DEEP SECRETS

THE DISCOVERY AND EXPLORATION OF LECHUGUILLA CAVE

Deep Secrets

The Discovery & Exploration of Lechuguilla Cave

Stephen Reames
Lawrence Fish
Paul Burger
Patricia Kambesis

CAVE BOOKS

Published by CAVE BOOKS, 756 Harvard Avenue, St. Louis, MO
63130, U.S.A.

CAVE BOOKS is the publications affiliate of the Cave Research
Foundation.

Layout and typesetting by Rob Kolstad.

Cover design by Roger McClure.

Cover photograph by David Harris.

Library of Congress Cataloging-in-Publication Data

    Deep Secrets: the discovery and exploration of Lechuguilla
       Cave / Stephen Reames ... [et al.].
          p.   cm.
       Includes bibliographical references (p.   ).
       ISBN 0-939748-18-5. – ISBN 0-939748-28-2 (pbk.)
       1. Lechuguilla Cave (N.M.)   I. Reames, Stephen,
         1957-   .
       GB606.L3D44 1999
       551.44'7'0978942--dc21   99-21728
                                     CIP

Printed in the United States of America.

Dedication

To Donald G. Davis, who more than any other person represents the true spirit of Lechuguilla caving.

STEVE REAMES

Lechuguilla \ lay-choo-GEE-uh \, a member of the agave family
having a basal rosette of sharply pointed leaves.

ACKNOWLEDGMENTS

We are deeply indebted to many people who helped us write this book. Larry Fish was responsible for taking the diverse writing styles and stories of the four authors and integrating them into a single story with one coherent voice. Stan Allison, Ann Bosted, Peter Bosted, Don Coons, Don Doucette, Roy Glaser, Jim Goodbar, Joanne Greenberg, JoAnn Hall, Rob Kolstad, Ted Lappin, Greg Miller, Bill Mixon, Emily Davis Mobley, Steve Mosberg, Patricia Seiser, Vi Schweiker, Norm Thompson and Carol Vesely told us their stories, verified facts, and reviewed the manuscript.

Many thanks go to Donald G. Davis, one of the most respected cavers in the country. His encyclopedic knowledge of Lechuguilla Cave and his personal recollections were invaluable.

To provide a non-caver viewpoint, Connie Conine and Rebecca Miklich spent many hours reviewing revision after revision of the text. Their patience was invaluable, although we suspect that just one more draft might have driven them crazy.

Special thanks go to cave photographers Stan Allison, Ann Bosted, Peter Bosted, Dave Bunnell, David Harris,

Peter Jones, Ray Keeler, Greg Miller, Dave Milligan, Art Palmer, Bob Stucklin, Norm Thompson, Carol Vesely, and cartoonist Sandra Svoboda.

This book would not be possible without the patience, skills, and guidance of Red Watson our editor. We also thank Anna Watson who copy-edited the manuscript.

Most of all, we thank hundreds of explorers who are not mentioned in this book, but whose thousands of hours of work made the big discoveries possible.

TABLE OF CONTENTS

Table Of Photographs

Table Of Maps

Table Of Plates

1

THE DIGGERS

ave Allured crouched in the small round tunnel. The passage was barely big enough for him to sit up and he could feel the cold damp floor through his coveralls. Just a few feet away, he could see the outline of another caver haloed by a circle of pale orange light.

A muffled shout broke the silence. "Bucket!"

Dave braced himself against the walls of the passage. The person in front wrestled a large plastic bucket past his body and handed it to Dave.

"Bucket!" Dave shouted over his shoulder. He strained to lift the heavy, dirt-filled bucket and pass it on to the next caver wedged in the passage behind him.

They had been digging in this passage every weekend for about a year now. It was part of Dave's big dream. All his life he had wanted to find a new cave, but unfortunately he lived in Colorado. The Colorado mountains had only a few sparse outcrops of limestone and there had not been a major discovery for more than fifteen years. In spite of these obstacles, Dave persisted. He was an engineer by trade and he approached the problem methodically. He read all the publications, studied all the maps, searched the cliffs and canyons, and crawled through all the known caves. Although he discovered a few small passages, none was spectacular.

In the end, he settled on a simple plan for finding new passage. The ends of many caves were blocked with dirt and rock. Dave's plan was to go to the end of a promising passage and dig out all the debris in hopes of finding new cave beyond.

Digging in a cave is difficult, but Dave was ideally suited for it. He was thirty years old, with the wiry, strong body of a caver. He was serious and intense with large owlish eyes and thick-rimmed glasses. A shock of sandy-blond hair curled around his narrow angular face.

Dave knew that if he wanted to run a major dig, he would need a small, dedicated group willing to toil for hours at a time at the ends of tight, cold passages. Colorado had a large group of experienced cavers, but he felt that most of them were too independent to work as a team on a long-term project. He wanted everyone to share the responsibilities and earn the rewards of a new discovery.

Dave had also observed that many Colorado cavers looked down on outsiders and treated novices badly. He thought this was unfair and a waste of talent, so he made every effort to include new cavers on all his trips. These newcomers made the perfect digging team. While experienced cavers had their own ideas about how to run a project, the new cavers were happy to follow Dave's direction.

The team's first big breakthrough came in Cave of the Winds, a commercial cave everyone thought had been thoroughly explored. After just a few days of work, the diggers broke into a narrow corridor just over a hundred feet long. The passage was lined with patches of glittering snow-white aragonite. In the soft clay clinging to the walls were impressions of ancient ice crystals left from the last ice age. It was not spectacular, but it was tantalizing and it proved that digging could uncover new passages even in the most thoroughly explored cave.

Dave's team was now working on another passage in the Cave of the Winds. Dave had noticed that the map of the cave had an empty space in the center. Dave reasoned that this would be a good place to find new cave. The passage they were digging in now was headed right into the center of that empty space.

The sound of excited voices once again broke the silence.

"What's going on?" Dave shouted up the passage.

"There's been a breakthrough!"

Dave and the rest of the diggers scrambled up for a look. Everyone stared at a small black opening at the end of the passage. Quickly enlarging the hole, they squeezed up through the narrow muddy opening into a small oval room they called the Whale's Belly. The room was drab and not very interesting and there were no obvious passages leading on.

"Hey, look up," somebody yelled.

The beams of their headlamps converged on an enticing hole thirty feet above the floor. They immediately tried to climb to it, but the walls were steep and slippery and they kept sliding back to the floor.

The next weekend they returned with climbing equipment, and when they bolted up the wall they found one of the most spectacular passages in Colorado. Although it was only fifteen feet wide and a little over 200 feet long, one wall of the passage was laced with delicate tendrils of pure-white crystalline calcite. Clusters of white helictites sparkled in the bright lights as the cavers walked down the ten-foot-high passage. It was so beautiful that they gave it the name Silent Splendor.

The next weekend was a circus. It seemed that every caver in the state wanted to see the new discovery. All day, cavers waited in the Whale's Belly to climb the rope, look at the passage, and return to make room for the next sightseer.

One person was conspicuously absent: Dave. Unfortunately, work had kept him up until 5:00 that morning and he missed the trip. By the time he was able to see Silent Splendor, it had already been completely explored by dozens of cavers. No one had even bothered to map the discovery. Dave had hoped to explore and survey slowly and carefully, but in the rush to see the new discovery his wishes had been ignored.

This experience had a strong effect on Dave. He had learned how to organize and lead a large digging project. But he had also developed a very strong conviction that the way you dig and explore is as important as what you find.

Dave had always been a conservationist. He wanted to explore caves in a way that would preserve them for future generations. This is not easy to do. Caves are delicate places that are easily damaged. Unlike mountains, deserts, and prairies where rain, wind, and sunshine can wipe away most traces of human impact in a few generations, caves repair themselves very slowly. In a cave, even something as trivial as a footprint can last for thousands of years.

Dave had seen many beautiful caves slowly deteriorate as they were explored. A carelessly placed hand or muddy boot can damage in a second what has taken millions of years to form. Thus, Dave imposed the most stringent conservation measures. He would mark a single trail through a cave with colored flagging tape to confine damage to a narrow path. He insisted on removing all human waste, on surveying a passage as it was explored, and on rotating participants so everyone had a chance to explore virgin passage.

Some cavers did not like Dave's ideas. Something as simple as flagging a trail through the cave provoked endless controversy. Even some of the most conservation-minded cavers felt that the brightly colored survey tape distracted from the natural beauty of a cave.

The Silent Splendor experience taught Dave how easy it was to lose sight of the welfare of the cave in the aftermath of a big breakthrough. Also, in the stampede to

RAY KEELER

The trail to Lechuguilla Cave.

see the new discovery, the diggers who did all the work often got pushed aside. Dave was now more determined than ever to do things right. All he needed was another project.

The ramparts of the Guadalupe Mountains rise out of the deserts of Texas and New Mexico. It is very dry, so plant life is scarce. With the exception of a few hardy grasses and scraggly bushes, the landscape is populated by small clumps of cactus and succulents. The topsoil is thin and patchy, and everywhere the bedrock peeks through the dirt cover.

These mountains contain one of the most spectacular caves in the world, Carlsbad Cavern. Carlsbad has over twenty miles of mapped passage, so it seemed natural that there should be another large cavern waiting to be found. Still, in the hundred years since Carlsbad had been discovered, no other cave found in the Guadalupes had even come close.

Map of Colorado and New Mexico.

In the dry, rolling hills on the other side of Carlsbad Caverns National Park was a little-known cave that had been mined for guano in the 1800's. The cave was called Lechuguilla and the first hint that there might be something special about it came in the mid-fifties. A park ranger visiting the cave happened to notice a great deal of wind blowing through some rocks at the back of the cave. In the late seventies, members of the Cave Research Foundation discovered his report and decided to have another look at this seemingly insignificant hole in the ground.

The CRF cavers knew that strong winds in a cave indicate the presence of an extensive network of passages. Caves react to changes in barometric pressure. When the pressure falls, the air inside the cave rushes out the entrance. When the barometric pressure rises, the outside air flows into the entrance and the cave inhales. The larger the cave, the longer and more forcefully this wind blows before equilibrium is reached.

In the case of Lechuguilla, the long periods of strong air movement could mean only one thing: miles of cave passage. In New Mexico, a land known for its beautifully decorated caves, these passages could be spectacular. And so, in 1976, motivated by the wind, the CRF cavers began working on a dig project in the rubble at the bottom of Lechuguilla Cave. The problem was that they were tunneling horizontally, and the walls and ceiling became more and more unstable as they dug. After only a few months, the threat of a collapse and the need for shoring forced them to abandon the dig.

John Patterson had been involved with CRF before moving to Colorado in the late seventies. He remembered the dig in Lechuguilla and the incredible wind that issued from the pile of rubble on the floor of the cave. This wind was the strongest he had ever felt. If you arrived at just the right time, the cave would exhale so hard that you could see a cloud of dust towering a hundred feet into the desert sky. At other times, the cave slumbered peacefully without a hint of the ferocious wind. Now, years after everyone else had forgotten about the dingy cave, the wind still intrigued John. He knew there had to be much more cave in Lechuguilla and it gnawed at him that no one else seemed interested in finding it.

The 1984 breakthrough at Cave of the Winds reawakened John's dream. John had worked long and hard on the Silent Splendor dig, and he thought that Dave's organizational skills and determination were just what was needed to find the source of the wind in Lechuguilla. Many people thought the dig was impossible, but Dave enjoyed this kind of challenge and was attracted to the project. He also thought that he could get a formal agreement with the

National Park Service that would give him control over how the cave would be explored and surveyed if the dig broke through. If the park accepted his plan, he could run the project the way he wanted.

Dave began to do research on the cave and on the previous digs. There was almost no data on Lechuguilla Cave other than some sketchy trip reports and a couple of old photographs. He decided that the best way to get information was to check out the cave for himself. He contacted park service officials, and was given a permit to visit the cave over the Memorial Day weekend of 1984.

It is an easy mile walk from the dusty access road to the cave. The path snakes along a low valley and over the top of a ridge. Dave scanned the drainage below, a shallow draw nestled in the rolling hills of the Guadalupe Mountains. On the opposite side of the arroyo, in a banded outcrop of tan limestone, Dave could see the black cleft of the entrance.

John Patterson, Vi Allured, Ted Lappin, and Donald Davis had accompanied Dave on the long drive from Colorado to Carlsbad. They walked down the hillside into Lechuguilla Canyon. It was named for the tough blue-green plant that lines the arroyos and hillsides in the area. In Spanish, lechuguilla means "little lettuce," which is an ironic description of the thick rosettes of fibrous spears. Each spear is about a foot long and tipped with a stiff, sharp spike that can easily penetrate the boots of unwary hikers or even the tire of a car. The lechuguilla plants were now in full bloom, their eight-foot flower stalks swaying gently in the breeze.

It was springtime in the desert. The bushes were green with new growth and the cactuses were blooming in a kaleidoscope of colors, covering the hillsides with patches of iridescent reds, purples, and oranges. Dave thought the blazing colors and towering stalks were a good omen.

As they walked up the opposite side of the canyon, the yawning mouth of the entrance came into view. Dave stepped cautiously toward the crumbling edge of the pit and squinted into the blackness below. He could feel the cool, moist air against his face and smell the sweet, earthy aroma of deep cave passages.

Dave tied a rope to a nearby tree and threw the coil into the pit. He fastened his seat harness, clipped his rappel rack into the rope, and leaned back, slowly working his way over the edge of the drop. For the first twenty feet he rappelled against the cliff, but then the rock walls belled out and he dangled free. He looked down. The dull, gray light barely reached the rubble floor sixty feet below. He slid down the slender nylon rope and landed on a rocky slope.

"What's that sound?" Dave asked after the rest of the group had rappelled down.

From somewhere in the back of the cave came a roar. It was like the far-off thunder of a train in the night. They moved toward the sound. With each step, it grew more insistent and powerful.

"Hey, look at this!" Donald yelled, pointing at the floor.

Small jets of air were hissing out of holes in the floor, forming tiny volcanoes that spit small rocks and sand into the air. The power of the wind was overwhelming and its meaning was clear: Lechuguilla had to be one huge cave. Two other caves blew air like this, Wind Cave and Jewel Cave in South Dakota. Jewel had just surpassed the seventy-five-mile mark; Wind Cave had just reached fifty miles, and both had plenty of unexplored passage.

Dave was enchanted by the wind. This was the best lead he had ever seen. It might take months or even years to find the source of the wind, so they would have to be very well-organized, disciplined, and patient. He would invite his friends and some of the promising newcomers. He now had a chance to set up a model project that he could run without any interference.

That night Dave, Vi, and Ted talked with Ron Kerbo, the park's cave specialist, about Lechuguilla Cave and the project they wanted to run. Ron, too, had visited the cave, but he thought there were much better prospects elsewhere in the park. Dave was not persuaded. He wanted to dig at Lechuguilla Cave.

Dave submitted a dig proposal to the park. The proposal contained one key provision: in the event that they were successful, the project participants would be allowed to explore and map the newly-discovered cave on their own terms. To Dave's delight, the park service granted permission to start the project. There was one concern: the permit made no mention of how the cave would be managed if the dig was successful.

In the Winter, 1985, edition of *Rocky Mountain Caving*, Dave outlined his plans for the cave:

> If the project ever opens up new cave, we will want to see it explored on a survey-as-you-explore basis. Although this may seem restrictive or bureaucratic, we feel that this system will best allow community participation in the cave's exploration rather than domination by some clique. It is good to run through your own virgin discovery once in a while, but not necessarily so in the case where dozens of cavers have helped you dig it open. We hope that everyone participating in the Lechuguilla project will feel the way we do about this.

The first dig was scheduled for Thanksgiving weekend, 1984. Steve Dunn joined John, Dave, Vi, and Ted on the long drive from Colorado to Carlsbad. A winter storm tailed them all the way through New Mexico, and as they pulled into the park the sky was filled with low stacks of slate-gray clouds.

By the time they got to the cave, fog was hanging on the rocky hillsides and floating up the valleys. Despite the approaching storm, there was no air blowing in the cave. The barometer had been stable, so there was no change of air pressure to activate the wind. They began to study the cave for a dig site. One spot at the bottom of a shallow pit looked good, but they hit bedrock immediately. They tried again, this time in the nearby guano pile. The digging was easy but the walls kept collapsing. If the dig went much further here, it would be too dangerous unless they shored up the passage with wooden supports. They finally gave up. Without the wind to guide them to the best location, it was hopeless.

The next day the weather turned cold and drizzly and the wind returned to the cave. Jets of air were gushing and hissing from the floor. They quickly settled on a new site. It seemed ideal: there was a strong blowhole to follow, and they were digging under a solid rock ceiling, so they did not have to worry about a cave-in. Most importantly, the trend of the dig followed a narrow crack in the ceiling that indicated a weakness in the limestone. They had followed a similar crack in the Silent Splendor dig.

The more they dug, the more excited they became. By the time the weekend was over, they were five feet down and the blowhole had expanded to two inches in diameter.

The blue sky had returned and the sun was shining brightly as they pulled out of the parking lot to head back to Colorado. The weekend had been a success and they could hardly wait for the next expedition.

John led a short trip on Memorial Day of 1985. He was able to recruit only enough people for one day of digging. The wind was blowing more violently than ever. John estimated the windspeed to be twenty-five to thirty-five miles per hour.

They had developed a system for removing rubble using a six-man bucket brigade. Ted Lappin was chipping furiously at the dig face with a small green army shovel and filling a five-gallon plastic bucket with dirt. He pulled the dust mask and goggles off his face and lifted the heavy bucket over his head, waiting for someone to grab it and give him an empty one.

"Hey John . . . bucket!" Ted yelled over his shoulder.

John looked down the tunnel.

"Hey Ted, you look just like a Martian," John said, laughing so hard that he could barely lift the heavy bucket.

"What?" Ted said.

Ted was covered with mud from head to toe. His face was completely coated with brown dirt except for white

BOB STUCKLEN
Lechuguilla Cave entrance viewed from the inside.

THE DIGGERS wait

circles around his eyes and mouth. John burst into another fit of laughter. Ted pulled his dust mask and goggles back on and dropped back down into the tunnel.

The dig was getting very messy. In the beginning, the wind had been friendly as it guided the diggers through the chaotic jumble of dirt and rubble. But as the work progressed, the wind made the digging more and more difficult. Cave dirt is usually damp and easy to dig, but here the wind quickly sucked all the moisture out of the soil. The dry dirt crumbled at the slightest touch, exploding into clouds of dust that were then driven into the digger's face. It was so frustrating that the diggers started calling the cave Misery Hole.

Dave organized another trip for the long Thanksgiving weekend. He invited several of John's old friends from New Mexico and a few Colorado cavers. A total of thirteen people converged on the park to help with the project.

The dig was getting steeper. It started at a twenty-five-degree angle, but the rock ceiling curved down and the slope was now approaching forty-five degrees. Normally this would not have been a problem, but as the wind dried out the mud walls, they softened and collapsed, sending avalanches of debris tumbling down the hole, threatening to fill the dig.

Still, the project was progressing nicely. They were opening up more and more blowholes and they could see small, dark openings in the rubble face. During the second day, one of the cavers pushed a shovel into the dig face and felt the dirt give way. A hole appeared and everyone squeezed in for a look. The back of the passage had opened into a small alcove about fifteen feet long. It was a tantalizing hint of the prize they were seeking, but still not the real thing. By the end of the trip, the dig was more than twenty-five feet long.

On the drive home, Dave could not stop talking about the cave. He knew they had to be close to a breakthrough. The number of air pockets had increased, and the wind seemed stronger and more concentrated. He ran through his plan over and over again. How would they explore and survey? How would they protect the cave, and who would they invite?

2

BREAKTHROUGH

The Colorado Grotto of the National Speleological Society is one of the oldest caving clubs in the country. Grotto meetings are the hub of all activity for cavers. They are times to socialize, talk about trips, and brag about discoveries. As the next grotto meeting approached, Dave Allured and John Patterson prepared an announcement. They wanted to concentrate all their efforts on one big push, so they decided to organize a week-long expedition around the 1986 Memorial Day weekend. The only concern was whether they could find enough people to mount a serious digging effort. Dave carefully worked out all the details: the trip size, what they wanted to accomplish, and what the guidelines would be if they broke through. The day of the meeting finally arrived.

The setting sun cast long shadows across the street in front of the old church as the cavers gathered. Cars began to arrive from every direction. Lumbering pickups barely held together by coats of primer, compact cars filled to bursting with people, and large family sedans squeezed into every available space along the narrow street. Nearly every car, no matter how old or new, how clean or battered, had a tiny yellow sticker with the silhouettes of several bats in flight – the emblem of a group brought together by one thing, caving. The people were as varied as their cars. They walked up the sloping lawn of the meeting house and went inside. Dave picked his way through the crowd, to a pew near the front.

The chairman called the meeting to order. "Everybody find a seat; the meeting is about to start."

A few late arrivals squeezed into the crowded pews. The meeting proceeded through the usual topics of business to the most anticipated part.

"Any trip announcements?"

Dave stood up.

"I have a few announcements to make. First of all, John and I have scheduled a Lechuguilla dig trip for the week of Memorial Day. It looks like we're about to break through, so we're planning to spend the whole week. The park service will allow only six people in the cave at a time, so we'd like to get about twenty people for the trip so we can keep the dig running with fresh people. If you're interested, see me at the end of the meeting to sign up."

The room was quiet.

Dave had a stern look on his face; he scanned the room, his eyes locking onto individual faces as he spoke.

"Now remember," he said, "we have some special requirements for this project. If you want to go on this trip you have to follow all the rules. I know some of you like to explore virgin passage without surveying it. If we break through, the park service wants the cave explored according to the guidelines we've set up."

People began to fidget impatiently.

"Dave," the chairman interrupted, "could you talk about this after the meeting? We have a lot of things to cover."

"No, I have the floor and there are things I need to talk about," Dave replied, his voice hard and determined.

Several people in the back of the room groaned in exasperation and began to whisper to each other. Dave could go on for hours about the minute details of an issue. Politics was not the average caver's idea of fun. Most people came to the meeting to hear about new discoveries, to plan trips, or to see the slide show. Still, no one wanted a confrontation, so they let him talk for another half an hour until he exhausted the subject.

He finished by again inviting everyone to participate on the next trip. After the meeting, several new people hurried to the back of the room to sign up. Some of Dave's old friends, the ones who had worked with him on the long digs at Cave of the Winds, left the meeting quietly without adding their names to the list. Without the more experienced diggers, Dave had trouble filling all the expedition slots. Still, the energetic newcomers would take up the slack.

BOB STUCKLEN
Digging in the breakdown of the entrance passage.

The following weeks passed quickly while Dave worked hard planning the expedition. There were a thousand things to do. He gathered survey instruments, books, pencils, flagging tape, ropes, and digging tools. He made sure each member of the trip was prepared. He checked their climbing abilities and their surveying skills and made sure they understood the rules. At least once a week he called Ron Kerbo, the cave specialist at the park to work out the details. But the most important task was organizing the work crews. The dig was now nearly thirty feet long and it took six people to pass buckets up the steep passage. Dave laid out a work schedule so that the dig would be fully manned every day of the expedition. By Memorial Day, everything was ready.

On the first day of the expedition they made good progress. By the second day, however, the work schedule was starting to fall apart. First, Roy Glaser decided to take a short trip to Mexico and would not be back until the next day. Then, two others decided to go to Carlsbad for the afternoon. Finally, the park service representative who was required to supervise the project did not show up until late afternoon. When the ranger finally arrived, he told them he had other things to do and they could go in without him. Although the rest of the diggers thought this was a good idea, Dave did not. There were only three people available to work, and he wanted six people to run the dig. Instead, Dave took Neil Backstrom and Rick Bridges to work on a surface survey above the cave.

Neil crouched next to a catclaw bush, taking care not to get stuck by the razor-sharp spines as he waited for Dave to scribble notes into a small, yellow survey book. A long, white ribbon of measuring tape trailed across the rocky landscape, hanging limply from clumps of grass and tangled bushes. Neil stood up, pulled the survey tape tight with one hand, and read the distance from the last station. A tall, muscular rock climber in his mid-thirties, he had long, sandy-blond hair and a mountain-man's full beard.

Dave wrote down the final numbers, sketched a few details onto the gridded paper, and closed the book. Neil shouted to Dave as he began to reel in the tape.

"Hey Dave, let's go look at the dig."

Dave was still reluctant to enter the cave. He wanted to go back to camp to look for reinforcements. But Neil and Rick wanted to see the cave. They had spent two days in the park and still had not been underground. They argued that it was the quality of digging, not the quantity that was important. Dave was also eager to start working on the pile of rubble that had captivated him for the last two years. He finally agreed.

Neil was the first to climb down to the dig face. He was in a narrow, tubular passage about four feet in diameter. The ceiling was solid limestone, but the walls and the floor were a conglomeration of loose dirt and rocks. The tunnel angled steeply downward and the right-hand wall was overhung and unstable. Several huge boulders were wedged precariously along the side of the passage, ready to fall. Neil began to pull rocks out of the bottom of the dig. It was like a house of cards and each time he removed a rock, boulders in the wall and floor shifted ominously. To make matters worse, the wind was whipping furiously through the dig and Neil was using a carbide lamp. Every minute or so a gust of wind would snuff out the tiny flame, plunging the passage into total darkness.

In spite of the difficulties, Neil was making good progress. Soon he uncovered several openings that got bigger as he dug. Neil was convinced that they were close to a breakthrough and he began digging like a man possessed. The rocks rumbled and shifted more frequently now and Dave became concerned about the stability of the dig face. He thought it might be better to dig in the clay fill along the ceiling instead of straight down into the loose debris.

Rick wanted a turn at the dig. Neil was getting tired; besides, Rick was using an electric light that was much better suited for digging in the wind.

Rick gingerly made his way to the bottom of the chimney, trying not to knock dirt from the fragile walls down into the dig. He braced himself against the walls of the narrow tunnel and began to remove slabs of rock from the floor. He put them into plastic buckets and handed them up to Neil who was wedged in the passage above him. Dirt and debris constantly rained down upon them as the buckets were laboriously passed upward.

Rick had just set an empty bucket on the slope above him when a section of the wall near the top of the tunnel collapsed, sending a fifty-pound boulder bouncing down the passage toward him. By a stroke of luck, it careened off the far wall and landed in the empty bucket.

"Hey, watch out!" he shouted, even though he knew it was no one's fault.

The wind howled insistently through several large cracks in the floor. Usually the cave exhaled, blasting sand and dirt into the digger's face. Today it was inhaling. In fact, it was like a vacuum cleaner sucking dirt and loose rocks down through a couple of screaming holes in the floor. Rick had an idea. He began pushing the smaller rocks and loose dirt through the holes.

"Hey, what are you doing?" Dave yelled from above.

"This is a lot better than having dirt rain down on my head every time a bucket goes up."

"If we do that, we'll just have to carry the same dirt out later from deeper in the dig," Dave said.

Rick was getting tired of Dave's rules and when Dave turned his back, he pushed all the loose dirt down one of the suck holes. "Mother Nature gave us a vacuum cleaner, and we might as well use it," he muttered under his breath.

Rick Bridges was very much the opposite of Dave Allured. Physically, he was a big man in his thirties with dark hair and a short beard. He had a broad face and bright, intense eyes. Where Dave was cautious and methodical, Rick was confident and quick-witted. He was a businessman who made a living buying and selling land in the oil fields, and he had followed the energy boom to Colorado in the mid-eighties. Above all, Rick was articulate and persuasive. It was easy to picture him closing a multi-million-dollar oil deal with a handshake and a slap on the back.

The wind was sucking harder now and the dirt rained down around his head as the buckets were pulled up the narrow dig. Rick wedged a crowbar under a large rock and levered it out of the dirt. To his amazement, a small hole formed right where the rock had been. He looked closer; the hole was getting bigger. Three inches, four inches, five inches. He suddenly realized that if it got any bigger, he would have no place to stand.

"What if I'm standing on top of a five-hundred-foot pit?" he thought.

"Throw down a rope, I think I need a belay!" he shouted to Dave who was pulling buckets out of the dig above him.

"What do you need a belay for?" Dave said, not quite grasping the seriousness of the situation.

"Look, you asshole, the bottom's dropping out and I don't want to fall in."

Dave threw a rope into the tunnel and Rick tied it around his waist.

"On belay." Rick shouted.

Dave wrapped the rope around his hips and braced his feet against each side of the passage, ready to catch Rick in case the bottom fell out of the dig.

Rick felt more secure now and he started kicking at the floor. The wind whipped past his body, sucking violently through the opening at his feet. It was almost as though the cave was trying to pull him through the small hole. It was an eerie feeling; gravity and the wind were trying to drag him from the cozy confines of the tunnel into the dark world below.

Tempting fate, Rick dangled his foot through the opening, trying to find the bottom. There was no bottom.

He kicked a small rock through the hole and listened. It rolled out of sight, clattered down a rocky slope and echoed to a stop in the distance. "Wow, I gotta look at this." He bent over, cocked his head and aimed the beam of his head-lamp through the hole.

"Hey, I can see a room."

Dave and Neil scrambled down the tunnel and squeezed next to Rick for a good look. They could see a rock wall on the right, a flat bedrock ceiling above, and a dirt slope that slanted out of sight to the left.

"Give me some room," Rick said indignantly. He pushed the two unwelcome visitors back up the tunnel.

He looked down into the hole. One side of the opening was lined with large boulders stacked in a chaotic jumble. If he was not careful, the wall would collapse and crush him. It was frustrating, like looking through the window of a toy store. There was one room and maybe more on the other side, but it was going to take some very delicate dig-ging to get through.

He decided to dig downward to try to avoid disturb-ing the dangerous boulders. The digging went quickly because he shoveled most of the dirt through the opening into the room below. As he cleared away the dirt, he discov-ered a large slab of rock blocking the way.

"I think we have a problem," Rick shouted over his shoulder.

He could not dig left or up because there was solid bedrock, nor could he go right because of the delicate boul-der pile. Dave and Neil came down the passage and looked over his shoulder.

"Can you pry it out of the way?" Dave asked.

"I'm afraid that if we try to move it, the wall is going to collapse," Rick said as he studied the jigsaw puzzle of boulders and rocks. One end of the rock slab was wedged in the boulder pile. If it was moved, it might bring the whole wall crashing down.

"We could get some plywood and shore up the wall," Neil said.

"It would take days to buy the wood, haul it to the cave, and build the shoring," Rick said, obviously frustrated by the thought of a long delay.

"Well, whatever we do, there's no way around that boulder; it's got to go," Dave said.

"I think if I'm careful, I can pull it out without bringing the wall down. I'm willing to give it a try, but be ready to pull me out if it collapses," Rick said as he moved into position.

He wedged a crowbar under the rock and shifted his hands toward the end of the bar to get maximum leverage. A low grinding sound vibrated through the floor of the cave as he put the weight of his body on the bar. The rock slowly pivoted backward, and then with a loud crunch, lurched down the hole, disappeared into the darkness, and landed with a thud.

They held their breaths as they watched the wall of the tunnel for the slightest sign of movement. The wall held.

Rick turned to Dave and Neil, a big smile on his face. "Gentlemen," he said with a flourish of his hand, "Welcome to Lechuguilla Cave."

The hole was probably big enough to get through, but it still looked dangerous. Rick had been working for nearly two hours in the blasting sand and choking dust, and he needed a rest. "Somebody else want to dig awhile?" he said as he picked his way back up the steeply sloping passage to relative calm above.

"Sure," Dave said. He pulled the dust mask over his mouth, the goggles over his eyes, and slid down the slope to the dig. He began cleaning loose rock from around the opening and very soon set the shovel on the floor and shouted up the passage. "I think it's big enough to get through."

Neil and Rick climbed down the passage and peered over his shoulder. Dave was shining his headlamp through the opening, trying to figure out the best way to get through.

"It's going to be tricky. We'll have to be real careful not to bring down the wall. It's going to be even harder to get out, and if the entrance collapses while we're in there, we'll be trapped."

Neil seemed hypnotized by the opening. "I know I can get through," he said, "and even if it does collapse, I know you can dig me out." He pushed his way toward the hole.

He closed his eyes against the wind, held his breath, and wedged his body, feet first, into the hole. He was now totally blind, feeling his way over the sharp rocks that lined the opening. He tried not to bump the walls because the slightest touch of an arm or an elbow sent an explosion of sand and gravel blasting past his face. His body was now almost blocking the passage, and the wind rushing past him seemed stronger than ever. He felt as if he was being sucked violently into the hole.

Slowly, he disappeared into the jagged opening. Suspended only by his arms, he lowered himself into the blackness, feeling blindly with his feet for a solid floor. Then he felt the soft dirt of the rubble slope under his feet.

"What do you see?" The voice was barely audible over the roar of the wind.

Still half blind, Neil crawled further down the slope, opened his eyes, and looked around. The wind was quieter here.

He spit the dirt out of his mouth and yelled. "There's a low room. About twenty feet wide and five feet high."

Neil turned around and climbed back up to the hole. He was in a good position to work on the opening to make it safer. With Dave working from above, they soon enlarged and stabilized the opening. Dave slid through the hole and joined Neil. He turned to Rick who was still peering into the new room from the safety of the tunnel above.

"One person needs to stay behind as a precaution in case the entrance collapses. Wait here while we check things out," Dave said.

"Yeah, I can report where the bodies are," Rick said.

Dave and Neil scouted around the room. At one end was the rubble slope they had just dug through. At the other end, the rocky floor sloped down into a low crawlway. All the air was rushing into the crawlway so they decided to follow. They soon found two small pits in the floor that swallowed most of the air. They were about to climb into one of the pits when the sound of Rick's voice interrupted them.

"What do you see?" Rick yelled from inside the tunnel.

Dave turned to Neil. "We should give Rick a chance to see this. I'll trade places with him," he said as he climbed back up toward the opening.

Rick quickly joined Neil who was examining a large boulder that nearly blocked the smaller pit. He had just decided that he could probably squeeze past it, when Rick started down the bigger hole.

"Shouldn't we be surveying this stuff?" Neil asked.

"Before I do any surveying I want to make sure there's really a cave here, not just another dig," Rick said as he reached the bottom of the pit.

Rick's feet landed on a dirt floor. He turned around and discovered that he was at the top of a rocky slope that descended fifteen feet to the edge of a twelve-foot sheer drop. Neil was right behind him.

"Let's see if we can find a way down," Rick said as he headed left along the top of the slope. Neil went to the right and found a small room that led to a balcony. There was a large passage below, but no way down. "Damn!" he said as he headed back to where Rick was waiting.

"Nothing this way. How about you?" Rick said as Neil approached.

"I could see a big passage down there, but no way to get to it. We'll have to climb down here." He pointed at the twelve-foot drop-off straight ahead.

Rick picked his way down the steep dirt slope to the edge of the cliff. It was sheer, but he could see handholds, and he thought he could climb down. He turned around, swung one foot over the edge, and felt for a foothold. He worked his way down the wall until he was close enough to the floor to jump.

"Come on down," he said.

They were at the junction of several passages. The main trend led down and to the left into a large room, about sixty feet long and fifty feet wide. The floor was covered with rimstone dams. These rock formations had been dried by the hot wind and were soft and sugary, like Christmas candy. Everything was coated with a thin layer of sand that blew and shifted in the relentless wind to form a miniature desert scene of tiny sand dunes.

The room was big, but there was no obvious way out of it. Still, there had to be more cave; there was too much wind to be explained by only a couple hundred feet of

BOB STUCKLEN
Walking passage beyond the breakthrough dig.

passage. The trick now was to follow the wind and let it guide them to the rest of the cave.

They back-tracked to the place where they had climbed down and then took the other walking passage leading east. They had gone only a few steps when, once again, they felt the breeze blowing gently past them. They ran down the tunnel to the top of a small rise where the bright glow of their lights was swallowed by the passage ahead. The sandy ground sloped into darkness; the cave was not going to end here.

Neil looked at Rick. "What about Dave? We should get back to him. Besides, we're supposed to be surveying this stuff."

The wailing siren of the wind and the promise of virgin cave was luring them deeper, tempting them to go on. But they remembered their promise and with great reluctance turned around and headed back to Dave.

It was late when the team of exhausted, filthy diggers climbed the rope out of the entrance. The night was warm and the cloudless sky was full of a million crystalline stars. They were exhilarated. They had broken through and were the first to explore what had to be an immense new cave.

Rick walked over to Dave and thrust out his hand. "Congratulations," he said.

Dave seemed a little uneasy, but he laughed and joked as they started down the long trail to the dirt road.

Walking back, Rick began to think about the day's events. He had been lucky in caving before. Years ago he had been involved in a spectacular breakthrough at Run-to-the-Mill Cave in Tennessee. A team of diggers had labored weekends for more than four months without success. The day Rick joined the project, they broke into 16,000 feet of new passage. Now, it seemed, history was repeating itself. The Lechuguilla dig project had started nearly two years ago, and on Rick's first trip there was a history-making breakthrough. This kind of luck was uncanny, and it gave Rick the feeling that he was destined

to be there, destined to play a key role in the exploration of
this cave.

✤   ✤   ✤

Word of the breakthrough quickly spread through the
camp. Everyone crowded together to listen to the stories.
They talked into the early morning hours.

The next morning, everyone was up early, ready to
survey the big find. Two teams were sent into the cave, one
to survey the passage that had already been explored, and
one to push a survey line into the unknown.

Rick trudged slowly up the sandy slope following the
footprints left in the dirt from the day before.

He turned to John and Neil. "This is where we
stopped yesterday."

They stood once again on the frontier of a new world.
Rick began to unwind the measuring tape and stretch it
down the passage. Neil cut a strip of bright red flagging
tape, wrote the letters "A1" on it with a large marking
pen, and placed it on the floor to mark the location of the
first survey station.

"On station," Neil said as he held one end of the measuring tape over the red flagging strip on the floor.

Down the passage, John pulled the tape tight and
said, "Length: sixty-seven point two feet. Light on station."

Rick pulled out the compass and clinometer that
were hanging on cords around his neck. He held the compass to his eye and sighted down the passage toward Neil.

"Bearing: fifty-five point five degrees."

Next he sighted through the clinometer, measuring
the slope of the passage. "Inclination: plus three degrees."

Rick studied the passageway trying to estimate the
distance from the station marker to the walls, ceiling, and
floor.

"Left: thirty; right: eight; up: nine; down: one."

John wrote the numbers in the survey book and drew
small sketches of the details of the passage. The process of

surveying the cave was tedious. Again and again, the survey tape was stretched down the passage and the numbers recorded in the book as they pushed into the unknown.

As they surveyed deeper into the cave, the passage got bigger, over thirty feet wide and, in places, twenty-five feet high. The walls were dry and covered with dust. Thick, bulbous knobs of calcite popcorn lined the ledges and lower sections of the floor. They surveyed their way slowly through the dry passage, following the gentle breeze that hinted at even better things to come.

Neil was in the lead, pulling the survey tape down the passage, trying to find the best route onward. The passage began to narrow and a crevice in the floor blocked the way. He found a narrow ledge leading around the crevice and down the left side of the passage. The ledge ended at a small slope of wet flowstone that glistened in his light. He climbed up the slope and squeezed through the opening into a small room. The walls were covered with draperies of flowstone streaked bright red, yellow, and black. Small, crystal-clear pools of water multiplied and reflected the colors.

"Hey, look at this!" Neil said. He was kneeling at the side of the passage looking at something on the floor. The others climbed up to join him.

"Cave pearls," he said.

A small pocket in the floor was filled with a half-dozen beautiful white spheres that glistened in the glare of their headlamps. It was easy to imagine them forming in a giant oyster deep in the ocean. Actually, dripping water over thousands of years had coated grains of sand with calcium carbonate to form the jewels.

"We'd better mark these babies so no one will step on them," John said as he secured a band of brightly-colored flagging tape across the floor to warn future visitors.

As they surveyed down the corridor, John marked a narrow path on the ground with two strips of red plastic tape. It looked like a pair of railroad tracks, snaking down the passage and around the corner into the shadows beyond. They wanted to confine all traffic to a single path through these beautiful rooms.

The character of the cave changed gradually as they pushed deeper. The front part of the cave had been dry and dusty, but the inner passages were wet and glistening. The flowstone here looked like a stone river. It was as though molten rock had flowed down the wall to splash across the floor, forming velvet-textured ripples and eddies of stone. In some places tiny dams and intricate terraces formed contours on the rock like miniature rice paddies perched on the sides of tiny hills.

They surveyed through this short room and under a low arch on the other side. The passage opened into a large chamber over fifty feet high. High on the right wall was a huge flowstone cascade twelve feet tall and six feet wide at the base, tapering into a rounded dome at the top. The sides were streaked red, gray, and white. Tangled draperies of snow-white flowstone and pencil-thin soda-straw stalactites hung from its base.

"It looks like a bell," Neil said. "Let's call it the Liberty Bell."

Across from the Liberty Bell, a steep fissure led off perpendicular to the passage, but the main trend went down a steep flowstone slope. It was not vertical but steep enough to be treacherous. Rick stared down the slope. He could barely make out the outline of a large room in the darkness below.

"I'm going to try to climb down." He crouched next to the edge, feeling for handholds to start the climb. He grabbed a mushroom-shaped nodule as he lowered himself down the slope, feeling with his feet for footholds. The flowstone was coated with a thin layer of water that made it slick as glass. There were no footholds.

"I think we need a rope," he said as he hoisted himself back up the slope to the safety of the level floor above.

They had no rope, so they were forced to stop. They turned and made their way back toward the entrance. On

Donald Davis climbing bare-foot beside the Liberty Bell.

the way, they ran into Dave, Randy Brown, and Dave
White who had just finished surveying the front part of the
cave. Allured's team was anxious to see the new discoveries, and they had a rope, so the two groups decided to com-
bine forces.

Neil led the way back down the flagging-tape trail to
the edge of the flowstone slope. He tied one end of the rope
to a knobby stalagmite and threw the coil down the slope
into the darkness. He then looped the rope across his back
for a shoulder rappel. The slope was not very steep and,
with a rope, getting down was easy. At the bottom, the passage continued under a low overhang covered with dripping stalactites and soda straws. Neil slid through the
opening and turned to look down the passage ahead. His
light spilled across the surface of a deep, blue pool over
forty feet long and twenty feet wide. Ripples from the
breeze and dripping water moved silently across the surface.

"Hey, come on down, there's a lake," he said.

BOB STUCKLEN

Caver pauses at the edge of Lake Lechuguilla.

Soon the others were standing beside him gazing into the cool blue water. They immediately christened it Lake Lechuguilla, and brought the survey to the edge of the water. No one wanted to dirty the pool by swimming in it, so they had to find another way across the deep body of water.

Neil scanned the edge of the lake carefully. There was a thick flowstone shelf just above water level. He grabbed a handhold for balance and stepped out onto the ledge. Slowly, he worked his way around the margin of the pool, clinging to a few small knobs with his hands as he shuffled his feet along the ledge. After twenty feet, he was able to step onto the dirt floor on the far side. They made a survey shot across the pool, and the others crossed on the ledge. They moved deeper into the cave.

The scenery became more beautiful and strange as they surveyed down the passage. On the other side of the lake they found rows of sand dunes, fifteen feet high, that shifted slowly in the underground wind. The passage got bigger as they walked along and the walls slowly receded into the shadows. The passage was now nearly thirty-five feet wide and over a hundred feet high. Rick tilted his head back to try to find the ceiling with the beam of his head-lamp, but all he could see was blackness.

They were discovering and surveying new cave so fast that John was having trouble keeping up with the sketches. All the features and landmarks of the passage had to be recorded in detailed drawings of each room. The rooms were so large that it took John more than thirty minutes to complete each sketch and the others were getting impatient.

Neil could wait no longer. While John was sketching, he explored the passage ahead, ostensibly to find the proper route to survey. He returned within a few minutes to announce that he had been stopped.

"Big pit," he said. "I don't think we can climb this one."

"Have you tried to climb it yet?" Rick said.

"No."

"Well, how do you know, if you haven't tried?" Rick's tone was confrontational and it startled Neil.

"If you think you can climb down that damn pit, then you can go do it yourself," he said, his face red with anger.

The survey was momentarily halted while everyone went ahead to check out the pit. They walked to a place where the passage split, each branch going only a few feet before ending in a dark void. As they approached the edge, they noticed that the floor was rocky and uneven and sounded hollow under their boots. They were apparently climbing over large boulders that were wedged in the mouth of the pit. Rick climbed down between a pair of large white boulders and along the left wall to a ledge covered with loose rock. He crawled toward the edge, testing every hold. A few rocks tumbled into the abyss as he reached the lip. He focused his light over the edge into the void below.

John had gone to the right looking for a path around the pit or a place to climb down. He had a better view of the pit than Rick, and he could see that there was only one way they could go, down.

"How deep do you think it is?" John asked, as he examined the walls of the pit with his headlamp.

"Throw a rock down and we'll find out. I'll time it," Rick said.

"Ready?"

"On three."

"Okay. One. Two. Three."

John pitched the rock underhand in a high arc over the pit. It seemed to float for a second and then fell downward.

Rick counted the seconds on his wristwatch: One second, two seconds, whack, boom. There was the loud cracking sound of a heavy rock shattering in the distance. As the echoes died away, they could hear the faint clatter of smaller rocks ricocheting deeper and deeper.

"Two point eight seconds," Rick said after a pause. "Let's see, sixteen feet after one second, sixty-four feet after two seconds and one hundred forty-four feet after three seconds."

"Yeah, and that rock was still going after it hit," John reminded him.

"There could be another hundred feet after that."

The pit was at least 150 feet deep and they would need another hundred feet of rope as a safety margin. The pit would have to wait for another day.

☞ **3** ☜

BOULDER FALLS

esearch expeditions were always headquartered at the CRF huts, a couple of rough stone cabins that blend perfectly with the craggy, arid hills of the Guadalupe Mountains. Hidden behind the park administration building and away from the visitor center, the huts are strategically located to keep curious tourists and rowdy cavers far apart.

Roy Glaser stepped out of the cabin door into the moonlight when he saw the carload of tired, dirty cavers pull into the driveway. The van crunched to a stop on the loose gravel in front of the hut and everyone piled out. Rick was in the lead. He grinned at Roy.

"Well, you lucked out," he said as he stepped into the cabin. "We got stopped by a big mother pit, about two hundred fifty feet deep."

Roy was relatively new to caving and still had things to prove to himself and his friends. He was tall and strong, in his early thirties, with reddish-blond hair, a friendly smile, and a crude joke for every occasion. He was fiery and sensitive, so it was easy to read his emotions by the color of his face.

Roy still regretted running off to Mexico and missing the big breakthrough. But he saw this new pit as a fresh opportunity to prove himself and as a chance to be part of a big new discovery. Still, the pit made him uneasy. It could be deeper than 300 feet and his longest rappel underground had been only 145 feet. The thought of the deep pit plagued Roy's sleep.

Roy was not the only one who could not rest. The lure of a big new cave and a mysterious pit had everyone up at 6:30 the next morning. But it was a morning of frustrating delays. As usual, Dave had a long list of items that needed to be done. First, he had to talk to Ron Kerbo at park headquarters. Next he had to check all the equipment. By the time everything was done and Dave was ready to leave, it was nearly ten o'clock.

Once they reached the cave, there were still more details to attend to. Dave was very concerned about the dig collapsing, so they spent several hours trying to make it safer. All these delays were pushing Roy to the limit of his patience. It was already afternoon and Dave still had a few more things to do. Roy and Neil Markovitz decided to run ahead to set up the rope for the rappel into the new pit.

They cautiously approached the crumbling edge of the drop. Several large boulders looked stable enough to serve as anchors, but the slope below them was covered with loose rocks and debris. The rope could easily dislodge the rocks while they were rappelling. Roy thought for a moment and then tied one end of the rope around the largest boulder. He then ran the rope down the side of the passage and behind another large boulder to keep it away from the loose rocks.

A voice interrupted his work.

"Hey Roy, Dave doesn't like the way we've fixed the dig. He wants us to go back up and do it over."

He looked up. Several members of Dave's work crew were making their way into the room.

"Not again," Roy muttered, his face red with frustration. "We can fix it later. I'm gonna do the pit now!"

He put on his seat harness, tightened the straps and began to lace the rope through the bars of the rack fastened to a carabiner at his waist.

"Six bars, maximum braking," he said to himself. Each bar would put more friction on the rope and slow the speed of his rappel. Finally, he tested the strength of the anchor by putting all his weight on the rope.

"Did you tie a knot in the end of the rope?" he asked Neil Markovitz. "I'd hate to rappel off the end."

"I think so," Neil said.

Everything was ready and it was too late to check. Roy leaned back and began to rappel down the steep slope leading to the pit. The room was glowing brightly from the lights of the cavers crowded around the edge.

Just then Dave appeared. He had finally finished repairing the dig and he arrived just in time to see Roy approaching the lip. He pushed his way to the front of the group.

"Roy, are you sure you want to do this? Because if you don't, I'd be glad to."

Roy looked up. "Do you think I would be here if I didn't?"

Roy's face was bright red with anger as he felt the critical eye of Dave watching his every move. Sweat poured off his face and he could hear a strange whining sound ringing in his ears.

"Oh great, now I'm freaking out." he thought, as he gripped the rope tighter. The sound was getting louder when he realized that it was just the whine of a flash gun. Someone was taking pictures.

He let the rope slip slowly through his hand as he worked his way to the brink of the pit. There was a layer of loose rock at the edge that Roy kicked and sent whizzing downward. Then he descended smoothly over the lip and vanished from sight.

"Hey Roy, what's going on? What can you see?" Dave called from above.

BOB STUCKLEN
Roy Glaser begins the first descent of Boulder Falls
as Steve Dunn looks on.

Roy turned his head and peered over his shoulder.

"I can see three ledges, and then it goes free. I think I'm at the top of a big room," he shouted toward the glowing lights above.

He paused on the lowest ledge and studied the situation. Just beneath the ledge, the wall was undercut, and he could see that he would soon be hanging in space.

Roy relaxed his grip, letting the rope slide through the brake bars. The rock curved away from him as he descended, causing him to swing free and rotate slowly in the center of the pit like a spider at the end of a thread. In every direction he could see only the vague shapes of the faraway walls.

He began to gain speed. The rope was buzzing through the brakebars and he could smell the acrid aroma of hot metal against the nylon rope. Loose rocks dislodged by the rope whizzed past his head and crashed in the darkness below.

Suddenly, he jerked to a halt. "What the hell," he muttered as he grabbed at the rack looking for a problem. The rope below the rack had twisted into a tangle of tight knots that jammed into the brake bars and stopped his descent. He pulled at the kinks, twisting the rope, trying to straighten the knots and feed it through the rack. The kinks slipped past the rack with a lurch and he was once again sliding free into the pit.

By now he could see a dim pile of rubble looming out of the darkness below. He aimed the beam of his headlamp at the floor to look for a soft landing place. He gripped the rope and pushed the brake bars closer together, increasing the friction against the rope. The rack chattered loudly as he slowed his descent and landed in deep soft sand.

It was dangerous at the bottom of the pit with all the loose rock above, so Roy trudged up the steep slope toward a big limestone block that was well out of the way. He looked around. He was in a huge room. The sound of water dripping into some unseen pool echoed in the distance.

"Off rope," he shouted and turned off his light.

He leaned back and watched the pale lights flickering on the ledge high overhead. After a minute or so, he could see the dark figure of another caver swing over the edge of the balcony to dangle from the slender thread of rope. It was a beautiful sight, a tiny point of light floating like a star on a dark night. As the light hovered closer, Roy recognized Neil.

"Over here," Roy shouted. Neil trudged up the slope and sat down next to Roy.

The rest of the team quickly followed Roy and Neil. Dave waited at the top to check each person's rigging before he started down. When Dave finally joined the others at the bottom of the pit, he noticed that one of the explorers was missing.

"Where did Neil go?" Dave said.

"He said he was going to get his rope bag," Roy said, pointing toward the unexplored part of the cave, past where the packs had been left at the bottom of the drop. They called down the passage but there was no response.

"Maybe he fell into a pit," Dave said.

Roy thought it was more likely that Neil had given in to temptation and was off exploring. After a few minutes, a light appeared in the distance. Neil walked up the slope and joined the group.

"How far did you go?" Roy asked.

"Oh, just a couple hundred yards. I came to a really big room, but I stopped because I knew you guys would get mad."

Roy looked at Dave. He knew that Dave didn't like cavers exploring on their own and he was expecting him to reprimand Neil, but at the moment Dave seemed more interested in the cave.

They were in an immense room seventy-five feet wide that formed the bottom of the pit. The walls were streaked with black flowstone and a few stalagmites dotted the lower slopes. Over the centuries, thousands of tons of debris had fallen down the shaft of the pit to form a huge pile of rocks and sand in the center of the room. They named the pit Boulder Falls for the incessant rain of rocks that fell during their rappel.

"Okay," Dave said. "We'll go as far as the room Neil found and then survey on the way out."

Dave led the way as they marched down the steep slope. The pile of sand and loose rocks continued downward, funneling into a large tubular passage about thirty feet in diameter. The walls were darker here, and scattered along the floor were big white gypsum boulders. They were just climbing past one of the boulders when Dave held up his hand signaling for the group to stop.

"Be careful where you step," he said, pointing toward the ground. Along the floor were dozens of small

DAVE MILLIGAN

Ten-inch-diameter gypsum rim in Rim City.

round openings about five inches in diameter. Each opening was encircled by a thin shell of white gypsum.

"Gypsum rims," Dave said. "They're very rare. They are caused by humid air rising out of those holes."

Everywhere they looked there were gypsum rims of all sizes. In some places they were thin and fragile, like broken egg shells. In other places, the rims were fat and thick and looked strangely like giant ears. Even the walls had rows of the unusual openings and some of the rims

were connected by narrow ridges of white gypsum that
meandered across the walls and ceiling.

"We should call this place Rim City," Dave said, jot-
ting a note in his survey book.

On the other side of Rim City, the passage continued
to angle downward. They were already 500 feet below the
entrance, and the deeper they went the hotter the cave
seemed. Everyone was sweating profusely.

"There's the room were I stopped," Neil said, pointing down the passage. Just ahead, the path seemed to be
blocked by a large white wall. As they got closer, they could
see that they were coming into the side of a room. The wall
was actually the edge of a twenty-foot-thick gypsum
deposit that covered the floor of the room. There was a narrow fissure leading up and to the right where the gypsum
had separated from the wall of the chamber.

Roy climbed along the fissure until he was near the
upper edge of the gypsum wall, then reached over the top

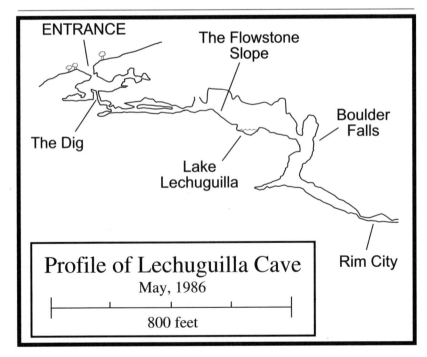

ENTRANCE

The Flowstone
Slope

Boulder
Falls

The Dig

Lake
Lechuguilla

Profile of Lechuguilla Cave
May, 1986

Rim City

800 feet

to pull himself up into the room. The others followed and they all gathered at the edge of the chamber. They were in a strange and beautiful room. It was big, over 150 feet wide and 40 feet high. The ceiling was flat and wide and arched slowly down to meet the floor. Even with the combined power of their headlamps, they could not see the end of the room.

"Boy it's hot in here," Dave said as he took off his shirt and wiped his forehead. The wind usually kept the cavers cool, but here it was lost in the vast expanse of the big room. The exertion of climbing up into the fissure made it feel even hotter.

"I'm going to call this place the Inferno Room," Dave said, making another note in his survey book.

They began to scout around the chamber. The floor was surprisingly flat and level, probably because of the thick gypsum deposits. It was covered with a thin veneer of brown dirt, but the gypsum underneath was pure-white and crystalline.

"Hey, look at this," Neil shouted. He was standing beneath a thick cluster of milk-white stalactites. Directly under the stalactites was a strange looking pit. It was oval and nearly vertical, with smoothly carved walls that looked like white porcelain. Deep vertical grooves ran from top to bottom down the walls of the pit. The dripping water from the stalactites above had bored a hole right through the soft gypsum floor.

Everywhere they looked, small clusters of stalactites hung from the ceiling, and another pit was drilled into the floor directly below each cluster. When they peered into the pits, they could barely make out the outlines of passages eighty feet below.

Beyond the pits and holes, there were deep crevices in the floor cutting across the width of the chamber. Toward the far end of the room, the passage tilted steeply downward. The crevices were wider here and huge blocks of gypsum had broken free and were stacked at various angles on the slope below. Even these blocks were riddled with drill-holes bored at various angles as the blocks slowly shifted down the slope over eons of time. It was like an Alaskan glacier complete with deep crevasses and icebergs floating off the end. By the time the expedition was over, they had forgotten all about the heat and renamed the room Glacier Bay.

"We should start surveying out now," Dave said. Everyone was reluctant to leave, but they had been in the cave for many hours, and still had the difficult task of surveying back to Boulder Falls. Dave opened his survey book and they began the long trek out of the cave.

Everyone was ecstatic. The cave was expanding rapidly with new passage everywhere and there were still four days left in the expedition. The next day, they pushed even farther. Beyond Glacier Bay, the passage narrowed and the wind returned with a vengeance. They called this passage Windy City. They had already surveyed nearly a mile of cave and yet the wind was stronger than ever.

Beyond Windy City they found a passage they called Sugarlands. Here, the floor is coated with a brittle layer of gypsum the color of brown sugar. It is like walking on crusted snow. Every step they took, their boots broke through into a layer of soft, loose gypsum sand that looks like pure white sugar crystals.

Just as they began to get spoiled by the easy discoveries and gentle walking passage, the cavers suddenly hit the most difficult obstacle yet. Just beyond Sugarlands at survey station C-61, the passage narrows, the floor drops out, and the ceiling vanishes to form an impossible-looking vertical fissure: the Rift.

Everything about the Rift is hard. The walls vary from three to twenty feet apart, but most of the time it is just a little too wide for easy chimneying. There are footholds everywhere, but half of them are made of crumbling gypsum that gives way the second you put your weight on them. Deep pits open in the floor and make

The Rift at C-61.

ART PALMER

climbing nerve-racking and dangerous. It is a lot like climbing into an empty elevator shaft halfway up a tall building.

More than anything else the Rift is tedious. You chimney up, climb down, and jump from ledge to ledge, over and over again. Everywhere the walls are coated with cave popcorn. These grabby little nodules snag your clothes and you must move carefully to avoid being thrown off balance. By the end of the expedition, they had been able to survey only 200 feet into the Rift.

They kept hoping to find a bypass, but although there were leads everywhere, none of them had any wind. All the air now funneled into this foreboding fissure. They

STAN ALLISON
Paul Burger at the dig culvert; wind measured at 40 mph.

reluctantly concluded that the Rift was the only route onward.

As the long, exciting expedition week finally drew to a close, there was one more thing that had to be done. The breakthrough dig had gradually become more and more dangerous. The constant wind continued to dry out the dirt, and the incessant traffic of dozens of cavers trekking in and out of the cave made it even more unstable.

On the last night of the expedition, Dave, Roy, Neil Backstrom, and Don Kluever worked through the evening stabilizing the dig. The park service provided a twelve-foot section of highway culvert to line the tunnel. There was a steel security gate at one end to protect the cave and a metal ladder had been welded to the inside. They dragged it across the desert in the moonlight, lowered it down the entrance pit, and spent the rest of the night removing rock and debris so it would fit. Then they backfilled around the steel tube, hoping it would provide enough support to stabilize the dig.

It was not until the reports had been filed with the park, the cabins had been cleaned up, and they were on their way home that Dave had a chance to think about how much they had accomplished. His plan had worked and he was now the leader of one the most promising new cave projects in decades.

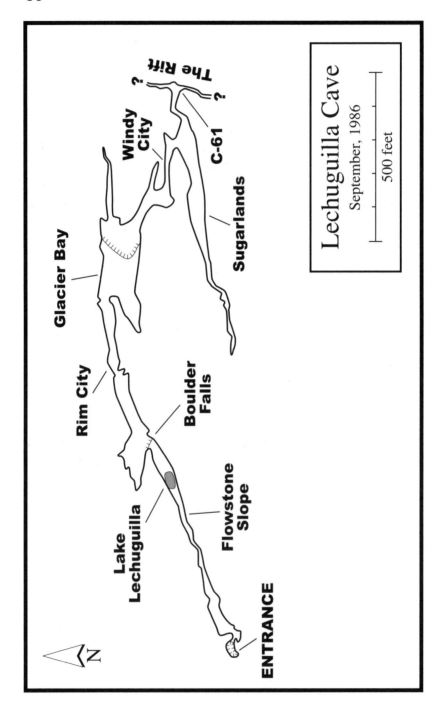

Lechuguilla Cave
September, 1986

500 feet

4

TRIUMPHS
AND TRIBULATIONS

ews of the discovery spread rapidly through the Colorado caving community. Roy told the story of his Boulder Falls descent at least a dozen times to groups of eager listeners. Detailed accounts of the breakthrough dig and the exploration of the cave up to the Rift were published in *Rocky Mountain Caving*. At the grotto meeting, Dave showed slides of the Liberty Bell, Rim City, and other landmarks in the cave. Together the explorers described a cave of great beauty and tremendous potential. Unexplored leads were everywhere.

Despite the excitement, the summer dragged on and Dave still had not scheduled a return expedition. After the initial breakthrough, Dave talked again with Ron Kerbo at the park. Kerbo knew this could be a major discovery. He wanted to make sure that a firm policy was in place before exploration was resumed, but he was too busy to work on it right away. Dave decided to wait to give Kerbo enough time to write a proper management plan.

Roy Glaser could not wait. The rappel down Boulder Falls had been the thrill of a lifetime. One way or another, he was determined to return to Lechuguilla Cave. A few weeks after the breakthrough, Roy asked Dave for permission to return to Lechuguilla with some friends. Dave was reluctant at first, but Roy was persistent. Dave finally agreed that Roy could lead a small expedition in the fall. A few days later, Roy contacted the park and soon had a permit for the first week of September, 1986.

In a way, Roy's expedition fit right into Dave's plans. Dave wanted to use Lechuguilla as a model project and Roy was one of the newcomers he wanted so desperately to help. Roy's expedition would show that new cavers could be trusted to lead expeditions and play a prominent role in the project. Still, Dave was nervous about Roy's intentions. To reassure himself, he composed a long list of rules for the expedition. The dictates were strict: only six people in the cave at one time. Only one day could be devoted to exploring new passage. The remaining four days had to be spent re-surveying the front parts of the cave where the survey notes were incomplete. Finally, all survey data and materials had to be turned over to Dave as soon as the expedition ended.

All of these rules were meant to protect the cave and to give everyone an opportunity to share in the joys of discovery. The idea was to survey the cave carefully while it was being explored. Surveying is a slow and tedious process. A team of three might survey as little as 150 feet of passage in an hour. But this slow pace left plenty of unexplored passage for future teams. Dave could then rotate personnel between trips to insure that everyone would have a chance to explore virgin passage. The technique worked well in small Colorado caves, but in Lechuguilla the plan had a subtle and fundamental flaw: it went against human nature.

Although the rotation of personnel gives everyone an equal opportunity to explore, big discoveries attract hordes of cavers. With so many people lining up to see the cave, once you took your turn, it could be months or years before you would get another. For some people, this was not a problem. For others — those who loved the excitement of exploration, who yearned to see what lay around the next corner — waiting was not an option.

Many Colorado cavers could not wait. As the excitement spread through the caving community, more and more people clamored to see the new discovery. Since Dave had yet to schedule an expedition, Roy was quickly inundated with requests. He tried to keep the preparations low key, but it was not long before Dave caught wind of the size of his expedition. The unbridled enthusiasm and the large number of cavers worried Dave. How could he be sure the cave would be protected? Would they adhere to his principles? Dave added even more rules and threatened to cancel Roy's expedition if they were not followed. Roy was forced to accept Dave's conditions. Ten people were already committed to the trip and he did not want to let them down.

Roy was beginning to feel the heavy responsibilities of leadership. He had never organized a cave expedition before, but he quickly discovered just how much work it was. There were hundreds of things to do. He had to gather all the equipment, get it to the cave, and organize all the participants into working teams. To add to the tension, some of the best cavers in the state would be on his trip and he wanted to make a good impression. The heaviest burden was being responsible for the safety of his friends and fellow cavers. All these anxieties weighed heavily on Roy, and Dave's demands served only to increase the pressure.

Just when Roy was beginning to feel overwhelmed by the job, Rick Bridges offered to help. He had been one of the diggers on the breakthrough team and was eager to get involved. He was energetic, a good organizer, and most of all, seemed unfazed by Dave.

A week before the expedition, Roy got another phone call from Dave.

"What do you want now?" Roy said angrily when he heard Dave's voice. With so little time before the beginning of the expedition he was afraid that Dave would have a whole new set of rules and unreasonable demands.

"Let's meet tomorrow night and we'll talk things over," Dave said. He suggested that they meet at a restaurant between Denver and Boulder. Roy knew the restaurant. It was an expensive French restaurant with a gourmet menu. Roy felt flattered that Dave had invited him to such an elegant place. Its location between their respective homes seemed to imply that Dave was actually trying to meet him halfway. Roy pictured them working out a friendly compromise over a good meal.

Roy arrived at the restaurant early wearing his best suit and tie. When Dave showed up he was dressed in shorts and tennis shoes. Roy quickly realized that Dave had no plans for dinner and intended only to talk in the parking lot. The roar of the highway was too loud for serious discussion, so they moved to the grass of a nearby park. Dave spoke for over an hour, jumping from subject to subject, reiterating his rules and concerns. Roy hardly got in a word edgewise and he left the meeting feeling confused and worried.

Despite Roy's best efforts to understand him, Dave remained an enigma. Why had Dave not organized a return expedition? Why did he insist on such unusual and awkward rules? Why did he keep changing these rules? Roy made a special effort to understand Dave's point of view and tried to control his anger, but he was rapidly approaching the breaking point.

Later that evening, Roy called Rick, looking for support. Rick laughed. His enthusiasm was contagious. Rather than struggle with a problem, Rick made plans and devised strategies. He had a no-nonsense approach to caving and a natural ability to organize. The two of them formulated a simple plan. They would obey Dave's rules to the letter. They would do such a good job on the expedition that Dave would be unable to find anything to criticize and the park service would be impressed. The caving community would view them as leaders. If Dave was left behind, then so be it.

The final week passed quickly, and soon Roy was back at Carlsbad Caverns National Park for the start of the expedition. The first problem to be addressed was the fact that the initial survey started 200 feet into the cave at the dig site, rather than at the entrance. They would have to add a connecting survey from the surface down to the dig. Roy and Rick also noticed inconsistencies and lack of detail in the sketches in the original survey notes. The sketches would have to be completely redone. In effect, they would have to re-survey the entire cave in addition to mapping five passages left unsurveyed from the breakthrough expedition.

Adding to the expedition's problems, some of the best sketchers would be available only at the beginning of the expedition. Many cavers had come down just for the Labor Day weekend and would be driving home on Monday. With a limit of six people in the cave at a time, Roy and Rick realized that the re-surveying might take all week. It did not seem likely that any new exploration would take place.

On Saturday, August 30, 1986, six cavers headed for the entrance of Lechuguilla Cave. When they reached the entrance pit, they split into two groups. Roy led a team deep into the cave, while Rick's team began surveying from the entrance.

Working in Lechuguilla was deceptively easy. When they first entered the cave, the damp air and cool temperature felt good compared to the dry desert heat. But as the two teams progressed inward, away from the dry entrance pit, the warm, damp cave air became stifling. The humidity of Lechuguilla Cave, like most caves, was near 100 percent. As the cavers climbed and crawled, sweat soaked their clothes and poured down their foreheads. The evaporation of sweat normally cools the body, but the high humidity of the cave kept the moisture from evaporating.

Relief from the oppressive heat came only when they rested. After a half-hour break, they even felt chilly. But once they started moving, they soon would be drenched with sweat again.

Both teams worked long and hard. When they returned to camp they had detailed survey notes for all of the cave from the entrance to Boulder Falls, and much of the cave back to the Rift.

The next day, two teams were sent into the cave with the ambitious goal of connecting all the existing surveys together. One team would survey from below Boulder Falls to Glacier Bay, while the other would have the unenviable task of surveying down Boulder Falls. Roy was anxious to see where the cave was leading, and connecting the surveys would provide the information they needed to make a map. Only then would they be able to assess the cave's true potential.

By the end of the second day, the teams had connected all the surveys and finished most of the short side passages. The computer plot was now a continuous line from the entrance to the far side of Glacier Bay. They were close to finishing all of the re-survey. When the cavers returned to camp the next night, exhausted from three consecutive days of hard work, they realized they really were finished and had the rest of the week to explore.

Roy and Rick could not believe their good fortune. They had completed all of the tasks Dave had laid out for them in record time. With the holiday weekend over, the number of Colorado cavers had dwindled from ten to four. Those remaining needed a day off before pushing any farther into the cave.

The day of rest began slowly with a big breakfast. Before the meal was half over, however, Ted Lappin sat down in front of the computer to make improvements in his cave mapping program while he finished a slice of toast. Rick tore the latest maps from the printer and brought them to the table where Roy and Donald Davis were looking at the survey notes. Lechuguilla Cave was now just over a mile long, most of it in a straight line running due east from the entrance. The profile map impressed the explorers most. The cave cascaded into the depths of the earth. Where Sugarlands met the Rift at station C-61, the cave was 672 feet below the entrance.

The cavers considered their options. There were still unchecked leads near the Liberty Bell and beneath Glacier Bay. But the wind was strongest at Windy City, telling them that the bulk of the cave lay beyond that point. That left only a few small crawlways in Sugarlands and the unexplored passage in the Rift, which was already the deepest point in the cave.

"If we can go just a bit deeper," Rick said, "Lechuguilla will be one of the ten deepest caves in the country." Rick's argument was compelling, so they decided to return to the Rift.

The next morning, the hut was full of activity. Ted Lappin moved quickly about the cabin gathering his equipment and loading his already overstuffed pack. He paused, a thoughtful look on his face, as he tried to remember where he had put his vertical gear. Ted was a computer programmer in his early thirties. He had all the appearances of a mad scientist, although he preferred the term "disgruntled scientist." His face was almost hidden behind a full, bushy beard. His gray-black curly hair formed a tangled mound on his head. His clothes hung loosely about his thin, seemingly frail body, but everyone in the room knew that Ted had as much strength and endurance as any of them.

Despite the cavers' enthusiasm, it was after eleven before Roy, Rick, Donald, and Ted managed to assemble their gear and start toward the cave. They were prepared for more vertical work — each of them carried a rope in addition to a cave pack. Ted also brought a camera. The four entered the cave shortly after noon.

They rappelled down the entrance pit and climbed down the culvert. The telluric smell of the cave greeted them as they entered. They crawled twenty feet and then stood up in walking passage. The route was obvious between the two strips of flagging tape on each side of the trail. They went quickly through the entrance passages to the top of the Flowstone Slope. There they stepped carefully among the gours, rimstone dams, and cave pearls. Ted still felt guilty every time he walked through this passage. They were trampling across formations that would be the highlight of most other caves, but there was no way around them. The only option was to walk across the delicate area taking care to step in the same footprints as the person before.

They rappelled down the steep Flowstone Slope and inched their way past the margin of Lake Lechuguilla to reach the top of Boulder Falls. Ted was first on rope. The lip of the pit was still covered with large rocks and dirt waiting to fall. He walked backward, being careful not to dislodge any of the loose rocks, and reached the bottom in three minutes. He quickly detached his rack and moved out of the rockfall zone to the safety of a large slab they called Packs Peak.

"Off rope."

Ted could tell when the next person started over the lip of the pit by the continuous stream of dirt and small pebbles that rained down the shaft. At the top of the pit, the others talked in whispers so they could hear any shouted commands from the caver on rope.

Half an hour later, the four cavers regrouped at Packs Peak. They dropped off some bottles of water, packed their gear, and continued deeper into the cave. They passed through Rim City and crossed Glacier Bay to climb down the huge blocks of gypsum at the far end of the room. As they passed through Windy City, they noticed that the flagging tape hanging from the ceiling was fluttering wildly. It was a strong wind day – good for tracing the route through the cave. They passed through Sugarlands and soon arrived at station C-61. They had reached the Rift.

The large, oval walking passage they had been traveling through abruptly stopped. Perpendicular to the passage lay a great fissure. The cleft cut through the bedrock as if tremendous forces had ripped the earth apart, creating this crack far beneath the surface. From their vantage point at C-61, the cavers headlamps illuminated neither the top nor the bottom of the Rift. They could see boulders wedged between the walls that could be used as stepping stones. In places they were clumped together to form false floors hundreds of feet long at various levels.

They paused for a short break to catch their breath. They were hot and sweaty, but anxious to continue. They shouldered their packs again and started into the Rift. The route began with a ten-foot climb down to a large chockstone, and then a climb back up the other side to the opposite wall of the fissure. They turned south and walked along a narrow ledge before entering the long stoopway passage that made up this part of the Rift. They moved south in the fissure to the final survey point only 200 feet away. Now the work began.

They stood at the edge of a pit. Here they could either traverse across to a ledge on the far side or drop down the pit.

"You don't set depth records by traversing," Rick said.

He tied a rope around a large boulder and threw the coil down the pit. Donald rappelled first, taking the end of the measuring tape with him. The drop ended on a slope of gypsum rubble that slanted steeply down the narrow fissure. The walls were only two feet apart, making it almost easier to chimney down than to walk.

Ted watched as Roy and Rick followed Donald. At each station, Roy read the compass and clinometer while Rick recorded the numbers and sketched the passage. Ted brought up the rear, stopping frequently to take photos. The fissure went down for a hundred feet and then turned sharply upward, at a forty-five-degree angle. Now the slope changed from loose dirt to flowstone. A river of stone cascaded down the walls in shades of orange, cream, and white. All along the floor were small pockets filled with tiny white cave pearls. Ted paused again for more photos, occasionally dodging blocks of gypsum and small pebbles dislodged by the others above him.

The first thing Ted noticed when he got to the top of the slope was a beautiful fossil embedded in the wall. It was a cephalopod — the family to which both the nautiluses and ammonites belong. It was sliced almost perfectly in half as if designed to be part of a museum display. The second thing Ted noticed was that the floor dropped away precipitously into a void at least fifty feet deep. He did not dare get close enough to the edge for a good look at the bottom. The walls of the fissure widened inconveniently to six feet at this point, making it impossible to chimney over the pit.

They looked for a solid anchor point for the rope among the blocks of crumbly gypsum. The closest place to secure the rope was fifty feet back down the flowstone slope. They tied two ropes together so they could reach the anchor and still have enough length for the pit. Donald went down first to check out the route. Soon only the dim glow of Donald's light was visible, but the sound of crashing rocks told the others he was still descending. Thirty minutes later the waiting cavers heard the faint zip-whirr-zip-whirr sound of a ropewalker ascending system. Donald stopped on a ledge forty feet below the others and shouted up his report. He had rappelled down sixty feet and used the rope as a handline for another thirty. There were crawlways at the bottom that headed north and south, but they ended after only a few feet.

"I think I can chimney to the opposite side of the pit," Donald said, pointing across the fissure.

The route was exposed — a slip would most likely drop him into the chasm. Donald disconnected himself from the rope and climbed easily up the fissure to a ledge straight across from the other cavers. Then Roy rappelled down the rope and stopped on the ledge where Donald began his climb. Ted leaned out over the pit and lowered the end of the measuring tape from his survey station down to Roy.

Traversing the passage was a formidable task, but surveying added to the difficulty.

"Hey you guys," Roy shouted up to Ted and Rick.
"I'll bet you can rappel halfway down and then swing
across."

The trick worked; they pendulumed across the pit
and the team was reunited on the far side. Ted looked at
his watch. It had taken them three hours to overcome this
one obstacle.

The fissure had no floor here, which forced them to
chimney along the passage. The easiest route led them up
and down repeatedly, fifty feet at a time. Soon the floor
appeared again, rising from the depths to meet them.
Again it was covered with flowstone, this time dominated
by shades of blue and black instead of white. At the top of
the slope, they found a pocket of black cave pearls and
another pit.

They named the saddle Black Pearl Pass. Ted looked
around in wonder at the grandeur – and difficulty – of this
cave. He was beginning to understand it now. The Rift was
a giant, nearly vertical, two-dimensional maze. They had
the options of going forward, back, up, or down. What
appeared to be floors were actually just rocks and dirt
wedged between the fissure walls. It was possible to walk
down the passage for a hundred feet, chimney down
through a hole in the floor, and then walk back under the
"floor" you had just traversed. The cave was proving to be
far more challenging than expected and they were beginning to wonder if they were in over their heads. Ted had
been caving for years and had spent most of his time in
Colorado caves. Even the exposed climbs of Fixin'-to-Die
Cave – one of the most difficult in Colorado – had not prepared him for this.

It was now 11:30 p.m. and the strain of the long day
was beginning to show. If this pit ahead of them was anything like the last one, it could take hours to cross. They
were almost out of drinking water, and the entrance was

five hours away. It was time to go. They packed their survey gear and moved slowly toward the surface. By the time they reached the entrance, they had been in the cave for sixteen hours.

The exhausted cavers arrived back at the huts just before dawn, just in time to see the bats returning to Carlsbad Cavern. The return of the bats in the early morning hours is unlike the famous mass departures in the evening. One by one, from every direction, single bats race back to the enormous entrance of Carlsbad. As they cross over the entrance pit they fold their wings and drop like stones, the air whistling past their bodies making a sound like a falling bomb. After diving eighty feet and reaching the level of the entrance corridor, they open their wings with a soft pop and resume their flight into the cavern. Two to three bats dive into the cave every second, filling the morning air with an eerie music. The tired explorers marveled at the sight for only a moment, and then turned to walk up the stone steps.

As they entered the cabin, curiosity got the better of them. They had made only twelve survey shots and it would just take a few minutes to process the data with the computer. The results were as expected: they had pushed the cave 330 feet further south, but only 65 feet deeper – not enough to set a record. Ted started the computer on the slow task of drawing plots, and the cavers finally crawled into their sleeping bags and fell asleep.

Ted Lappin awoke at the crack of noon. He did not head for the shower, and he did not enter the kitchen. Instead he walked directly to the computer to see what the latest plots of Lechuguilla Cave revealed. He stretched and yawned as he tore the sheets of paper away with one hand. He walked to the central table and sat down with the plots, squinting in the bright sunlight that streamed in through the dirty window.

The cave was L-shaped. It headed almost due east from the entrance and then turned south at the Rift. The new survey extended the southern limit of the cave, making the fissure-like structure of the Rift more apparent. Ted scratched his beard and moved to the next page. The cave now appeared in profile, viewed from the south.

He marveled at how quickly the cave lost elevation. It was only a few thousand feet to the Rift and yet station C-61 was over 650 feet below the entrance. He looked for the lines of the survey they had just completed only to find overlapping zigzags of black ink on the page. This was what the north-south-trending passages looked like when viewed in profile from the south. To get a profile view of the new survey, the computer would have to draw the cave as seen from the west. Ted thought about the changes he needed to make in the program. He walked over to the keyboard and began typing. The early-model portable computer answered with rude beeps, obviously unhappy with Ted's initial input. He cursed the primitive programming language he had to work with. His frustration disappeared quickly, however, and Ted again became one with the machine. He worked all day, barely noticing the sun sinking below the horizon. It was late evening before he finally got the results he wanted.

⚜ ⚜ ⚜

Friday morning came too early for the explorers. Most of them were sore from a full week of hard caving. Blane Colton was the exception. He had arrived late in the week and was now eagerly anticipating his first trip into the incredible cave. Roy was the last to get up. He stumbled into the kitchen rubbing his eyes.

"I'm trashed," he said. "I don't think I'm going in this time."

"This will be the last trip," Rick said. "Tomorrow we have to clean the cabins and write our report. Sunday we'll be driving home."

"I know," Roy said. "But there's always next time. Besides, I want you guys to find the way out of that damn Rift so I can come in and scoop booty." Roy laughed.

"OK," Rick said. "But if we find a way out, we'll be the ones scooping."

Several hours later, Ted, Rick, Donald, and Blane made another late start, arriving at the cave shortly before noon. This time they entered with a single purpose: to find a way out of the Rift. Soon they reached the first rope drop, where they had started the survey on the previous trip. With the ropes already in place, and everyone but Blane familiar with the route, it seemed to take no time at all to return to the top of Black Pearl Pass.

Now they were confronted with the same dilemma as before: which way should they go? There were holes in almost every direction. Which way would lead them to more big passages? It was already early afternoon.

"Let's eat," Ted said.

Rick collapsed on the floor with a sigh of relief. He was breathing heavily from the exertion of the long, strenuous trip.

"You know," Rick said, "the first part of this cave was real easy. Only a few rope drops, big walking passage, well-decorated rooms. Traveling through the upper cave is kind of like a monkey swinging from tree to tree. It's easy."

"But the Rift is different," Ted said, taking a bite from his candy bar.

"Yeah," Rick said, breathing more slowly now. "This Rift stuff is like that monkey turned into a big gorilla and is pounding on my head."

"It must be the Lech-a-Gorilla," Ted said. "It must have climbed onto your pack back at C-61." They laughed.

The four cavers considered their options. They could go up, but the fissure overhead appeared too wide to chimney. They could go down, which seemed to lead farther south, but they would have to place another rope. Or they could go east into a small crawlway that branched away from where they were sitting. They finished lunch and started into the crawlway, the path of least resistance. It ended after only sixty feet. They quickly returned to the top of Black Pearl Pass with only one viable option: down.

They descended twenty-five feet to a large ledge. The fissure continued down, but the easiest route appeared to be forward, where they would have to chimney over the depths. The awkward, narrow passage was opening up to a comfortable five feet wide. Abundant hand and footholds made route finding simple and it was much less stressful to chimney over a mere twenty feet of exposure, rather than the fifty feet that was common in the passages behind them. They continued to survey over the hole in the floor, along the fissure, and over another low pass.

Ahead of them lay what, by Rift standards, could be called a room. The walls were ten to twenty feet apart. For eighty feet the floor was smooth and flat, and was covered with soft dirt and a few small rocks. The ceiling of the fissure was not visible far over their heads. Although it was not a large room compared to others in the cave, it was definitely the most comfortable spot they had found in the Rift. The room was big enough to deserve a name: Lech-a-Gorilla Hall.

They continued onward with renewed vigor. Perhaps the fissure was finally opening up and the Rift was finally ending. Blane was in the lead when he let out a shout, "It goes!"

The others scrambled forward to see the new passage. Their hearts sank as they caught up with Blane. What his feeble carbide lamp had shown as a black void ahead was only a mound of dark red flowstone. The passage ended. The disappointed cavers returned to the center of Lech-a-Gorilla Hall for a break. As they ate and drank, they scanned the walls and floor for leads, hoping desperately that they had not truly reached the end. They split up and climbed into several small holes, each of which ended after twenty feet.

Then Donald yelled that he had found a small fissure that continued. The others gathered their packs and survey gear and followed Donald into the one- by three-foot elliptical hole. The passage quickly opened into a walking

fissure with a steeply descending floor. They followed the
passage down while Rick sketched the route in the survey
book. With each survey shot he updated the plan and profile sketches, calling out the incremental depth. Minus 50,
minus 100, minus 150; the passage continued steeply
downward. After dropping nearly 200 feet below Lech-a-
Gorilla Hall, the fissure ended abruptly in a small pool of
water. The walls and floor were covered with a thick layer
of flowstone – there would be no leads from here.

The explorers finished their survey and climbed back
up to Lech-a-gorilla Hall. It was late evening. Ted was
ambivalent about their discoveries. They had pushed the
survey much deeper than anything yet found in the cave
and Lechuguilla was now one of the ten deepest caves in
the United States, but they had not found a way out of the
Rift. Worse, they had checked dozens of leads in the area
and come up with nothing. Ted looked over at Rick to see
him staring upward.

"Look up," Rick said.

"I don't see anything," Ted said.

"Up there. That's where we need to go."

"Yeah, right. How do you plan on getting up there?"

"I don't know yet," Rick said. "But just look at it."

Ted had to admit that climbing the fissure looked
promising. It seemed to get larger as it ascended toward a
fifteen-foot hole in the ceiling far overhead. It almost
looked as though it opened up into another passage beyond
the hole.

"Well, we aren't going up there tonight," Ted said.

"Next time," Rick said. "Next time."

The next morning, Ron Kerbo dropped by the cabins
to find five ecstatic cavers. Roy eagerly showed him the
computer plot of the cave. It was not a formal map, but
simply a sequence of lines leading from one survey station
to the next. Although no wall or floor detail was shown, the
line plot illustrated the basic structure of the cave. Rick
presented a list of the deepest caves in the United States,

with a bold line drawn between number seven and number eight. At 925 feet deep, Lechuguilla had become the eighth deepest cave. The cave was 7,440 feet long – almost a mile and a half.

Roy understood the implications of what they had accomplished. In addition to doing everything Dave had asked for, they had doubled the surveyed length of the cave and had set a new depth record. The expedition had run smoothly and Kerbo was pleased with the results. The expedition had succeeded beyond Roy's wildest hopes. There was nothing Dave could complain about.

Roy should have been happy, but a troubling thought kept nagging at him. Dave's rules dictated that other cavers had to be given the chance to explore. With the number of people who wanted to go to Lechuguilla, it would be two years or more before Roy could return.

Roy wrestled with an ethical dilemma. He knew there was an unwritten rule among the cavers that gave Dave the right to direct the exploration of the cave as he wished. It was only fair. Dave and John had led the dig project that uncovered Lechuguilla. For two years they had toiled with those few cavers they could badger into helping. Lechuguilla Cave was Dave Allured's dream come true. It belonged to him.

Still, the memories of the dazzling passages haunted Roy. He remembered the thrill of descending Boulder Falls, the excitement of finding Glacier Bay, the lure of the Rift, and the wind. The wind that whistled through the entrance with such incredible force, the wind that spoke of passages yet unseen. Roy had been bitten by the bug – he craved the adrenaline rush that accompanied exploration.

"This is crazy," Roy thought. "This cave is difficult: you can't just take a bunch of novices to the last survey station and say, 'Start here.' This cave needs strong and experienced cavers. Cavers who have been here before are the ones most likely to contribute to the project. Strong cavers cannot be brushed aside and told, 'See you in two years.' It's not right for Dave to keep us out of this cave."

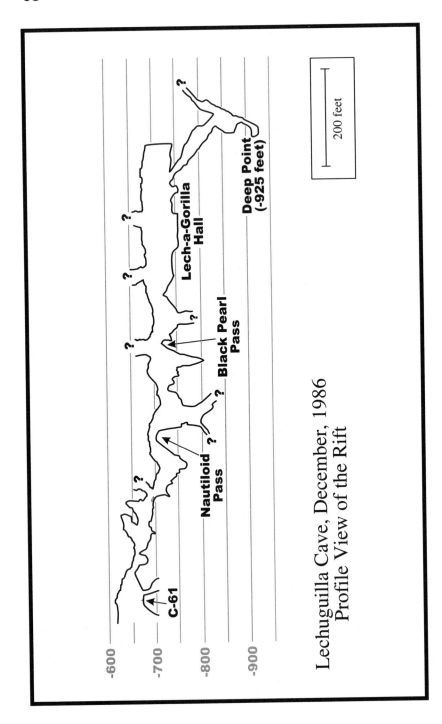

Lechuguilla Cave, December, 1986
Profile View of the Rift

He was now thinking thoughts that bordered on heresy. Roy wanted back into Lechuguilla Cave and he was willing to do anything in his power to accomplish it. He felt guilty when he confessed his feelings to Rick, only to discover that Rick felt the same way.

"I'm willing to flag the trail, I'm willing to take out my waste, I'm even willing to survey as we explore," Roy said. "But whatever it takes, I want to go back into Lechuguilla Cave."

Roy and Rick talked late into the night, discussing how they could get around Dave's rule that would not let them return.

It was easy. They had done so much work in one short week that Ron Kerbo was very impressed. By the time they left Carlsbad Caverns National Park, they had obtained another permit to return in two months.

Roy and Rick talked about Dave all the way back to Denver, trying to figure out a way to deal with him. They knew that Dave believed he had the right to run the project the way he wanted and would not budge.

Within a few days, Dave discovered that Roy and Rick had a permit to return to Lechuguilla and the battle lines were drawn. It was Roy and Rick against Dave and John, and the controversy polarized the cavers. Each side tried to sway the cave community and to recruit supporters to their camp, which only divided the cavers further. The more level-headed people knew that the battle was destructive and unnecessary. Worst of all, the conflict could jeopardize everyone's relationship with the park. Neutral cavers began pushing both groups for a compromise.

A meeting was organized to bring the two factions together to try to establish some common ground. Two impartial cavers, Ed LaRock and Steve Dunn, invited both factions to a meeting in Rick's office.

The meeting started. Dave asked Rick for copies of the survey notes taken on their expedition.

"Will you let us back in the cave?" Rick asked.

"No," Dave replied. "You have to wait your turn like everyone else."

"Then you don't get the notes," Rick said.

"You agreed to turn over copies of the notes," Dave said angrily.

"Not until you let us back into the cave," Rick said. His voice was hard and determined.

Roy and Rick had a trump card, and they were playing it. Without the notes, Dave's survey efforts would remain disjointed and inconsistent. He would have to re-survey the entire cave before meaningful progress could be made. The person who held the survey notes had control of the cave, and Rick knew it.

The meeting quickly degenerated into a shouting match. Dave accused Roy and Rick of stabbing him in the back and breaking their promises. Rick, the more eloquent speaker, accused Dave of making arbitrary and illogical rules. Roy did not take the lead in the arguments. He was torn. He knew he had broken his promise to Dave by not delivering the notes, but he also knew that once the notes were turned over, Dave would never let him into the cave again.

As mediators, Ed and Steve tried their best to find a compromise – Rick would turn over the notes and Dave would let Roy and Rick back into the cave. But neither side would budge. Three hours later, the meeting ended unresolved. Dave did not have copies of the survey notes, and Roy and Rick still had a permit to return to Lechuguilla Cave.

Dave finally scheduled his own expedition for the Columbus Day weekend in October, 1986. It was more than a month after Roy and Rick's Labor Day trip. His expedition was small by comparison since he invited only close friends and a couple of newcomers. Without the new data, Dave was forced to use the original survey notes from the breakthrough expedition. He prepared a simple map to present to the park.

Roy and Rick were not idle during the intervening month. Rick had one of the draftsmen in his company make a pen and ink version of the map. When he was done, the poster-size map was a thing of beauty. All the fine detail of the cave passages had been committed to paper in both plan and profile views. Rick's and Dave's maps were as different as a fine oil painting and a rough sketch. Roy and Rick sent the three-by-four-foot map to the park by overnight mail, so it would arrive just before Dave's expedition.

For Dave, the expedition was a disaster. Instead of exploring the cave, Dave spent most of his time at park headquarters lobbying to get Roy and Rick banned from the cave for life. He insisted that they had not been operating "in the spirit of the project."

When it came to results, however, Dave failed miserably. Where Roy and Rick had been careful to invite the most experienced surveyors and cartographers on their trip, Dave was saddled with novices. In the course of a week, Dave surveyed less than 1,000 feet compared to Rick and Roy's 3,000. Roy and Rick had pushed the cave farther and deeper. Dave surveyed only a handful of insignificant side passages.

Ron Kerbo was in a bind. As the cave specialist for Carlsbad Caverns National Park, he was responsible for protecting the caves and administering access to them. He had made numerous phone calls to all the parties involved but found only anger and bitterness. On the one hand, he acknowledged that Dave was the permit holder for the original dig. Dave had organized the trips. Dave had been responsible for the breakthrough. Now Dave was applying his principles to working in Lechuguilla Cave. Kerbo did not agree with all of Dave's ideas, but he knew they were motivated by the highest conservation standards. On the other hand, Dave was not a great leader. He was organizing expeditions as if this were some small Colorado cave, rather than a world-class cavern.

Roy and Rick were producing results. They had re-surveyed the entire cave in record time. They had pushed the limits of exploration, and they had produced an excellent cave map. But they refused to cooperate with Dave, and they refused to abide by the project rules Dave had established.

Kerbo had his own constraints to deal with. Despite Dave's demands, he could not ban Roy and Rick from the cave. The cave was on public land, a part of the public trust the park service was charged with protecting for future generations. It would be unwise to take sides in a dispute between cavers; it would be much better to encourage them to work it out among themselves. Kerbo also knew that the cave had potential. A new discovery of this magnitude could reflect well on the National Park Service. He could see that an opportunity to improve the image of the whole park system was about to disintegrate in a wave of petty politics and infighting.

In the end, Kerbo felt he had no choice but to close the cave. He sent letters to the expedition participants announcing that all future trips had been canceled and that the cave would be closed until a management plan had been developed. Kerbo hoped that by giving everyone a few months off, tempers would cool and reconciliation would be possible.

Closing the cave, however, had the opposite effect. Each group blamed the other for depriving cavers of the opportunity to explore. At the same time, both groups began intense lobbying campaigns to influence the park service. The fierce battle that followed became known as the Colorado Cave Wars. Letters were written to senators and congressmen. Heated debates consumed grotto meetings. Editorials and commentaries were published in national caving publications. A rift had formed between the opposing factions, and the gap was becoming wider with time.

Finally, in May, 1987, one year after the breakthrough, the park service released a management plan offering co-leadership of the project to Dave, John, Roy, and Rick. Dave and John were acknowledged for their work in discovering the cave, and Roy and Rick were acknowledged for their contributions to surveying and mapping. The four of them would be equal co-leaders reporting to Ron Kerbo.

John, Roy, and Rick sent the park a letter of acceptance that included a list of agreed upon responsibilities. Dave, however, refused to participate unless Roy and Rick were removed from the newly formed project. The park service refused to change the management plan, so Dave declined.

Over the next few months, Dave Allured wrote fewer letters and stopped attending grotto meetings. He watched silently as the project took off and the cave began to expand. What had started as a humble, unglamorous dig beneath the desert of New Mexico was fast becoming the greatest cave discovery of the century.

Dave Allured never returned to Lechuguilla Cave.

5

BEYOND THE RIFT

ust after noon on July 30, 1987 a two-car caravan
arrived in Colorado Springs. Rick Bridges was
driving his four-wheel-drive Suburban that still had a new-
car look and feel. He had enough room for six people without their gear. Roy Glaser followed in his battered,
early-70's pickup truck. Rick parked in front of Steve
Reames' house and Roy drove into the driveway. Leslie
Clarfield arrived in her small pickup and immediately
started loading her gear into Roy's truck. Steve's gear was
stacked and ready in the living room and was loaded in a
few minutes. They were ready to go. They made a final stop
to pick up Neeld Messler, and then headed south.

The 530-mile drive gave the explorers ample opportunity to speculate about the future of the newly formed
Lechuguilla Cave Project. In addition, they talked about
more general topics: the pros and cons of various vertical
ascending systems, carbide versus electric headlamps, and
the best survey techniques to use in the new cave. Finally,
some of them drifted off to sleep.

Just before 11:00 p.m., the two vehicles reached Carlsbad Caverns and pulled up in front of a small stone cabin

CRF Hut #5, one of two buildings that housed visiting cavers.

with the words "CRF 5" over the front entrance. Fumbling with the combination lock, Roy opened the thick wooden door. He turned on the lights and smiled as he surveyed the room. The decor was Early American Garage Sale, common among volunteer organizations. The entry room, the largest in the hut, was an eating and general gathering area occupied by an old, olive-green sofa and several odd chairs. Sections of the tile were missing from the dusty floor, and the wall paint was peeling. The room was set up for overflow sleeping, with a thin mattress in one corner and a mattress on a sagging frame in the other. The room to the right was the kitchen, equipped with a stove and refrigerator from the fifties. A wide, low window on the south side provided light during the day, but now the only illumination was a single bare bulb hanging from the ceiling.

On the other side of the entry room, a small hallway led to a bedroom and a small bathroom. In the bedroom there were two triple-bunk beds made from two-by-fours, canvas, and galvanized pipe. They creaked and groaned whenever someone climbed in or out of bed. Sleeping on the top bunk was always interesting, with the whole bunk twisting and moving every time someone below turned over. There were no shelves in the room, so caving gear was stacked on the floor. Over the years, the hut's solid wooden doors had been painted so many times they would not shut.

Roy walked through the hut flipping on every light switch as he went.

"There's a light out in the kitchen," he said.

The hut quickly filled with gear and, since more people would be arriving later in the evening, each caver claimed a bunk by tossing a sleeping bag on it. Rick, Roy, and John sat in the kitchen making plans for the next day.

"Who's going in tomorrow?" John asked.

Roy looked at the list of names.

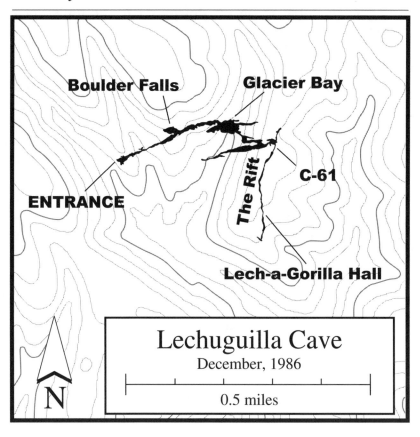

Boulder Falls Glacier Bay

C-61

The Rift

ENTRANCE

Lech-a-Gorilla Hall

Lechuguilla Cave
December, 1986

0.5 miles

N

"Rick, Leslie, Don, Art, and you will be one team; Kirk Branson, Norm Thompson, and Alan Williams will be the other. Bruce Zerr and his son David want to take wind measurements at the entrance and Barb am Ende and Tish Korbly are scheduled to go along with them."

"But, what's the plan?" John said.

"Find a way out of the Rift into virgin cave," Rick said. "We lose the wind somewhere just before C-61 in the Rift so the air is probably going high and disappearing into a ceiling fissure. Kirk, Norm, and Alan are going to take some pictures around Glacier Bay and then check for leads in the north Rift."

"What if the wind goes into holes too small to follow?"

"Then thirty people are down here for nothing. Let's go to bed, we need some sleep."

At seven o'clock the next morning, a few cavers began to move about, preparing for the trip. Those who were going to spend the day on the surface had no reason to get up early, but by eight o'clock, the noise in the hut was too loud for anyone to sleep. Ropes, rope pads, helmets, cave packs, water bottles, and headlamps were gathered, inspected, and hauled out to the awaiting vehicles. Inside the hut, the normal sounds of breakfast preparation were absent – no one wanted to waste time on anything more than cereal and milk.

The temperature was already over eighty degrees by the time the explorers were ready to leave. The cars lined up single file behind Rick's four-wheel-drive Suburban. Roy walked up to the driver's-side window and shook hands with Rick. "Good luck."

Rick smiled, "See you tomorrow."

As the caravan rolled down the service road toward the cave, twenty minutes away, Rick was happy. All the ideas and plans that had been brewing for over a year were finally going to be tested. Every caver in the truck had seen the map of Lechuguilla and had a different opinion about where the cave would lead. Rick was particularly inter-ested in the fissure above Lech-a-Gorilla Hall. Even with powerful headlamps, the holes in the ceiling were just barely visible. Rick did not have the skills needed to make the climb himself, but he knew two climbers who did. The lure of virgin passage had brought Don Doucette and Art Wiggins to Lechuguilla Cave.

Don was strong and slender, with light-brown hair and brown eyes. He was nearly forty but he looked much younger. He had a warm smile, a wry sense of humor, and a quiet confidence that pervaded everything he did. Don had grown up in Colorado Springs and learned to climb by scrambling up the spires and canyon walls at the edge of town. When he was just eighteen, he climbed El Capitan in Yosemite, and during the next six years he established new routes on Devils Tower and made first ascents in the canyon country of Utah. He was among the best.

Don had been caving for years, mostly in the high alpine caves of Colorado, but Art Wiggins had never been underground before. In fact, even though they had known each other for years, Don and Art had never even climbed together. Still, Don knew that Art was a superb climber. Like Don, he had climbed in Yosemite and on the sand-stone towers in the desert. He had long hair and a bushy mustache and, like Don, he was quiet and confident.

At the parking area, each member of the team took a portion of the group gear. Everyone had a small cave pack except the two climbers; they had huge packs filled with climbing equipment. Between the two of them they had all the specialized gear needed to deal with every imaginable climbing situation.

Half an hour later they were at the entrance. The desert was hot and they were all eager to enter the cool air of the cave. John rigged the entrance drop, and one at a time the members of the first team rappelled into the pit. Air rushed through the entrance culvert, moving at its typ-ical fifteen to twenty miles per hour.

They went quickly down the entrance corridor, past the Liberty Bell, and down the Flowstone Slope. They paused at the edge of Lake Lechuguilla to fill their bottles with drinking water. It was the last water they would see on this trip. The team waited at the top of Boulder Falls while Rick rigged the rope, then each rappelled down. They continued on through Rim City, Glacier Bay, and Windy City, finally arriving at C-61. Everyone was sweating heavily now. The large walking passage they had been traveling in ended abruptly. Before them lay the Rift. Standing at the edge, one could look up, down, left, and right and see only darkness. This was the last good resting spot until they reached Lech-a-Gorilla Hall; the next four hours would be spent traversing 1,200 feet of tortuous passage.

Leaving some water bottles for the trip out, they continued onward. Three hundred feet of scrambling through the Rift brought them to the first rope drop, twenty feet deep. Over Nautiloid Pass and then Black Pearl Pass, they finally reached their destination. Now the real work would begin.

They paused to eat and to drink some precious water. Rick pointed to several holes in the ceiling, the largest directly above them. The Rift was only six feet wide here and tilted at a sixty-five degree angle; the wall before them was a nearly featureless slope of packed gypsum. Art and Don studied the slope. They looked for lines, curves, and handholds, and began get to a feel for the rock. The angle of the wall was low at first, but became increasingly steep toward the top. There were not many places to hang an anchor for protection, so bolts would be needed.

"Getting to that first rock should be easy," Don said, as he pointed at the wall and traced the route with his finger. "After that you can go left a bit and then up."

Art took the first lead. A boulder the size of a small pickup truck was wedged in the fissure fifty feet overhead. Art climbed effortlessly to the rock and set up a belay. John and Don followed with the rest of the gear. Down below,

Rick and Leslie decided to remove some rocks from a nearby crawlway while they waited.

The gypsum wall was crumbly like partially-dried brown sugar. Double-checking everything, Art prepared to start out onto the face.

"Belay on?"

"On belay," Don said.

"Climbing."

"Climb."

Art started climbing diagonally, to the left. He could see a shallow, irregular fissure about fifteen feet away that would be the best place to find holds. He slowly and delicately worked his way across the wall. He reached the crack, relaxed for just a moment, found a reasonable foothold, and drove a piton into the soft gypsum. He clipped the rope into the piton and examined the crack above him. The fissure appeared to fade away about twenty-five feet overhead, but he would worry about that when he got there. Moving upward, Art reached the end of the crack sooner than he expected.

There were no irregularities that would hold any kind of anchor. Looking at his last piece of protection far below, Art decided it was time to place a bolt. Maintaining a delicate balance on the rock face, he reached into his pack and pulled out the drill, hammer, and bolt hanger. Each had a tether to keep it from falling. Art began hammering on the end of the steel drill, driving the bit into the rock. Normally, if the rock was solid, the drill would sing out with a high-pitched ringing sound. The dull thuds above Art indicated that the rock was soft and might not hold the anchor. The thought made Don nervous. Fifteen minutes crept by before Art declared he was finished.

"How solid is it?" Don asked from below.

"It's bombproof. This bolt isn't going anywhere."

Art clipped his figure-8 rappel device to the rope and prepared to come back down to the belay ledge. Don would continue the lead from here.

It took Art only seconds to descend what had taken almost an hour to climb. Arriving at the belay ledge, Art turned to Don.

"Your turn."

"Your hammering sure didn't sound good. I hope that bolt holds."

"The gypsum is too soft. It's not a very good placement, but I think it's fairly solid."

"Thanks," Don said as he tied into the end of the rope. He took the bolt kit and climbing gear from Art, and loaded every piece of exotic gear he had. He had no idea what would be needed or what would work on the difficult section ahead.

"Belay on?"

"On belay."

"Climbing."

"Climb."

Don moved out onto the face, searching for the same holds he had seen Art use. As he placed his fingers on a small knob, it gave way and crumbled into dust. Don instantly shifted his weight and caught himself.

"I sure hope that bolt is solid," Don said.

"Well, actually it's a little loose," Art said.

"Loose!" Don exclaimed. "I thought you said it was bombproof!"

"It is," Art said, "for gypsum."

Don reached the crack and paused to catch his breath. Then he quickly climbed to the bolt and tugged on it. As he expected, the bolt was solid. Art, the eternal pessimist, would never overstate the strength of an anchor. Maybe that was why he had lived as long as he had.

Don continued climbing methodically. The wall was rapidly getting steeper and the hand and footholds were farther apart. After twenty feet, he stopped to place another bolt. It took fifteen minutes of difficult hammering to set the anchor in place, and Don's arms were tired. While he rested, he grabbed the anchor and leaned back, trying to see the route above. He could see a passage up there, but the angle of the wall was over eighty degrees and the climbing was going to be even more difficult. Moving much more slowly now, Don gained another ten feet. Here, the slope was almost vertical and handholds were nonexistent. He decided to place a third and final bolt to protect the next dozen feet of climbing.

After inspecting the wall above the bolt, Don yelled down to Art, "There's nothing here. I'm going to use the cliffhooks."

Art tensed and readjusted his stance to prepare himself in case Don fell.

"I've got you covered," he called up.

Don reached for his gear sling and removed a small metal hook no larger than the end of a tablespoon. A thin nylon sling with footloops hung from the hook. Don found a tiny irregularity in the wall and placed the curved end of the hook over the protrusion. Putting one foot into the loop, Don began to shift his weight carefully to the cliffhook. The tiny tip of the hook dug into the soft gypsum wall and felt stable. Don slowly took another hook from his gear sling and placed it above and to the side of the first.

"Slack!"

Art relaxed the tension on the rope, still ready to arrest a possible fall. Don did not like having slack in the line, but he knew that the slightest tug on the rope might pull him off balance. Like a dancer in slow motion, he raised his other foot into the sling of the second hook. It shuddered and then held. The cliffhooks now held Don's entire weight, and would continue to do so provided he did not do anything radical – like take a deep breath. Shifting all of his weight to the second hook, Don moved the first hook higher and placed its tip on another tiny ledge. He could see the passage above him clearly now; in fact, two large passages took off in opposite directions. To get up there, he would have to scale a ten-foot section of wall that was perfectly smooth. He had no choice but to create a placement for one of the cliffhooks. Moving carefully, he took out his hammer and drill. With the lightest possible taps, he hammered a small depression into the cliff face. Don hung the cliffhook over the edge of the depression and stepped up into the footloop. Now he was within reach of a solid handhold. With one swift movement he grabbed the hold and swung himself onto the ledge.

"Belay off," he shouted, and relaxed for the first time in forty minutes.

"What do you see?" John yelled from below.

"Let me check it out," Don said. "Give me five minutes."

Don chose the southward trending passage. It was fifteen feet wide and a dozen feet high. After a hundred yards, the passage widened into a small room, twenty feet wide and more than twenty feet high. Pure-white soda-straw stalactites over three feet long hung from the ceiling. The passage continued around the corner, splitting into two oval-shaped corridors the size of subway tunnels. There was no doubt in Don's mind that this was the breakthrough they were hoping for. Returning to the top of the climb, he shouted to the others below to come up using the fixed rope he had anchored. Don moved aside and leaned against a large rock in the passage. He named the climb Captain Hook's Ladder.

6

TRAVERSING
THE OVERPASS

oy Glaser paced impatiently into and out of the main hut. Eight cavers, including Roy, stood ready to leave for Lechuguilla Cave. Rick had estimated twelve hours for his trip, the first exploration visit to Lechuguilla in more than ten months. Roy glanced at the clock again. It was after 8:00 a.m., and the morning sun was beginning to make its effect felt on the desert below. Nearly sixteen hours had passed since Rick and his team had entered the cave.

Roy's team could not enter the cave until Rick returned. The new park rules allowed only eight people in the cave at one time. This limitation spawned an idea the cavers called tag-team caving. When members of one team left the cave, they quickly briefed the members of the next team about their discoveries. Armed with this knowledge, the new team would push the cave farther and deeper. It was like a children's game of tag and turned out to be a very efficient technique for exploring a cave with a limited number of people.

"If they aren't here by nine, we're going in after them," Roy said to no one in particular.

"That probably won't be necessary," one of the cavers said as the dirty brown Suburban appeared on the service road.

"They're back," someone yelled from the kitchen. Roy was already standing in the driveway, ready to meet the vehicle as it pulled to a stop in front of the hut. Cavers came out of both doors of the hut to hear the news.

The grin on Rick's face said it all. They had discovered a way past the Rift. Half-a-dozen excited conversations started all at once. In a rapid exchange, Roy and his teams learned where the passages were and how to get to them. There were three leads: two south from the top of Captain Hook's Ladder and one that cut back north over their approach route. If the northern passage connected back to one of the earlier surveys, it might provide a shortcut around the long and tedious route through the Rift.

Several hours later, Roy's team reached C-61 at the start of the Rift where they stashed some bottles of water for the return trip. Two climbers, Neeld Messler and Neil Backstrom, started checking leads by climbing up into the Rift. Their job was to try to find an easier way to the top of Captain Hook's Ladder. The previous day's team had spotted a good lead going back north from the top of the Ladder – that passage had to come out somewhere. The others turned right and started making their way through the narrow fissures of the Rift.

The two climbers made an unusual team. Neil Backstrom had been on the breakthrough expedition and knew the cave well. He was in his mid-thirties and had been caving and climbing for years. Neeld, on the other hand, was only eighteen and this was his first trip to Lechuguilla. He was tall and blond and had spent most of his youth scaling the rocks and mountains near Colorado Springs. Although he had been caving for only a couple of years, he had already earned the reputation of being nearly inexhaustible on caving trips.

Neeld and Neil were looking for a shortcut. It might be above or below them, but there was no way to tell. They could see many high leads, but most seemed to be heading in the wrong direction. They climbed down and across the fissure. One look into the small, gypsum-lined holes on the far wall told them this was not the route they were searching for. They worked their way south along the Rift, climbing up at every point that seemed to have promise. Every lead they checked was eventually blocked or became too small for human travel.

It took them over an hour to move 300 feet south. They stopped at station C-71, where the first rope drop led into the lower Rift. Neil looked across the pit and could see that the fissure continued at the same level on the other side.

"Has anyone tried to climb out there?" Neil said, pointing into the Rift.

"Rick said that none of the side leads have been checked," Neeld said.

"I'm gonna go for it."

Neil shoved his foot into a slanting pocket on the left wall of the pit. He swung his right foot to a small knob on the far side, shifted his weight to the new foothold, and stepped onto a breakdown bridge.

"No problem."

Neeld repeated the maneuver and the two of them worked their way south over mounds of large boulders wedged in the fissure. The passage widened to twenty feet and then a large, slanting pillar divided the passage into two routes. They followed the main trend straight ahead through the fifteen-foot-high fissure, but were soon faced with another pit that they could not climb around.

They backtracked and tried the passage to the left. It wound around a corner and then into a twenty-foot-wide corridor that ran straight ahead, vanishing into the darkness. They were off and running.

Soon they were stopped by another deep pit. This one was not as imposing as the first, but the only route appeared to be a traverse across a steep slope of loose dirt and rock. To make matters worse, the best route would force them to step around a large rock balanced delicately on the slope.

Neil led the way, carefully kicking steps into the dirt, which sent showers of debris rattling into the pit below. He worked his way two dozen feet along the sloping left wall until he reached the obstructing boulder. He tugged on the boulder, hoping to move it safely out of the way; but the rock refused to budge.

Cautiously, Neil slid one foot around the boulder to a ledge on the opposite side. He slowly shifted his weight, placing his hand on the large rock for balance, careful not to make any rapid movements. He glanced into the pit below. One slip here would send him, along with several hundred pounds of rock, sliding into the void. Neil swung his left foot around the boulder and quickly took three final steps to safety. Sighing with relief, he gestured for Neeld to follow.

"Where do you think we are?" Neeld said as he joined his partner on the other side of the pit.

"I'd guess we're about sixty feet directly above the lower Rift route."

Neil took a computer line plot out of his pack and began to study it.

"If this map's right, we should be pretty close to the top of Captain Hook's Ladder."

As they continued down the passage, they noticed numerous high leads and several low crawlways heading off of the main trend. Their goal, however, was south, and the huge twenty-foot-wide corridor led in that very direction.

They traversed past another pit and looked down it for any sign of people or fixed ropes. They did not really expect to see anyone. They had left the other team a little over an hour ago, and the lower Rift route always took three or four hours to negotiate.

The color of the cave had changed dramatically. What had begun as bare rock or thick crusts of gypsum now gave way to patches of sooty black residue on the walls. They continued onward, passing yet another pit. The ceiling was covered with long white soda straws standing in bright contrast to the dark cave walls.

The passage turned left into a flowstone-floored stoopway that led to a junction. A large walking-sized tunnel led to the right, but the main trend continued straight ahead. The cave looked as though it would never end. They moved faster, passing many side leads, ignoring everything but the main passage. The black residue now covered every square inch of floor, wall, and ceiling. It was slippery and stuck tenaciously to the bottoms of their boots.

They came to a sharp rise in the passage. To continue on, they would have to climb up a slope to the left. The surface was coated with a thick deposit of the slimy residue, making the footing treacherous. If one of them fell here, he might slide all the way into the tight fissure below.

Neeld put one foot out onto the steep slope, digging in with the edge of his boot. His gloved hand sank into the soft, brown-black coating as he braced his back against the ceiling. He stepped back, pulled off the glove and shook out several pieces of the black mud. Once again, he stepped out and pushed hard against the ceiling, hoping the pressure would be enough to keep his feet from slipping. As he moved his other foot onto the slope, the first foot began to slide out of its hold. He tried to move his hand upward for a better grip as both feet began to slide.

Moving faster now and knowing that no amount of finesse could keep his feet on the greasy rock, he stepped into a small pocket where he could dig in his toes. Balanced on only one foot and with one arm pressing against the roof, he planned his next move. Just ahead, the passage seemed to level out, which would make the footing easier. Neeld treadmilled up the last three feet to the relatively flat floor above. Even here the floor was not as safe as it appeared. His feet continued to slide slowly down the barely perceptible slant of the floor.

The soft, rusty-brown walls swallowed much of their
light and made it difficult for them to see down the passage. Ahead, the tunnel curved to the right and then the
floor dropped out. Neeld and Neil moved carefully to the
edge of the pit, not trusting their traction on the treacherous black slime. A gentle breeze cooled their faces as the
cave exhaled from below. They stared into the pit, looking
for a route down. Neeld dropped the coil of rope from his
shoulder and began to unwind the stiff loops.

Back in the lower Rift, the others wormed their way
along the surveyed route: C-61, C-62, C-63. They crawled
up, then down, then sideways through the crystal-lined
corridor. After 300 feet, the passage finally opened into a
walkway six feet wide. They paused at the top of a short
drop where a small piece of flagging tape marked the last
station of the C-survey, C-71.

"This is the beginning of the D-survey," Roy said.
"The route starts getting tough now." Roy clipped his fig-
ure-8 to the fixed rope and disappeared over the edge. He
quickly arrived on the ledge fifteen feet below and moved
down the steep slope while the others rappelled. The passage was narrow and soon they were strung out single file
as the angle of the fissure floor sloped upward. The last
member of the party was just starting down the first rope
drop as Roy reached the top of the slope.

"Nautiloid Pass," Roy said to the next person to
reach the top. Roy sat on the floor, leaning against the east
wall with the cephalopod fossil only a couple of feet from
his right shoulder. To his left the passage dropped precipitously, a single rope dangling down the drop.

"Who wants to go first?" Roy asked. The platform of
Nautiloid Pass was uncomfortably small; someone would
have to continue on before the rest of the party could come
up. Steve Reames had been right behind Roy.

"I'll go," he said.

Roy explained the procedure. "The problem here is
that you can't go to the end of the rope − it doesn't reach

the bottom of the pit. What the first person needs to do is go down about halfway and start swinging. The route goes into that fissure on the far side of the pit." Roy pointed to a two-foot-wide and ten-foot-high crack about fifty feet away. "We usually shoot for that chockstone you can see in the passage; it seems to be securely anchored."

"How do you hold yourself in the fissure once you've reached it?" Steve asked.

"If you time it just right, you can jam your elbows into the walls. Then you can chimney backward into the passage until you feel secure enough to untie from the rope."

"And if you don't time it just right?" Steve said.

"Then you just swing back into the pit and try again."

Steve was less than thrilled about trying this trick, but he wanted to make a good impression on his first trip into Lechuguilla. He pulled up a loop of rope and fed it though his figure-8. After double checking the knot anchoring the rope, he backed slowly over the edge of the drop.

"Rappelling."

Steve slid slowly down the white nylon rope.

"OK, stop there," Roy shouted. "See if you can swing to the other side."

Steve flexed his knees and pushed softly off the nearby wall, swinging five feet out over the pit. He swung back to the wall like a pendulum and once again pushed off, feeling for the rhythm of the rope. This time the swing was longer and, as he swung back to the wall, he pulled both knees up to his chest for one big push. Just as his feet touched the wall, he kicked hard, flinging himself across the void. Although he was moving fast, swinging across the pit felt like slow motion.

As he approached the fissure on the far side, Steve and the others above could see that he was about eight feet too high; the desired chockstone was well below his feet.

Like the pendulum he was, Steve slowed as he reached the other side. Just touching the fissure, he began to swing back toward the near wall of the pit. He bent his knees to absorb the shock, and slammed back into the wall where he started. The force of the impact knocked several rocks loose and they vanished down the shaft below, bouncing noisily off the walls.

"You're too high," Roy shouted down into the pit.

"Yeah, I'm going to go down a little bit."

Looking at the fissure on the far side, Steve judged the distance and slid downward on the slender strand of nylon supporting him. He stopped abruptly and tied off his figure-8 so he would not descend any farther.

"No!" Roy shouted. "Now you're too low. You're going to have to get out your ascenders and . . . ."

Steve ignored the protests from above and shot out across the pit again. Swinging into the fissure on the far side, he jammed his elbows into the walls and stopped.

The cavers shouted encouragement. Chimneying backward in the fissure, Steve worked his way toward the chockstone. Arriving at the large boulder wedged between the narrow walls, he slackened the rope and relaxed. The trickiest part of the journey through the lower Rift was now over.

He anchored the rope to the chockstone, and one by one the others rappelled down the rope and were pulled to the far side of the pit. Another rappel and another ascent took them to the top of Black Pearl Pass. Small cave pearls, stained black by traces of manganese, lay in tiny pools of water. The black flowstone covering the walls and floor stood in stark contrast to White Pearl Hill, which they had passed a few hours ago.

Two more rappels and one more ascent took them to Lech-A-Gorilla Hall. A single white nylon rope hung in the middle of the room, suspended from some unseen anchor high above. They collapsed on the dry gypsum floor and began pulling food and water out of their packs. Occasionally

someone would shine a headlamp into the darkness overhead trying to see what lay above.

After twenty minutes, they had recovered enough to
move on. They split into two teams. Roy, Alan Williams,
and Dave Logan would ascend to the top of Captain Hook's
Ladder and begin surveying the new passage to the south.
Steve Reames, Pat Kambesis, and Dave White would continue the survey up Captain Hook's Ladder and look for an
alternate route back to the north.

Steve was glad to be a part of Pat's team. Pat was one
of the best and most experienced cavers that Steve had
ever met. She was a geologist and had been caving since
1974. She was small and slender and was often sent ahead
to check out the tightest crawlways. But she was most
admired for her ability to make accurate and detailed
sketches of cave passages. She moved to Colorado in the
early 1980's where she helped map and explore the high
mountain caves, as well as participating in many long
expeditions to Mexico.

Although she had moved away from Colorado by the
time Dave Allured broke through in Lechuguilla, she was
among the first invited to participate. The project needed
as many good people as possible, and Pat was among the
best.

Dave White went forward with the tape and held the
end on a small projection of rock. Pat held her end of the
tape against the previous survey marker and read the distance.

"Thirty-two point one."

"Thirty-two point one," Steve repeated and recorded
the number in the survey book. Dropping the tape, Pat
looked through the compass to sight the next station.

"One hundred seventy-three," she called out.

"One seven three point zero," Steve echoed.

"Hello!"

"Hello?" Steve said, looking up from the survey book.

"That came from up there." Pat pointed to the hole
in the ceiling high overhead.

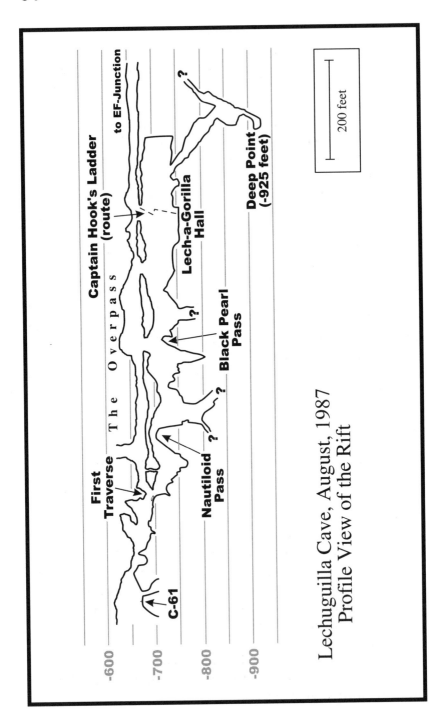

Lechuguilla Cave, August, 1987
Profile View of the Rift

"Hello." the voice said again. The three of them turned and looked up Captain Hook's Ladder. There was a single headlamp at the top.

"Neeld. Is that you?" Steve shouted.

"Yeah. Where are you?"

"We're in Lech-A-Gorilla Hall," Pat shouted. "You're at the top of Captain Hook's Ladder."

"That's what I thought," Neeld said. "We found another route. I think it's shorter than the way you came."

"Good!" Pat yelled. "Mark the route and we'll survey it."

"You can't miss it," Neeld said. "Just turn left when you get up here. I'm going back to check out some more side leads."

"I guess we have our work cut out for us," Pat said.

They resumed their survey and reached the top of Captain Hook's Ladder in under an hour. Large walking passage, ten feet high and over a dozen feet wide, went in both directions. The southern route was being explored by the first team, although neither lights nor voices could be detected in that direction. The northern passage was Neeld's promised shortcut. The passage would have to be surveyed, especially if it proved to be easier than the tedious lower Rift route they had just completed.

They had gone just a hundred feet down this new bypass when they reached a large pit that dropped into the lower Rift more than eighty feet below. A small ledge on the right permitted safe passage around the obstacle, and they continued along the passage.

Large boulders littered the floor. They seemed to be in the upper reaches of a large funnel that started fifteen feet wide and gradually narrowed as it descended into the lower Rift. They were walking on a suspended floor made of boulders, dirt, and smaller rocks wedged halfway up the immense fissure of the Rift. They knew that if the floor shifted, there would be little to stop them and several tons of rock from crashing to the depths below.

As if to confirm their fears, another pit appeared in the passage ahead of them. Here the boulders had failed to wedge securely between the two walls. As they leaned out over the edge they could make out shadowy shapes far below. A small ledge started on the right side only to be blocked by a six-foot-high rock. This pit was going to be trickier than the last one.

Dave volunteered to be the first one across. Steve set up a belay and Dave tied the end of the rope to his seat harness. Edging his way along the right wall, Dave moved out to the obstructing boulder. He kicked and pushed it but the boulder did not budge. Dave extended his left leg around the boulder, feeling for a solid foothold. Finding it, he shifted his weight around the rock, hugging it like a bear. Sliding to the opposite side, he breathed a sigh of relief.

But he was not finished yet. The small ledge petered out after a few feet, turning into a wall of gypsum that sloped steeply into the pit. Dave picked his way from handhold to handhold, testing each one before committing his weight to it. The soft gypsum crumbled underfoot, threatening to break away with each step. Several tense minutes later, Dave reached the far side of the pit.

After taking compass and tape measurements across the pit, Pat and Steve followed one at a time, each in turn checking the security of the boulder before carefully stepping around it. On the far side, they continued down the spacious passage.

It was not long before they reached another chasm, the fourth to block their path. This time there was no ledge along the side and no handholds or footholds anywhere on the surrounding walls. There appeared to be no path onward.

But where was Neeld? He had started down the corridor ahead of them, and they had not passed any side passages. Where could he have disappeared to?

Pat frowned as she looked back down the hallway they had just surveyed. Since Neeld could not have vanished into thin air, they must have missed something. Clearly the route was not as obvious as Neeld had promised. Twenty feet back, along the right wall, a small crawlway led off the main corridor. Pat crawled into the hole. Dave and Steve rested on the rocky floor, taking food and water from their packs.

Fifteen minutes later, Pat returned.

"I found the way," she said. "I didn't want to lead you guys on a wild goose chase, so I kept going until I could see where it connected to the lower Rift. I could see a rope and a survey marker, so I know we're on the right track. It's not as bad as it looks; it opens up just on the other side. It's all walking passage after that."

They started mapping through the crawl. Pat held the spool of tape as Dave stretched the end to a bend in the crawl.

"Distance to DC-10: three point five feet." Steve scratched the numbers on the page. After recording the compass and clinometer readings, Steve closed the book and followed the others through the hole in the wall.

It took them an hour to survey to the place where Pat had seen the rope and survey marker. To their great dismay, they stood on one side of the pit looking at the rope on the other.

"Where are we?" Steve asked.

"I'm not sure," Pat replied. "I don't recognize that rope over there. We must be somewhere in the lower Rift because we've been traveling over it the whole time. Besides, the Rift is the only area nearby that has any fixed ropes."

"I wish I knew what was written on that survey marker," Steve said. "Then we'd know where we are."

"We'll get there," Pat said. "We just have to figure out how."

The pit was not as wide or imposing as the ones they had crossed earlier. It almost seemed possible to leap across to a large flat boulder on the far side – provided you could jump fifteen feet. Dave moved to the edge and tested a handhold on the right wall. Starting out over the edge, he made one move forward and came back. He continued to examine the walls, looking for a secure way to cross.

Neeld Messler appeared on the other side of the pit.

"Hi guys!"

"Neeld! Did you cross this?"

"Sure! It's easy. See those handholds on the right?"

"Yeah."

"Well just use those and that big foothold over there, then step across."

"Easy for you to say."

"Wait," Pat said. "Neeld, could you throw us the end of that rope?"

"Sure," Neeld said, "but what about the other guys returning from the lower Rift? Shouldn't we leave the rope in place so they can get out?"

"Once they see this shortcut, no one will ever be using the lower Rift route again," Pat said. "By the way, what does that survey marker by your right foot say?"

Neeld bent over to read the strip of blue plastic. "C-71."

"Wow!" the three of them exclaimed at once. "We're almost out of the Rift!"

"Yeah, C-61 is just around the corner," Neeld said, pointing behind him as he coiled the rope. "Don't you guys know where you are?"

"We do now!"

Neeld tossed the rope across the pit. Anchoring the end of it to make a horizontal traverse line, they quickly crossed over. One final shot connected the new survey to the old. Steve recorded the numbers, closed the survey book, and put it inside his pack.

"We should go back to show the others the new way out," Pat said. In twenty minutes they were back at the top of Captain Hook's Ladder; the same trip had taken them four and a half hours via the lower Rift route.

ART PALMER

Caver crossing the namesake rock at
Freakout Traverse; the rock fell in 1989.

They were excited about finding a bypass to the Rift, but there was still the question of whether it led to any new cave. The answer came quickly when Roy, Alan, and Dave returned from their explorations to the south. They had surveyed to a major intersection where two large walking passages went in different directions. One of them was designated the E-survey, the other the F-survey. They had continued down the E-survey past two promising pits that were blowing lots of air. In addition to these three major leads, many small side passages branched in all directions. They were ecstatic; they had found more cave than they knew what to do with.

It was near midnight and they were all exhausted from a long day of caving. The members of Roy's team were pleased to hear they would not have to return through the dreaded lower Rift. Returning north, the tired explorers worked their way past the first two pits along the shortcut, soon arriving at the edge of the third.

One by one they crossed the void, each person belaying the next. Each caver kicked and pulled on the boulder that blocked the traverse along the narrow ledge. Each caver in turn stretched across the rock; the smart ones declined to look down.

Finally, it was Roy's turn. Roy was not afraid of heights, but was not especially fond of them either. Like the others before him, Roy also tested the security of the large boulder blocking his path. Moving cautiously he reached around the boulder.

No one was looking at Roy when they heard him shout.

"Holy Shit! It moved!"

Leaping around the boulder, Roy dashed from the ledge to the safety of the far side of the pit. He collapsed trembling on a large flat boulder.

"It moved." he repeated. "I thought I was a goner."

From their perspective on the far side, the boulder appeared unchanged.

"Yeah Roy, sure it moved," someone teased. The others laughed. "That rock is solid; it must have been your imagination."

"No way," Roy insisted. "I tell you that rock moved. It completely freaked me out. I thought I was going all the way down that pit while hanging onto that rock." Roy's heart was still pounding. The others snickered at Roy's active imagination.

"It did move," came a voice from the other side of the pit. Steve had approached the boulder and was examining the wall. Deep vertical grooves marked the wall for several inches where the rock had slid downward.

"These grooves are fresh," he said. "They weren't here when we crossed earlier. I specifically looked for signs like this to see if the rock had shifted recently. It looks like the rock settled about four to six inches."

The laughter stopped. Roy stood up and shouldered his pack. "Let's get out of here."

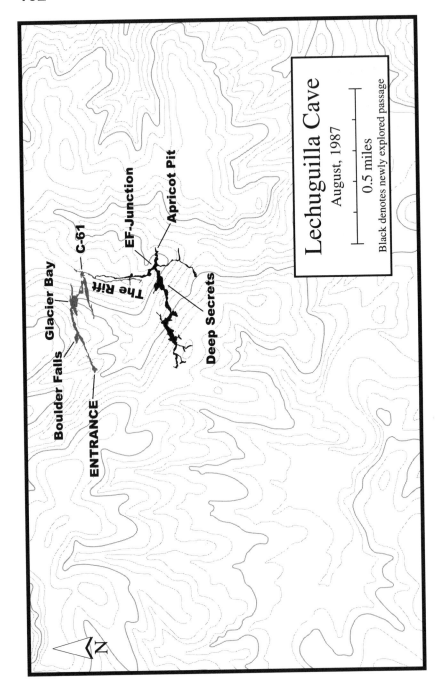

Lechuguilla Cave
August, 1987

0.5 miles

Black denotes newly explored passage

Apricot Pit
EF-Junction
C-61
The Rift
Glacier Bay
Boulder Falls
ENTRANCE
Deep Secrets

N

7

IN SEARCH OF DEPTH

lan Williams sat in a corner of the CRF hut, hair matted and face covered with sweat-streaked dirt from his recent trip into the cave. He was motionless, his back propped against the wall, staring across the room at nothing in particular. It was too noisy to sleep, yet he was too tired to stay awake. Occasionally he took a handful of potato chips from the bag in his lap. A half-empty two-liter bottle of pop sat on the table next to his elbow. His body, not his mind, selected his breakfast foods. An intense thirst left his mouth dry as cotton, and yet he had an incredible craving for something salty. Both were the result of dehydration.

The long, hard trip in the warm, humid cave caused everyone to sweat profusely. In the excitement of exploration, none of them realized how much water and salt their bodies had lost. They did not know they were dehydrated until they woke up the next morning with an unquenchable thirst. It would take two days to recover fully.

"Where were those leads you guys found on your trip?" Steve Reames asked.

Alan turned slowly to the computer-printed map on
the table.

"Is this the new map?" he asked.

"Yeah. You guys were out here," Steve said. He
pointed to a small line on the page. Alan sat up and swung
his feet around beneath the table, momentarily forgetting
his fatigue as he looked at the crooked lines showing the
route they had surveyed. Rick had named the new shortcut
the Overpass because it passed directly over and avoided
the tedious lower Rift route. Alan traced the route across
the page with his finger. "Then this must be the Freakout
Traverse, where Roy and that big rock almost fell into the
pit."

Steve nodded. They talked for several minutes about
the passage. Within the hour, the next team would head
into the cave. Tomorrow, they would be as beat as Alan was
now.

Ted Lappin, resident computer expert, sat hunched
over his keyboard on the opposite side of the room. He had
been on the first trip to explore the newly discovered exten-
sion to Lechuguilla. Rick Bridges had brought along a
portable computer, and Ted had been volunteered by the
rest of the cavers to write a program to process the survey
data into a map.

Before long, his original simple BASIC program had
grown into pages of complex code. Ted went caving with
everyone else, but while the others rested on their days off,
Ted worked on the program. The latest version, TEDDY20,
was almost complete.

The brrrrrrrap-brrrrrrrap sound of the printer coming to life immediately caught the attention of the others in
the room. The latest map was about to appear. A half-dozen
cavers crowded around the printer.

"Ted, how deep is the cave now?"

"Ted, could you plot a profile of the cave?"

"Hey Ted, could you zoom-in on this section of the
Rift?"

"Ted, what's the total length of the cave so far?"

Ted sighed and resumed typing. No matter how much information he produced, they always wanted more.

Rick and Roy stood near the bulletin board where Rick had just posted the team assignments for the next few days.

"I want to go tomorrow," Roy said.

"You can't," Rick said. "I'm going tomorrow with these people here." He pointed to a column on the page.

"But I'm ready," Roy insisted. "I want to push the end of the E-survey."

"Look, I've already made the team assignments," Rick said. "You're scheduled to go in the day after tomorrow."

"But why can't I go in on this team here," Roy said pointing to the list, "and Jim can be shifted back two days."

Rick was annoyed. Roy did not appreciate how much coordination was required to assemble teams to go into the cave. The limit of eight people a day constrained them to two survey teams at a time. Each team needed a sketcher, an instrument reader, and someone to set survey stations. Cavers skilled enough to be sketchers were few and far between. The team assignments were largely controlled by which sketchers were available, how tired they were, and how long a trip they were willing to endure. Rick was carefully orchestrating the exploration of the cave. He did not want to waste time on people who wanted to go on wild goose chases. He used his caving experience to decide who would explore and where they would survey. On this expedition, Rick wanted to make Lechuguilla Cave deeper than Carlsbad Cavern.

The two leaders continued to argue for several minutes. Occasionally other cavers in the room would interject a few words in an attempt to settle the disagreement peacefully. Their efforts were in vain; Rick and Roy were locked in a struggle for dominance of the project. Finally, Roy gave up and stomped outside.

Ron Kerbo came into the cabin through the back
door, through the busy kitchen, and into the main room.
He was immediately surrounded by cavers anxious to talk
to him. Rick soon drew Kerbo aside. Rick was prepared this
morning, as he had been every morning that week, with
every imaginable fact and figure. He knew the surveyed
length of the cave to the nearest tenth of a foot. He knew
the exact depth of the cave and where it stood in the list of
the ten deepest caves in the United States. He recited the
number of feet surveyed per person per hour, the average
passage height and width, and the total number of man-
hours spent in the cave. Rick reeled off these numbers
while Kerbo looked at the map on the table. Rick continued
with a painfully detailed report on every step taken by each
of the survey teams that day.

Kerbo frequently interrupted Rick's monologue to
ask about things of more global importance. "Have your
teams been careful not to leave scuff marks on the Flowstone Slope?" "Have you been confining travel in the cave
to a single path?" Rick assured Kerbo that he had taken
care of these things. Rick pointed out that he had person-
ally recruited all the cavers that were here, and had
selected only the best.

Rick had a fondness for history, and often thought
about how others would someday view the mark the group
was making on caving. He was careful to point out every
accomplishment that could be used to highlight the importance of this expedition. "This is one of the best-equipped
teams of cavers ever put together on short notice." "This
cave is growing in surveyed length faster than any other
cave explored in the Guadalupe Mountains." "This cave
has more gypsum per square foot than any other in North
America." The list was nearly endless.

Rick was sitting on the table talking to Kerbo when
Barb am Ende entered the room.

"Oh, Ron, I have something for you." Barb went
back into the other room and returned with a rubber
stamp.

"This is what you ordered," she said. As Kerbo examined the surface of the stamp, a large smile broke out over his face.

"This is perfect!" he said. "Do you have a stamp pad I could borrow?"

Barb returned with a rainbow-colored ink pad and handed it over. Rick continued to ramble on about Lechuguilla Cave.

Kerbo approached Rick with rubber stamp in hand. "Don't move," he commanded. Rick would normally hold still for no one, but in view of Kerbo's importance he sat motionless. Kerbo could hardly contain himself, and chuckled as he carefully wiped the perspiration from Rick's forehead. Kerbo pressed the stamp firmly into the pad and then onto Rick's head, centered squarely above his eyes. In rainbow hues, the stamp said "I'm Somebody In Caving."

Everyone exploded in laughter.

"What's it say? What's it say?" Rick shouted.

"Rick," Kerbo said, "I was afraid that some people might meet you and not realize that you were a Very Important Person in Caving, so I thought it would be a good idea to label you." Rick laughed nervously.

"OK," Kerbo said, "now that we've had our fun, could you go find Roy and meet me in my office? We have some paperwork we need to finish."

⚜   ⚜   ⚜

While Rick and Roy sat with Kerbo in the tiny back office of the cave resources building, the members of a small team were making their way to the end of the Overpass survey. There were three major leads in the thousand feet of passage discovered south of Captain Hook's Ladder. The first lead was a walking passage heading south that started at the junction of the E and F surveys. Two hundred feet further down the passage there was a promising pit at the base of the right wall. Finally, another two hundred feet south, at the end of the main corridor, a strong breeze issued from a ten-foot opening they called Apricot

CAROL VESELY

Pat Kambesis on the first rope in Apricot Pit.

Pit. Neil Backstrom, Jim Dugue, and Ron DeLano, an optometrist from Grand Junction, Colorado, were heading for Apricot Pit.

The corridor was slathered with the dark slimy coating the cavers now called gorilla shit. Underneath the black residue was a layer of white moonmilk. The slippery surface was described by one caver as sugar, coated with white grease, coated with motor oil. Ron and Jim each fell twice before deciding to slow down and take smaller steps. As they approached the edge of the pit they moved with extra caution. Neil was uncoiling the rope as Ron and Jim arrived.

"This shouldn't be too hard," Ron said. "Dropping pits is much easier than climbing."

"You don't understand," Neil said. "I've been here before; this is no ordinary pit." He looped the rope around a six-foot-diameter pillar at the edge of the pit, tied a knot, and attached his descender to the rope.

"How hard could it be?" Ron said. "Just throw a rope down and rappel."

"Just wait until you get down there." Neil backed over the edge of the pit and started his rappel. "You'll see."

Neil completed the rappel in just a few seconds, and called for the next person to come down. Ron clipped into the rope and started descending. For the first thirty feet,

NORM THOMPSON
Randy Brown rappelling down Apricot Pit.

he was rappelling in a ten-foot circular tube that slanted down at a sixty-degree angle. For the last ten feet, the passage was vertical and Ron landed on some breakdown blocks on the bottom. He detached himself from the rope and called "Off rope" to Jim. He scrambled down to the edge of the breakdown pile where Neil was standing.

Neil was right. This was no ordinary pit. The tubular passage had intersected a broad, low fissure that sloped downward at a forty-five-degree angle. Ron squinted into the darkness to make out the details of the fissure. At the top of the slope, the ceiling was about five feet high, but it gradually narrowed until, twenty feet down, there was only one foot between the ceiling and floor. Obvious leads lay to the left, right, upslope, and downslope, but the most promising route angled down and across the sloping floor. It was not the awkward-looking route that concerned Ron, nor was it the low ceiling or the absence of a visible bottom. It was the layer of slick, black, gorilla shit that coated every visible surface.

Neil began scouting along the top of the fissure looking for another way down. When he got back, Jim had just arrived at the bottom of the rope.

"It doesn't go that way," Neil said. "It pinches out after a hundred feet. It looks like we need to go down there." He pointed to the route Ron had been examining.

"It looks pretty slick," Ron said. "We better use a handline."

Neil tied a thin nylon rope to a pillar and threw the coil down the fissure. He attached his descender to the rope as a safety precaution, turned to face into the slope, and began climbing down. Using small depressions in the floor as footsteps, he traversed diagonally, moving one yard to the left for each yard he descended. Neil had moved only fifteen feet down the rope when his feet shot out from under him. He grabbed the rope and tumbled in a long arc, rolling through the gorilla shit, before coming to rest in a prone position directly below the rope anchor.

"You OK?" Jim asked.

"Yeah. Damn, this stuff is slick."

Neil pulled himself along the slope to where the ceiling rose enough for him to get back on his hands and knees. He slipped repeatedly, but each time caught himself before traveling far. It was several minutes before he returned to his original path. He stood up again and resumed his descent, this time in a crouched position, taking extra care not to slip.

The minutes crept by as Neil progressed down the fissure. The floor would be smooth and featureless for a dozen feet, then the next dozen feet would be covered with small footholds. Neil could see a level platform below him as he continued his downward traverse. He reached the safety of the ledge just as he ran out of rope, 150 feet from where he had started. He tied the end securely to a large boulder and disconnected his descender.

"Off rope."

Following the anchored rope, Ron and Jim walked and slid their way down to Neil. The ceiling rose to a dozen feet here, and the six-foot-wide ledge was almost level. They studied the fissure, looking for a way down. The rift itself was slightly curved, like the inside of a shallow bowl, but the angle of the fissure below them increased until it was nearly vertical. The three cavers followed the ledge twenty feet to its end and then began to chimney down and along the fissure. They climbed cautiously on the slime-coated rocks, careful to avoid an uncontrolled plunge into the void below. Finally, they stopped at a small platform barely large enough to hold the three of them. The route was too steep to continue unroped.

Ron tied their last rope around the only available anchor point, a chockstone wedged between the walls. He rappelled down through a tight spot where the walls closed to within two feet, but it stayed narrow for only one body-length before opening up again. Ron estimated he had descended forty feet when he arrived at another ledge. He stopped and looked down. The end of the rope was dangling free, just above the floor of a room thirty feet below. Ron knew that the stretch of the rope as he rappelled would probably be enough to get him to the floor. There was just one problem: once he took his weight off the rope, it might contract out of reach leaving him stranded at the bottom. Ron tried to make out details of the room, but the gorilla-shit-coated walls seemed to swallow up the light from his headlamp.

He was too close to stop now. Ron continued rappelling cautiously, watching for the end of the rope. The free end of the rope slipped through his descender just as his feet touched the floor. With his weight removed, the rope contracted slightly, leaving the end hanging at eye level. Ron relaxed. He was confident now that he could reach the rope and would be able to climb out. He called to Neil and Jim to come down as he turned to explore his surroundings.

He was in a small room aligned with the fissure and floored with large pieces of breakdown. The slimy gorilla shit of the fissure above was replaced with smooth, undulating surfaces of shiny flowstone. When the others arrived, they all searched for passages leading from the room, and found only one. Pushing through a short, flowstone-lined tube in the floor they popped into a room fifty feet wide, twenty feet high, with twenty-foot-wide passages leading in two directions. They had bottomed Apricot Pit and found a new area of the cave, but they were also exhausted. It would be a long trip to the surface, so the three of them reluctantly started back.

✦ ✦ ✦

The next day, Rick led Leslie Clarfield and Donald Davis into the cave. They stopped 200 feet before reaching Apricot Pit; Rick was interested in a new lead that he thought might go even deeper.

Rick, Donald, and Leslie looked down into the unobtrusive, ten-foot-wide pit that lay along the wall of the passage. One of the other teams had gone a few feet down this pit the day before. What interested Rick most was the report that it continued going down. Rick wanted to go deep. His entire being was focused on the quest to make Lechuguilla deeper than Carlsbad Cavern.

Donald Davis was the quintessential caver. He lived to cave and he structured his life so he could spend as much time as possible underground. He was in his forties and made a living raising bees and selling honey because it gave him lots of free time to go caving.

Everyone knew Donald. His reddish beard and bright-silver caving helmet were familiar fixtures around many a campfire in the mountains of Colorado and New Mexico. He had been involved in so many major discoveries that people began to think that he had a special gift for finding caves. But it was not just his knack for big discoveries that drew people to him. Donald knew more about caves than just about anybody. If you wanted to know the best place to look for caves or the scientific name of some rock formation, Donald always had the answer.

To add to the mystique, Donald had a majestic speaking voice that commanded everyone's attention and added an air of authority to the things he said. It was rhythmic and hypnotic, almost like the oratory of a Shakespearean actor. It was so captivating that cavers who spent time around Donald would begin to unconsciously imitate his voice. People who had never met Donald would instantly recognize him because so many people mimicked his voice.

All his life Donald had searched for the perfect cave. A cave that was large enough, beautiful enough, and interesting enough to culminate his caving career. He was now beginning to think that Lechuguilla might be the one.

Donald studied the area around the pit. He noticed that the walls of the pit itself were lined with a massive coating of stark white crystalline gypsum, but the walls just above the pit were bare rock.

"Why such a dramatic difference over so few feet?" he mused. Perhaps this pit was a pathway for airflow. The air movement would accelerate the evaporation of moisture from the pit walls, thereby enhancing the growth of gypsum. Donald followed this train of thought to its logical conclusion: there must be a large volume of cave down this passage to cause that much airflow.

Rick had already anchored the rope and thrown it down the short drop. He clipped the rack to his seat harness and then to the rope and slowly inched over the edge. The first twelve feet of the pit were sheer, but below that it intersected a low room that sloped out of sight. Rick stopped at the edge of the room and called up for the others to follow.

Donald and Leslie tossed the extra ropes they were carrying down to Rick and then descended on the anchored rope. They were at the top of a broad, flat room that sloped steeply downward. It was about fifty feet wide and a dozen feet high, and the far end was more than eighty feet away. It would have been a good place to park a small airplane if

NORM THOMPSON
Rick Bridges (left) sketching while Phil Curtin looks down the
first drop of the Great White Way.

it were not for the forty-five-degree tilt of the ceiling and floor. The floor was smooth with few rocks or irregularities. One slip would put a person at the far side of the room in record time.

The most striking feature of the chamber was the brilliant white gypsum that coated every visible surface. A single headlamp made the room come alive, as millions of microscopic crystal surfaces refracted and reflected the light. Rick wrote the words "Great White Way" next to his sketch in the survey book.

Even though the floor was steep, it looked as though it could be climbed without a rope. Rick made his way down the slope, maneuvering across the floor to the right, toward a ten-foot boulder. He rested briefly on the boulder and peered down the steep passage as he tried not to pitch headfirst down the slope. The others followed him. After only a few more feet, the angle of the floor changed and gave them a clear view of the passage below. As they descended to the lower end of the room, the walls narrowed. The passage soon tapered down to a small, uninviting hole in the floor only two feet in diameter. Donald was in the lead with the survey tape. He placed the end of the tape on the wall directly over the hole. Rick and Leslie sadly assumed that this would be the last survey shot.

"I feel air." Donald said. He knelt down and put his outstretched hand over the small opening.

Donald dropped the tape, and squeezed feet-first through the hole in the floor. He descended just a few feet before he emerged in another room very similar to the one he had just left.

"Hey, come on through, there's a room," Donald shouted back to the others. Rick and Leslie quickly crawled through. There were several large boulders at the upper end and the floor slanted steeply downward. The far end of the room was lost somewhere in the darkness below.

"I'm glad we brought all that extra rope," Rick said. "This room is way too steep to climb."

ART PALMER
Three cavers ascending the Great White Way.

They returned to their packs and equipment on the other side of the crawlway and continued the survey into the new room. Rick found a suitably large boulder and tied the end of a 200-foot rope around it. He tossed the coil of rope down the incline, beyond the reach of their lights. Again, Rick was the first to rappel down.

The gypsum-coated walls of the Great White Way gradually gave way to stark limestone boulders. After twenty-five feet, the room widened to fifty feet and the ceiling rose in a long graceful arch that soared sixty feet above the floor.

"Off rope," Rick shouted.

He was in a large room over forty feet wide and sixty feet high. The lower half of the room – the bottom twenty feet – was completely filled with huge boulders. These immense, haphazardly stacked blocks of rock had been falling out of the ceiling for thousands of years. The smallest rocks were six feet high, the largest more than twenty. Holes in and around the boulders formed passages that branched in every direction.

Leslie and Donald descended the fixed rope, surveying as they came. Rick was working on a profile sketch that tracked their progress, carefully computing their depth below the entrance. When the others reached him, he was beaming.

"We're now eight hundred eighty feet below the entrance," Rick said. "If we can just get another forty feet, we'll pass the Rift for the deepest point in the cave."

Donald was also happy, but for a different reason. The more passage they found, the more it looked like this discovery would fulfill his dream of finding the perfect cave.

They followed the most obvious path into the pile of boulders. Moving up, down, and around, they made their way through the limestone maze.

"Hey, look at this!" Donald shouted.

They were coming into an area profusely decorated with formations. Orange- and cream-colored stalactites and stalagmites stood in thick clusters that nearly blocked the passage. Thin soda-straw stalactites hung from the ceiling high overhead. Although no bigger in diameter than a pencil, some were up to fifteen feet long. The centerpiece of the display was a huge, caramel-colored column thirty feet tall and five feet wide that hung from the highest point in the ceiling. Orange flowstone poured down the wall below the column, and a veneer of multicolored flowstone spread across the floor. Reds, oranges, yellows, and whites swirled together with infinite variety.

The most important discovery of all lay in a nearby alcove. It shimmered in the diffuse glow of Donald's carbide lamp. More common than sand, yet more precious than gold, it was the one thing they needed to find more than anything else. The pool of crystal-clear water lay only a few feet away from the hall of formations. Three feet across and six feet long, the small pool collected drops of water that had been falling from the ceiling for untold centuries.

Donald knelt beside the pool, dipped his canteen into the water, and took a long, deep drink. It was cool and clean. Rick and Leslie had heard Donald's shouts and now appeared around a corner. They looked with disbelief, first at the formations, then at the pool.

"I think this place should be called Deep Secrets," Donald said. They named the pool Little Lake Lechuguilla after its big sister near the entrance.

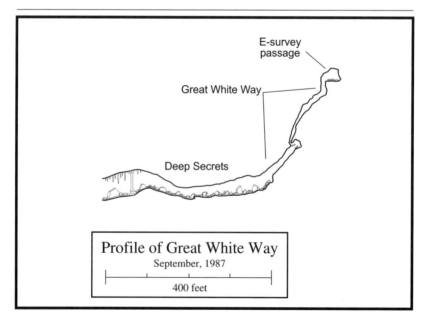

E-survey
passage

Great White Way

Deep Secrets

Profile of Great White Way
September, 1987

400 feet

It was early evening and the cavers were ready for a break. Little Lake Lechuguilla provided a convenient spot to eat and to refill their depleted water bottles.

The meal rejuvenated them. Rick showed Leslie and Donald the sketches of the territory they had covered. They had continued to lose elevation as they explored farther into the cave.

"We're now at minus 950 feet and we've just passed the Rift as the deepest point in the cave," Rick said. "Carlsbad is just under a thousand forty feet so all we need is another ninety feet." They picked up their gear and began to work their way past the delicate formations.

Down the passage, the formations quickly disappeared giving way to stark gray limestone walls. The passage continued sloping gradually downward, gaining a few inches of depth with each step. Just as the survey reached minus 1,000 feet, the passage split three ways. The main trend, which was still the largest and most promising, turned sharply upward. A short stoopway to the right went only a hundred feet before ending. To the left, a side

RAY KEELER
Paul Burger (left) and Ron Lipinski surveying in Deep Secrets.

corridor sloped down out of sight. Although the branch straight ahead looked more enticing, Rick was adamant; breaking the depth record was why they were there.

The route down started as a large walking passage, but quickly constricted to only five feet high and fifteen feet wide. As they proceeded, the ceiling continued to drop slowly and the walls narrowed. The depth continued to accumulate: minus 1,010, minus 1,020, minus 1,030 feet. It was a race to see whether the passage would end before the depth record would be broken. Donald was in the lead, trailing the end of the survey tape along like a hundred-foot leash. On his hands and knees now, he turned the corner and found the undeniable end of the passage. The walls, ceiling, and floor came together in a small pool. There were no side leads.

This would be the last survey shot. Donald paused for a moment at the edge of the quiet pool. Holding the end of the survey tape in his hand, he thrust his arm into the foot-deep pool. He held the tape against a small projection on the floor of the pool. "Tape," he called out.

Leslie held the spool of tape next to the previous survey station. She read the length from the tape and called out the numbers to Rick, who recorded them in the survey book.

"Seven point eight three," Leslie said.

Donald removed the carbide lamp from his helmet and held it near the surface of the water. "On station," Donald said.

Leslie sighted through the compass, to align it with the previous station and Donald's light. She repeated the procedure with the clinometer. Rick hastily wrote down the numbers. Then he drew the profile sketch that he used to measure their progress. They wanted to know if they had passed the 1,037 foot depth of Carlsbad.

Rick told them what Donald already suspected. The total of depth of Lechuguilla cave was now 1,058 feet. Donald dipped an empty can from his pack into the water and they all drank a toast in celebration.

Back on the surface, the next survey team was anxiously waiting their turn to go underground. They were scheduled to be the last trip of the expedition and they were beginning to worry. It was already late morning and, after more than twenty hours underground, Rick's team still had not come out of the cave. Ron Kerbo was worried too. He decided to tag along with the cavers on the hike up to the entrance to see if there was any sign of Rick and his team. As they approached the entrance pit, they heard voices far below and relaxed. As the fresh team readied their gear, Kerbo stood near the lip of the pit where the nylon rope was anchored.

Rick Bridges appeared at the top of the pit. His smile was a mile wide.

"Ron," he said, "I have a trivia question for you. What's the deepest cave in Carlsbad Caverns National Park?"

Kerbo nodded. He reflected on how this cave, open for less than two years, had grown faster than anyone could have imagined.

"Lechuguilla Cave," he said.

8

WESTWARD EXPANSION

ow that they had exceeded Carlsbad's depth, Rick
had a new goal. The deepest cave in the country
was Columbine Crawl, a difficult and dangerous stream
cave in Wyoming. It was 500 feet deeper than Lechuguilla
and Rick was convinced it was only a matter of time before
Lechuguilla would surpass it.

By the beginning of the October, 1987, expedition
Rick had formulated a plan to push Lechuguilla deeper.
There were still leads around Deep Secrets but most
appeared to be blocked by thick calcite formations and
pools of water. Apricot Pit was a different matter. Although
it had never been surveyed and the trip reports were mud-
dled, it was clear that it was at least 300 feet deep. That
would make the bottom of Apricot Pit slightly deeper than
Deep Secrets. Making progress in the treacherous pit, however, would be difficult. The steep fissure and the slick
gorilla-shit-coated walls would require a very skilled team.

Some of the best vertical cavers in the country come
from the region where Tennessee, Alabama, and Georgia
meet – often referred to as the TAG area. Rick had lived

there before coming to Colorado, so he assembled a team of friends from TAG and Texas. Their goal was to survey Apricot Pit and explore the passage at the bottom. Rick, Buddy Lane, Pat Kambesis, Marion Smith, Gerald Moni, and Mark Minton entered the cave with 500 feet of new rope. In just over an hour they were at the top of Apricot Pit. The group split up into two teams. The rigging team began to set fixed ropes along the best route to pave the way for the surveyors to follow. They replaced the rope that had been left at the first drop in August and then rigged the long, sloping second pitch.

Rick was particularly glad to have his old friend Buddy Lane on the trip. He was one of the most competent cavers in the country. He was in his mid-thirties, quiet, intense, and energetic. Most important of all, he was an expert at ropes, rigging, and vertical work.

The six cavers made their way down Apricot Pit. As one caver uncoiled the rope, another checked the knots, and a third fastened rope pads where the rope crossed sharp rocks. In the lead, Buddy followed the trail of scuff marks left by DeLano's team.

When they reached the third rappel, Buddy rigged a new rope to two large boulders and started his descent. He approached the point where the fissure narrowed to only two feet wide. He tried to avoid the narrow slot by swinging out to a wider place in the fissure, but his feet slipped out from under him and he pendulumed back into the slot. He continued to battle the slippery slope as he descended until he finally landed on a relatively level ledge.

"Off rope."

While the others followed him down the pit, Buddy looked for the route on. It was possible to go down here, but the fissure was even tighter than the one he had just come through. The other option was to traverse farther along the fissure by climbing across the wall to the right. Buddy climbed out a few feet until he could see farther down. It looked as though DeLano had gone across here, but it was much too exposed to do unroped. Once the other cavers and gear arrived, Buddy used the last rope to set up a traverse line. He climbed across the wall forty feet to another level place where chockstones were wedged between the walls. He smiled when he saw a rope anchored to a boulder below him. This was the route.

Buddy did not like the looks of the rock DeLano's team had chosen for an anchor. He pulled up the rope and re-rigged it while the others traversed. He clipped his rack into the rope, descended a few feet, and leaned out over the pit.

"The rope's too short."

"What?" Rick said.

"The old rig must have been just long enough to reach the bottom." Buddy pulled himself back to the safety of the ledge.

"We could use the rope from the Great White Way," Pat said.

"You're crazy," Rick said. "We'd have to climb back to the top of this pit, go over to the Great White Way, go to the bottom, get the rope, climb back up, and then drop back down here. It would take hours and it's already after midnight."

"We can't leave without surveying to the bottom," Pat insisted. "There've already been two trips down here and the survey still isn't finished."

Pat and Mark decided to make the long trip over to the Great White Way, and Rick grudgingly followed. In single file they ascended back up the four ropes in the 400-foot fissure that lay between them and the top of Apricot Pit.

Mark was the first one up the pit. When Pat arrived, he asked her for directions. As Pat rested, Mark raced the 200 feet back down the E-survey to the Great White Way. Ten minutes later Pat shouldered her pack and followed. When she reached the first handline in the Great White Way, Mark reappeared, the long coil of rope slung across his chest.

Rick arrived at the top of Apricot Pit just as Pat and Mark rounded the corner on their way back. Rick's face was bright red and sweat was carving thin white lines in the black smudges on his face. He pulled himself into the passage and let out a huge sigh. He was exhausted. Luckily, Mark and Pat were full of energy and were determined to reach the bottom of Apricot Pit. After a short discussion, Rick decided to solo out of the cave while Pat and Mark took the rope back down to the others.

The new ropes were already so dirty with gorilla shit that it was a struggle to feed them through the descenders. Even the cavers' familiarity with the pitches did not help much; it still took almost an hour to rejoin their team-mates. It was now two o'clock in the morning and they found the others sleeping on the ledge.

The events of the early morning hours became a blur, and the cavers only vaguely remembered what they saw. Once the rope was anchored, they rappelled down the fissure and landed in the small rubble-filled room at the bottom. A trail of footprints led across the room to a small hole in the floor. Beyond the hole was a flowstone-coated chamber they called the Low Tide Room. They made one long survey shot to the floor of the room for maximum depth and, with the last bit of energy they had, turned around and headed back to entrance. By the time they returned to the huts the sun was well above the horizon. Out of curiosity, they stayed awake long enough to enter the data into the computer and to find that Lechuguilla was now 1,125 feet deep. Then they collapsed on their bunks, too tired to care about anything but sleep. Apricot Pit was now the deepest section of Lechuguilla Cave. Pat and her survey team could attest, that with five pitches and 600 feet of rope, it was also the most difficult.

The depth record held for less than one full day. Now that Apricot Pit was rigged all the way to the bottom, a trade route was open for those who wanted to explore. The new passages expanded the cave to the east. The two main

PETER JONES
Glen Malliot admires a column near Nirvana.

exploration areas were now being called by their compass direction: the West was accessed via the Great White Way through Deep Secrets, and the East was down Apricot Pit and beyond the Low Tide Room. The contrast between the two areas was remarkable. Both routes started at the top of pits that were only 200 feet apart, but no connection had been found between them. The Great White Way was white and crystalline, Apricot Pit was black and slimy. The Great White Way was large walking passage with only one easy rappel. Apricot Pit was a nightmarish exercise in ropework through a tight fissure. Despite the difficulties of Apricot Pit, the lure of new passage was too great to ignore. Beyond the Low Tide Room, cavers found a labyrinth of huge passages they named the Mega Maze and a stunningly beautiful room filled with butterscotch flowstone and white columns they named Nirvana. Team after team charged into the East, each one finding new rooms and corridors and increasing the depth of the cave by a few feet. Before the end of the week, Lechuguilla was the third deepest cave in the United States at 1,207 feet.

One of the reasons the East was getting so much attention was the diminishing number of leads in the West. Most of the teams that went down the Great White Way came back with only a few hundred feet of passage and a dead end. The East still had more passages than there were people to survey them, but Rick wanted to send one last team to the West to finish off the remaining leads. Then he would be able to focus all his energy on the East.

Carol Vesely was a thirty-year-old substitute teacher from California. The best thing about her job was that it gave her free time. She spent that time caving in the Sierra Nevada mountains, in sea caves along the coast, and in the deep cave systems of Mexico. Caving was her life, and often she would sign her name "C. A. VESely." She was well known as a cartographer, surveyor, and tenacious sketcher, and she often drove her team to the breaking point, always encouraging them to survey "just another hundred feet."

Carol had reviewed the survey notes and knew that the West had only a few small leads left to be mapped. She also knew that, in all likelihood, this was going to be the last trip to that branch of the cave for a long time. The area was supposed to be nicely decorated and she had hoped to see it before the last leads had been surveyed. Carol volunteered to take a team to the West to mop up those last unchecked leads.

Carol recruited Bill Farr, Art Wiggins, and Steve Sims to go along. Rick Bridges told them to map the last of the leads in the West and then pull all the ropes so no one would be tempted to go back into this highly delicate area. Art had heard there were still some climbing leads in the West; he had earned his reputation by his ascent of Captain Hook's Ladder and was anxious to explore more cave. Bill was also a climber.

They arrived at Deep Secrets in less than three hours and began looking for the first unchecked lead. The floor was a jumble of blocks the size of small automobiles and there seemed little promise of anything leading out of the room through the tiny holes between the rocks.

"I think we should each take a section of the floor and check out holes until something goes," Steve said.

Steve Sims was a college student in his mid-thirties from Colorado Springs. He had served several years in the Air Force before deciding to go back to school to become a technical writer. He was relatively new to organized caving. Just two years earlier he had joined the local grotto to participate in the dig projects and to cave in the Guadalupe Mountains.

"We have to survey as we go," Bill said. "That's the rule. We should just map into everything we check."

"That'll take way too much time," Steve said.

"It's also going to be hard to sketch, but it's got to be done," Carol said. She did not look forward to sketching a route through the pile of rocks.

Each team member crawled into a different hole and began to worm through the breakdown. Bill had been working

The White Christmas Tree Room derives its
name from the white raft cones covering the floor.

his way steadily upward and could see past two large boulders
into blackness. He loved squeezing through tight passages,
and now it looked as though it was going to pay off. He
popped into a large chamber and yelled, "I've found a
room."

Steve started laughing and turned his light back on.
"Yeah, and it's got a survey in it. I did the same thing.

Almost all of these holes just loop back into the main Deep Secrets room.''

"Find anything?" Carol said as she, too, popped back into the main room.

"No. Did you?" Bill said.

"Well, nothing big but it's probably worth mapping. Let's wait for Art to see if he has anything."

As if on cue, Art emerged from the hole he'd gone into. "I'm not sure how good this lead is but it at least has real walls, not just loose rock," he said.

"Sounds good to me," Carol said.

Art led through a small, twisted path in the jumble of blocks. After a dozen short survey shots, the breakdown gave way to real cave. The passage was small but it was virgin and had many side leads. Soon the main trend ended, and they started back, mapping and checking all the leads.

"This is a waste of time," Steve complained.

"We need to map everything we find," Carol insisted.

"We should just mark them as leads; if we map all these holes, we won't have time to map the big stuff if we find it," Steve said.

"We can't leave any leads. Our job is to finish off this area. If we spend all our time looking for something big, we'd probably have to come back down here and do this anyway." Carol was firm.

Steve continued to argue to no avail, and in a couple of hours all the leads in Art's area had been mapped to their end. They crawled back to Deep Secrets.

"What now?" Carol asked, mentally going through her lead list.

"We can survey Carol's lead in the breakdown and some of the stuff I found could probably be mapped," Bill said.

"No way, I'm tired of mapping in these little holes. Let's go check out that high lead in the White Christmas Tree Room," Steve said, referring to a room that had been found a previous team.

The four cavers looked at each other and nodded in agreement. They repacked their survey gear and headed deeper into the cave, past the impressive columns that marked the end of the massive Deep Secrets flowstone, and past Little Lake Lechuguilla. Twenty minutes later they arrived at the last room in the West: the White Christmas Tree Room. The floor of the sixty-foot diameter chamber was covered with calcite raft cones consisting of hundreds of potato-chip-sized flakes of calcite stacked in conical mounds. They looked like two-foot-tall baby Christmas trees covered with a thick blanket of fresh snow. Carol stopped to take pictures while the others crossed the room to fill their canteens with water from a small pool called Lake Louise.

They turned into a side passage along the right wall of the White Christmas Tree Room, climbed a steep slope, and then walked and crawled another hundred feet to the end of the passage. On the left wall twenty feet over their heads was the promising looking hole that had been noted by the previous survey team. The floor where they stood was covered with a layer of small, brittle calcite rafts. Unlike the White Christmas Tree Room where the rafts were cemented together, the rafts here were loose and crunched with each step. As the four of them shuffled about, it sounded as though they were walking across mounds of cornflakes.

Carol, Bill, and Steve prepared to survey while Art examined the twenty-foot climb. The wall was a crumbly mass of bad rock. One thing that can be said about cave climbing is that the rock is never very good. Art stepped forward to the bottom of the climb, his feet crunching in the thick pile of cornflakes on the sloping approach. He tapped lightly on a thin blade of rock just within reach. The dull thud told him it would not make a good hold. Further to the right, he swept away the loose gypsum and old cornflakes to reveal a tiny pocket.

Art placed his right foot in the pocket. His boot crunched into the loose calcite coating, but the rock held.

He shifted his weight to his right foot and stood up, moving his left foot and hand upward. With a few swift moves he was safe in the passage above.

Art tied the end of a rope to a large rock so that the others could use it as a handline. He looked around and saw a maze of crawls and walking passages. A light breeze suggested they were probably heading in the right direction.

"Which way does it go?" Steve asked as he arrived at the top of the climb. Bill was right behind him.

"I don't know," Art said. "I only rigged the rope and waited for you guys to catch up with the survey."

"Which one do you want to survey first?" Bill asked.

"We should just explore for a while; that way we can map all the good stuff," Steve said.

"The only way we can be thorough is to map as we explore. Besides, who would want to come back and map a crawlway that he knew ended?" Bill said.

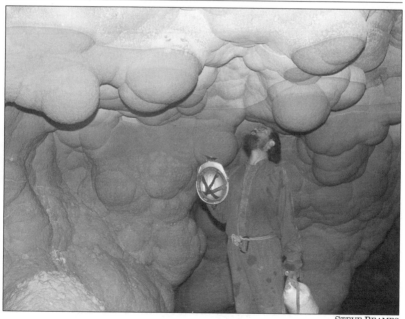

STEVE REAMES

Donald Davis examines a ceiling pocket at Lake Louise.

"Surveying as we go will be a waste of time." Steve said.

Bill and Carol were adamant about sticking to the survey-as-you-go philosophy. Steve wanted to explore; Art was indifferent and was happy just to be in such a fantastic cave. The majority ruled, so they continued their survey from the top of the climb into one of the three good leads.

The passage started at walking height, but after only a couple of turns degenerated into a crawlway that quickly turned into a narrow squeeze. The average shot length dropped to less than five feet, but the passage kept going. When it seemed that the passage would continue this way forever, it changed into a smooth-floored crawlway. The crawl made a few turns and then came right back to the place they had started. They had surveyed a 140-foot loop. Two of the three leads had been eliminated with one survey.

The remaining lead meandered for seventy feet to the bottom of a steeply ascending chimney. It would have been too steep to climb except for the large rocks embedded in the wall that provided good handholds and footholds. Many of the rocks were loose, so each climber had to be careful not to knock rocks down on the others below.

Steve was the first one up. At the top, he chose a hands-and-knees crawl to the right that led over a large fallen block.

"Wow, you've got to see this." Steve shouted.

It was not what Steve said that grabbed the attention of the others, but the echoing reverberations of his voice. The rest of the team hurriedly completed their measurements and then followed Steve.

They emerged from the crawl into the center of a large chamber. The size of the room was a stark contrast to the tight crawlways they had spent most of the day exploring. The ceiling arched forty feet above, and the walls were fifty feet away. When they looked to the west they could see Steve over a hundred feet away, the light from his headlamp dimly illuminating the end of the room 300 feet beyond. Even farther down the passage, a thirty-foot-diameter borehole led into darkness.

"Come on!" Steve shouted, waving for them to follow. "No," Carol said. "We should check out this room first." On the south wall of the room another forty-five-foot-diameter passage led upward. The floor of the chamber was covered with huge, sloping breakdown blocks coated with a thick gypsum crust. Crossing the room was like walking in freshly fallen snow; even the lightest step made an inch-deep impression in the soft, sugary gypsum. They regrouped to continue the survey, being careful, as

Steve Sims in the ABCs Room on the discovery trip.

always, to trample as little of the floor as possible. This time there were no arguments against survey-as-you-go.

They took a survey shot to the nearest wall and began working their way clockwise around the room. By following the perimeter wall they would be assured of finding and marking all the leads. This way they could choose the most promising one to follow.

"Hey wait a minute," Bill said, looking back toward the center of the room. "This room is big enough that we might not be able to find the way back out."

They had entered the room through a small hole near the middle of the chamber and it would have been very easy to miss the obscure opening among the breakdown blocks and boulders. He ran back and used twenty feet of flagging tape to mark the exit.

They decided to call it the ABCs Room, a name with a double meaning. They had followed the ABCs of cave surveying by mapping everything they explored, and the name was made up of the first initials of the discoverers, Art, Bill, Carol, and Steve.

They came to the twenty-five-foot-diameter hole on the south wall, beyond which were several small pools and a cascade of white and red flowstone. It was too tempting to pass by. They surveyed two shots up the flowstone to a large domed room. The passage continued up a steep slope of loose rock, but the cavers decided they should return to their perimeter survey.

Another five shots in the ABCs Room took them back to the place where they had started the survey. They now had two choices, either continue along the passage on the south side of the room or follow the thirty-foot opening on the west side. They chose the west side, and as Steve had promised, the passage continued; the ABCs Room was really just a wide spot in an immense borehole. Shot after shot, they kept moving to the west. Art and Bill were running ahead with the tape like dogs on a hundred-foot leash. Even sketching at a scale of fifty feet to the inch, Carol was

ART PALMER
The beginning of the Western Borehole.

finding it difficult to keep up. The passage varied in width from 30 to over 100 feet. The ceiling was almost uniformly thirty feet high, and the walls and floor were covered with thick, white gypsum snow. They named the passage Winter Wonderlands.

Winter Wonderlands continued this way for over 500 feet with only a few side passages. The cavers checked each side passage, just to make sure it was not a major lead. The main passage was amazing. Rather than tapering down, it now opened into a hundred-foot-wide, breakdown-floored room over forty feet high. Carol groaned. Her sketch was already going off the page every three or four shots and it was nearly impossible to judge the distances from wall to wall.

"Hey everybody," Carol said. "Let's take a break. It's four in morning and I need a break from sketching."

They sat on the floor in the center of the passage. As they rested and ate they could not take their eyes off the huge dark borehole that disappeared into the distance. Their tired bodies were telling them to sleep, but the cave beckoned.

"Let's take a short nap, and then we'll survey some more," Carol said.

Carol woke up half an hour later, too cold to sleep any more. She changed the calcium carbide in her miner's headlamp and found that she only had two charges left, enough for only about eight hours of light. Bill had three charges left; Steve and Art each had enough batteries for another ten hours of light.

"Okay gang, I've got about eight hours of carbide left; how long should we survey?" Carol said.

"It'll take us about four hours to get back to the surface," Bill said. "So why not survey until you have to change carbide again? That'll give you one charge of carbide to get out of the cave." It would be pushing their supplies to the limit, but they all wanted to explore as much of the cave as possible.

The passage continued heading west and stayed over 100 feet wide. Carol dimmed her light to make the charge last longer. It made it more difficult to judge distances, but she could still estimate the dimensions of the passage by the lights of the other cavers. The hours passed and soon Carol had barely enough light to illuminate the survey book. The only features she could see were the silhouettes

STEVE REAMES

The room known as Manifest Destiny features three gypsum
stalagmites called The Three Amigos (left of center).

of three ten-foot-tall pure-white gypsum stalagmites that
became known as the Three Amigos.

It was time to change carbide and head out of the
cave. The three stalagmites would make a good landmark
for the next party into this area. They packed their gear

and started out, knowing that with more than 2,700 feet of virgin cave surveyed, and more beckoning, the West definitely was not finished.

⚜   ⚜   ⚜

While Carol's team was still underground, Ron Kerbo walked between the main hut and the cave resources office, with Rick and Roy a half-step behind.

"Make it quick guys," Kerbo said. "I have a meeting."

"Ron," Rick said. "You know we've been finding lots of new cave. The trips are getting longer and longer. Even our best cavers are having to take a rest day between trips."

"Yeah," Roy added, "sometimes it takes two days to recover from a hard trip."

"We're finding a real bottleneck with the number of teams we're able to put into the cave each day," Rick said. "With more resources we could address some of the open leads we haven't been able to check."

Kerbo stopped, almost causing Rick and Roy to run into him. "Stop beating around the bush. You want me to raise the limit on the number of cavers per day going into the cave?"

"Well, it would certainly help us achieve our goals if . . .," Rick started.

"Fine," Kerbo interrupted. "How many do you want?"

Rick stammered, speechless at the abruptness with which Kerbo advanced the question.

"I've told you guys, if you need something, just ask for it," Kerbo said. "Is twenty people enough?"

"Er, uh, well, yeah," Rick said.

"OK, you got what you wanted. I've got to go," Kerbo said. He turned and walked off, leaving Rick and Roy with their mouths open.

⚜   ⚜   ⚜

It was late morning when Carol's exhausted team finally returned to the surface. As they walked into the hut, the rooms were surprisingly quiet. Nearly every available caver was underground. The only people left in the huts were Rick Bridges and his team who were getting a late start on another trip to the East.

"How was your trip? Did you find anything?" Rick said. He was expecting Carol to announce that they had finished off all the leads in the West. As an answer, she dropped a stack of survey notes on the table.

"Hey, this is interesting," Rick said as he flipped through the muddy survey pages. "There must be half a mile of borehole." The rest of his survey team crowded around to look at the notes. As Rick flipped through the pages, Carol pointed at the sketches and described the ABCs Room and the passages beyond.

"I think we should have a look at this new passage," Rick said looking at the rest of his team. They were nodding enthusiastically. He walked over to the signout sheet on the bulletin board and changed their destination from East to West.

When the other teams returned later that evening, the huts were full of excitement. Although there were still new discoveries in the East, the center of attention had shifted to the West. The latest computer plot showed that the new borehole was heading due west into a blank part of the map.

The next day, Pat Kambesis talked at length with Carol about the leads in the new area and decided that she would take a team out to the Three Amigos and continue the main survey to the west. She was just about ready to leave when a groggy Roy Glaser walked in from the back room, having returned only a few hours before.

"Pat, where are you planning on going today?" Roy said.

"I'm going to the end of Carol's survey to push it farther west," she said.

"I need you to do something else before you head out to the end," Roy said.

Pat set her pack back down on the porch and signaled her team to wait for a moment.

"Here," Roy began, taking out a copy of his notes from the day before. "This passage is drawn too small and I think there's something wrong here." He traced his finger along the wide pair of lines on the page. "There's also a high lead here that needs to be looked at."

Pat recognized the sketch as the area south of the ABCs Room.

"Why don't you fix it when you go in tomorrow?" Pat said.

"We need to have the data corrected right away so we can send new teams into the area tomorrow."

Pat was annoyed; there was huge going cave at the end of Carol's survey, but now she had to waste time fixing someone else's mistakes.

"By the way," Roy said as Pat turned to leave. "Be careful. There's a lot of loose rock in that area."

"I will," Pat assured him as she walked out the door.

The rest of her team, Mike Goar, Art Wiggins, and Terry Bolger, were already waiting in the truck when Pat climbed inside. As they bounced along the dusty road to the cave, she explained the problem. It was frustrating and everyone was disappointed.

"Once we fix the survey notes, we can go back to where Carol stopped," Pat reassured them.

They made their way to the Rift, along the Overpass, and down the Great White Way. Art took the lead as they turned at the White Christmas Tree Room. He repeated his ascent of the Cornflakes Climb, and led them into the ABCs Room. It took them just four hours to make the trip from the entrance.

Their first goal was the passage leading south out of the ABCs Room, but the enormous borehole heading west still drew their attention.

Art pointed into the passage. "We stopped surveying about a quarter mile down the borehole and it was still going."

More than anything, Pat wanted to go west but she knew she had to keep her promise to Roy and re-survey the passage to the south.

It took them only a couple of minutes to find the old survey markers.

"We should start surveying here," Pat said as she removed the survey gear from her pack.

"I thought we were just going to fix a couple of bad shots," Art said.

"Unfortunately, the notes are so bad we're going to have to re-survey the whole thing."

From where they were standing they could see that the passage climbed steeply to the south. From Roy's description Pat knew that the passage led 400 feet to a large room. In typical caver fashion Roy had named it the Reason Room, not for any characteristic of the room, but so he could name the next chamber Beyond Reason.

Pat, Terry, and Mike started surveying while Art scouted the route ahead. The most striking thing about the passage was how unstable everything was. The floor was very steep and covered with loose rocks and small boulders. With every step they took, the rocks shifted and slid under their feet sending small avalanches of rubble skittering down the slope. They surveyed for several hours, gaining more than 100 feet of elevation before reaching the Reason Room.

What happened next seemed to unfold in slow motion. Art was already scouting around the Reason Room, but the surveyors were still in the steeply sloping passage below, preparing to make the last shot up into the room. Pat sat on the floor sketching the passage while Terry stood next to her holding one end the of survey tape. Mike took the other end of the tape and trudged up the steep slope looking for a likely spot for the next survey station. He saw a large boulder about forty feet up the passage and began unreeling the survey tape as he moved toward it. The best spot for a station was high on the boulder, so he reached up and held the tape taut against the point he had chosen. He could not read the number from where he stood, so he climbed up on the boulder, putting his full weight on the rock.

Suddenly, the boulder shifted, throwing Mike backward down the hill. The big rock then broke free and began careening down the slope after him. Mike tried desperately to get out of the way but he was falling and rolling out of control. The sound of the heavy rock caught Pat's attention. She looked up just in time to see Mike falling head over heels down the slope, the beam of his headlamp casting wildly around the passage. Mike rolled into a fissure between two smaller rocks. The rolling boulder landed on top of him with a dull thud, like a lid on a coffin. The noises stopped.

Terry bolted across the slope, shouting Mike's name. Rocks rolled and slid under his feet. Pat dropped the survey book and ran uphill, dodging the small stones that tumbled down toward her.

Terry arrived first. He continued to call to Mike, but there was no response. He heard a faint groan. Terry placed his shoulder and both hands on the boulder and with a mighty push rolled it off to the side. Pat arrived just as Terry was helping Mike to sit upright.

"Are you all right?" Terry said.

Mike winced. "I can't tell. My side hurts pretty bad."

"Can you move?" Pat asked.

"Give me a minute and then I'll tell you," he said.

Art arrived, and the three of them helped Mike out of the fissure and over to a level area.

"I think I can get out of the cave, but I need to rest first," Mike said.

While Mike drank some water and ate some food, they discussed their options. Mike wanted at least an hour to rest. Pat suggested that they finish the last few shots of the survey and then head for the surface. during the next hour of surveying Pat, Terry, and Art were on pins and needles. They tested every rock and did not trust anything to be safe.

Terry and Art took Mike's gear, and the four of them retraced their steps down the passage. Pat vowed to herself never to go back to this area of the cave. Leads or no leads, it was just too dangerous to be worth pushing. "Mike got off lucky," she muttered.

146

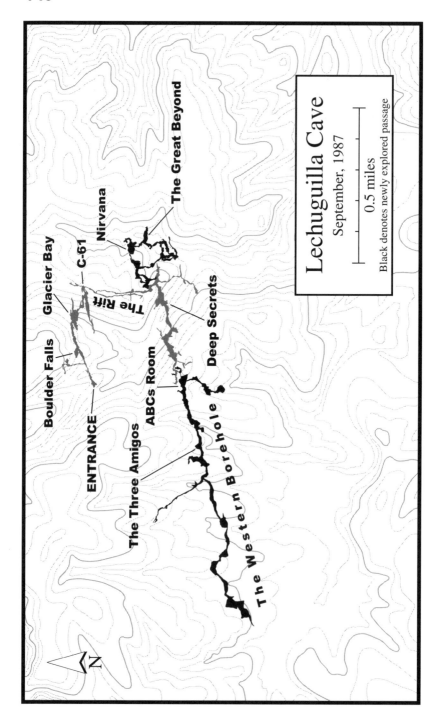

Lechuguilla Cave
September, 1987

0.5 miles

Black denotes newly explored passage

The Great Beyond

Nirvana

C-61

Glacier Bay

The Rift

Deep Secrets

Boulder Falls

ENTRANCE

ABCs Room

The Three Amigos

The Western Borehole

N

9

THE END OF
WESTERN DOMINATION

t was cold in the desert at the start of the January, 1988, expedition and dense fog enveloped the foothills. A chilly wind blew from the north and tiny frost crystals fell from the white ghosts of frozen yucca and sotols. Steve Reames sat in the corner of the CRF cabin packing his gear. He glanced out the window at the sunrise. The hills were briefly illuminated with a spray of orange as the sun rose above the horizon.

Steve was a thirty-year-old electrical engineer from Colorado Springs. He was thin and lanky, with blond hair and clear blue eyes. A study in contrasts, he was light-hearted and friendly, but when it came to caving he could be serious and intense.

He finished stuffing a survey book and some food into his cave pack. He was now prepared to chase the lead that had been on his mind for two months.

He fumbled through his pockets until he found the scrap of paper Ted Lappin had given him. It was crumpled and ragged, torn from a larger sheet. The message was cryptic, just a few scribbled lines and numbers, some with arrows. No one else could possibly make sense of the markings, but Steve remembered every detail of what Ted had told him.

Ted, Carol Vesely, Dave Bunnell, and Bill Farr had been surveying down the F-branch at the end of the last expedition. After mapping through several tight crawlways to dead ends, the California cavers had found an interesting lead. Still small, the final route took them through a squeeze, down a steep slope, to a narrow lake they named the Gulf of California. They were dirty, hot, and tired, but Ted had to look just a little farther. He climbed a slope at one end of the lake and followed the small passage as it switchbacked and twisted into a narrow walking passage. Not wanting the others to wait long, he walked another hundred feet to a large branching passage, turned around, and rejoined his team.

When they returned to the surface, Ted drew a diagram of how to get to the new lead but no one seemed interested. The Western Borehole was still going strong

NORM THOMPSON
Larry Johnson eyeing virgin passage at the start of the F-survey.

with no end in sight and Apricot Pit led to a maze of large rooms and seemingly endless passage. And everyone knew the F-survey did not go anywhere.

Steve thought differently. He convinced his caving buddy Stan Allison that Ted's lead was worth a look. Most cavers, Steve explained, had forgotten that the wind divided at EF Junction, some going down the E-survey, some down the F. The well-delineated corrosion features, the barren ceilings, and the aragonite-encrusted floors all indicated that air had been flowing through the corridors for a long time. If the F-survey was a dead end, where was all the air going?

"Are you packed?" Steve said to Stan, who was making his way toward the kitchen.

"I haven't started yet."

Steve shook his head and followed Stan into the kitchen. As Stan began to eat his oatmeal, Rick entered the room and was immediately mobbed by anxious cavers ready to explore. Steve finally managed to squeeze through the crowd and propose a trip to the F-survey.

"I want you to lead a team to the Apricot Pit area," Rick said.

"Lappin gave me directions to a good lead in the F."

"Look, Steve, we've already agreed that we're going to field teams to the East and the West alternately to push the cave. I don't want you wasting time surveying crawlways in the F."

Another caver interrupted Rick and put a crude map in front of him. "Now, where do you want us to go again?"

Steve slipped away and walked over to the bulletin board where the trip signout sheet was posted. He began to fill in the blanks on the form as Stan approached.

"Can we go?" Stan asked.

"Get your gear," Steve said.

"I talked Dave Logan into coming with us. Did Rick actually say it was okay?"

"Get your gear."

They grabbed Dave and hurried out the back door. Rick would be furious when he found out.

While they geared up at the entrance, Steve reported his exchange with Rick. Stan and Dave listened with apprehension and excitement. They were not really worried; Steve would take the heat when they returned, and there were promising tales of going passage in this area. The shock of the cold hit them as they stripped off their jackets, hung them on the tree next to the entrance, and rappelled into the cave as quickly as possible. Beyond the gale in the culvert was the warmth of the cave.

Stan went first, followed by Dave and then Steve as they raced down the passages. They stopped to rest and to drink some water at EF Junction. The wind drifted silently by, barely perceptible in the walking passage. Steve took the lead now, walking steadily down the large corridor. Only a few boulders and ceiling protrusions slowed the easy ten-minute walk to station F-21. Steve paused to make sure that he was still on the right route; very few people had been to this area so there was no distinct trail. Ahead lay a dead-end passage. To the right there was an eight-foot climb to a walking passage heading south. Steve took the survey notes and Ted's map from his pocket to compare with his surroundings. He pointed down the passage.

"Looks like we're here," he said, pointing to a line on the paper. "We should climb up there and then turn left again."

They climbed up and turned to follow the most obvious path. The route was confused by smaller side leads going in every direction. A short chimney led down to the start of a small crawl and a body-sized squeeze. They began to have doubts about this promising lead; while other teams in other parts of the cave were walking down 100-foot-wide passages, they were wasting time checking out leads at the end of tiny crawlways.

Soon the floor dropped away at a forty-five-degree angle, and after what seemed like forever, they arrived at a small pool of water, the Gulf of California at last. The ceiling was only four feet high and it was difficult to move without sliding into the pool. Steve wedged his body into a small pocket and carefully slid Ted's map out of his pack. He unfolded the scrap of paper, rotated it slightly and then pointed toward the entrance of a narrow passage.

"That way."

They continued along the length of the pool, alternately bumping their heads and slipping into the water. At the end of the Gulf, they could stand upright again. They followed the route Ted had described.

"Wow," Dave whispered, stopping without warning.

The other two hurried forward to look over Dave's shoulders. The floor dropped away into a pool of water twenty feet below. The walkway had intersected a much larger passage leading to the right. Twenty feet wide and forty feet high, the passage disappeared into the darkness.

"I need more light." Steve said.

They focused the combined beam of their lights into the passage below. It kept going. This was what they were looking for, every caver's dream. Any earlier doubts were now gone. They were ready to push ahead into the unknown, except for the small matter of a twenty-foot drop.

"Ted didn't mention anything about a pit," Steve said.

They stood at the top of the drop, looking for an alternate way down into the large passage. The walls were coated with soft gypsum and aragonite. Even if they had a rope long enough to reach the bottom, it would cut into the soft rock, making the climb back up next to impossible. As each possibility was considered and discarded, their excitement slowly changed to frustration. Here was the best lead any of them had ever seen in the cave, but it was impossible to reach. They sat down to eat lunch.

Stan stowed his trash in his pack and took a long drink from his water bottle. He put the bottle into the pack, closed it and leaned over the edge, looking for a way

down. Along the right-hand wall a narrow ledge angled up
from the floor of the big passage to the same level as the
balcony they were standing on. It looked as though it
would be an easy way to climb down, but unfortunately it
stopped short of the balcony leaving an eight-foot-gap. The
smooth, overhanging wall in-between made it impossible
to reach.

Stan looked across the pit. The opposite wall had lots
of handholds and the slope was relatively gentle. If he
could just get across, it would be easy to climb down.

He scanned the wall to his left. The shadows cast by
his light revealed small irregularities and pockets in the
loose rock surface. Stan stood up and leaned out into the
passage, his hand gripping tightly one of the few handholds
the soft wall offered. He leaned out farther to look down
the dark passage far below. His light reflected off a large
pool of water on the distant floor. He had always dreamed
of swimming down a flooded borehole. More determined
than ever to get into the passage, Stan scanned the rock
face. He traced a path along the steep left-hand wall, carefully planning his route.

"I think I can climb to there," Stan said, pointing to
the far wall.

"No way!" Dave said.

"How?" Steve said.

Stan carefully described each move along the left side
of the pit. He stopped just short of the goal.

"I don't know how to do the last few moves."

"You're crazy," Steve said, knowing this would only
encourage Stan.

"I could belay you from there." Dave pointed to a
large ledge on the left.

They had left their seat harnesses at Boulder Falls,
more than two hours back. They had no climbing rope, just
fifty feet of thin handline only one-third the strength of
regular rope. With twenty feet of webbing and a couple of
carabiners from Steve's pack, they constructed a simple
seat harness.

Dave and Steve left their packs behind and traversed to the ledge. Dave secured himself behind a rock to set up a belay. Steve remained on the ledge to provide light and advice for the climb.

"Belay on?" Stan asked.

"On belay," Dave said.

Stan stretched out onto the wall. The rock beneath his foot slumped slightly and then held. He slowly shifted his weight to his right foot, then moved his left foot past a crumbling bulge of gypsum. Small crusts of rock rained into the pool below. He tested each handhold and foothold before shifting his weight to them.

"Slack!" Stan shouted.

Dave let out a few more feet of rope so Stan could move forward unhindered. He was now more than twenty feet out on the wall and had reached the most difficult part.

"Slack," Stan shouted again, "more slack!"

Dave let out just one or two more feet of line. Stan called for more rope. Even though he was around the corner from Stan, Steve knew from his own climbing experience exactly what Stan was facing. Stan had climbed so far away from Dave that the rope would not save him; if he fell, Stan would pendulum across the sharp rocks and fall unchecked to the bottom. If he was lucky, he would land in the pool, if unlucky, he would hit the jagged, steep slope that led deeper into the cave. The rope was only hindering him now.

The crash of a rock echoed throughout the chamber and Dave braced for the inevitable jerk on the rope – but none came. A basketball-sized foothold had broken loose, leaving Stan with one foot dangling in space and the other foot and one hand glued to the rock. The time for slow, cautious moves was over. If he did not move now, he would cling there until his strength gave out. Left foot across, then right, stretch to the far hold, push back, reach to the ledge, done. In six rapid moves, Stan reached the far ledge, sweat dripping from his brow and his heart thumping wildly.

"Belay off."

"Yeah! All right Stan!" Dave and Steve cheered.

Stan now considered the problem of getting the others across the traverse and then getting everyone back. He did not like the idea of reversing the moves he had just made.

Dave released the rope, allowing Stan to pull it in. Stan worked his way to the bottom of the pit and disappeared out of sight. Twenty minutes later, he poked his head around the corner on the right-hand side of the pit.

"Hi."

"Stan!" Steve said.

Stan had followed the narrow ledge up the right-hand wall and was now just eight feet away, smiling at Steve. They were separated by the smooth overhanging wall.

"I'm not sure how we're going to get across this," Stan said.

"Just throw us the rope and tie off your end, we've got a plan," Steve said.

In minutes, a horizontal traverse line was stretched between the two points. Stan reached across the rock face and handed Steve the seat harness. Steve put on the harness, clipped it onto the traverse line, and gently slid along the rope across the crumbling gypsum to the ledge where Stan was waiting. Steve handed the harness back to Dave who was soon across. They agreed that they had managed to do the impossible with little more than a shoestring and a prayer, so they named the climb the Shoestring Traverse.

It took less than fifty feet to know that the five-hour effort had been worth it; before them lay a large pool of crystal-blue water. The underground lake stretched from wall to wall, over forty feet wide and thirty feet long. It was the largest body of water yet found in the cave. There was no obvious way around so they sat down to eat before continuing. Steve remembered a poem by Robert Service and began to chant the caver version of it: "The caver's lights have seen strange sights, but the strangest they ever did

ART PALMER

Peggy Palmer on the Shoestring Traverse.

see, Was that night on the marge of Lake Lebarge where I cremated Sam McGee."

They saw no way past Lake Lebarge, so they undressed and stuffed their clothes into their packs to keep them dry. Dave and Stan started off, choosing slightly different paths across the lake. Dave got wet only to his waist, but Stan, choosing the deepest part of the lake, got into water up to his chest. Following Dave's shallower route, Steve came across last.

They ducked under a twenty-foot-wide, ten-foot-high block and stared in disbelief at the passage ahead. Almost perfectly round and sixty feet in diameter, the passage disappeared into darkness: borehole.

They quickly put on their clothes, and Dave ran ahead with Stan close on his heels.

"Dave, wait!" Steve shouted, pulling on his pants. "This is going to take forever to survey!"

Steve groaned. There was no stopping them now. Dave and Stan, chased by Steve, raced hundreds of yards down the tunnel, hopping across gypsum blocks and skirting the edges of holes in the floor. All too soon, the tunnel pinched down into a stoopway and ended. They searched for leads at the end and found none. Remembering that a low passage took off to the right halfway down the borehole, they jogged back to push it. But Steve halted the madness, asserting his authority as trip leader. He insisted that they survey what had been found so far before exploring any more.

As they began the tedious process of recording the passage on paper, they noticed another lake just around the corner from Lake Lebarge. It was round, symmetrical, and funnel-shaped with beautiful deep blue-green water. It was Dave's turn to name something. This new discovery reminded him of a place he had been to in Canada, not far from the real Lake Lebarge. He named the new lake Chandelar.

Lake Lebarge looking back toward the Shoestring Traverse.

After completing the survey, they started the long trip out. As they crossed Lake Lebarge again, Steve noticed it was just past midnight.

"Happy Birthday, Stan," he said.

Stan grinned. "This has been the best birthday present I could have ever asked for."

As they were leaving, Steve's group ran into a team led by Pat Kambesis, who were on their way into the Western Borehole and told them about the big discovery. Pat caught up with the Apricot Pit team and told them. The Apricot Pit team ran into a group that was on their way out of the cave and told them the news. Pat continued into the cave and told the story to the group that was on their way out of the Western Borehole. In this way, everyone in the cave knew about the discovery in the F-survey before anyone on the surface.

⚜   ⚜   ⚜

Back at the cabins, Steve steeled himself to face a dressing down from Rick. It never came. All negative reaction to their trip was washed away by the news of the big discoveries. They described the dicey traverse over and over, how they got around it, and what lay beyond. As more groups arrived at the hut, they repeated the tale. Even those who had already heard it listened again to absorb all the details. The story of big passage filled everyone with enthusiasm to go back into the cave. They knew that only a few would get the chance. They also knew that there were other big discoveries yet to be made elsewhere and that they might be the ones to make them.

Images of the borehole and the still-going passage filled Stan's restless dreams. The next day was too long in coming, and when it did, even the task of eating breakfast and packing his gear seemed to take forever. He was going back to the Lebarge Borehole, although without Steve and Dave, who needed a rest day before going back into the cave.

Steve and Dave watched as Stan, Calvin Woods, Dave Hughes, and Ron DeLano packed their gear into the vehicles.

They were destined to discover what lay beyond the Lebarge Borehole. Stan was out of the car almost before it stopped. His three companions could barely keep up with him as he ran up the trail.

They caught him briefly at the entrance and barely kept him in sight as he ran through the cave. He finally stopped to rest and eat on the near shore of Lake Lebarge. The rest of his team was red-faced, tired, and sweat-soaked; it was a distinct disadvantage to have an impatient long-distance runner as their guide.

Even in the relative warmth of the cave, they quickly began to feel chilly and were soon ready to move again. Stan took them past the previous finds to the lead where Steve had put a stop to the frenzied exploration. The oval borehole tilted slightly down to the right, and along the right-hand wall, where the edge passage narrowed, a series of low small openings led downward.

"This is the first lead," Stan said, pointing to the first opening.

They scrambled down the hole into a narrow fissure lined with large, curving gypsum flowers. After a few hundred feet, they came to a short climb down. They could see a large passage disappearing around the corner below them. Stan was the first one down.

"Hey, looks like more borehole," Stan said as he pointed down the thirty-foot-wide oval tube before him. The others quickly followed, anxious to survey the new passage. As they rounded the next corner, however, the passage shrank back to modest walking size.

Still, the cave was beautiful even if it was not borehole. The cavers' lights danced off the white, crystal-lined passage and turned it into a magical world. A long, narrow pool stretched along one side of the passage. The floor was a shiny rippling sheet of pastel-yellow flowstone.

"We're on the Yellow Brick Road," Ron said.

Stan laughed. "Yeah, maybe we'll find something fantastic like the City of Oz."

Their hopes were quickly dashed when the smooth yellow floor abruptly ended at a fractured gray limestone wall. Dozens of small angular openings penetrated the wall forming a maze of crawlways that curved out of sight in every direction. Each crawlway was lined with tiny calcite crystals that glittered and flashed in the beams of their headlamps. Ron decided to call the place Tinsel Town.

Rather than survey each passage, they decided to try to push through the labyrinth and then survey once they had found the route. Stan chose one of the holes. He crawled, turned, and twisted his way through the maze of narrow tunnels, following a small tube into a taller fissure. He climbed to the end to find it choked with thick gypsum. A small hole to his right went for a few feet before it, too, became choked. He returned to the fissure and dropped into a small chamber. He pushed through another hole and followed it back into the same small room. He chose a different hole and followed the crawl to its end. It looked as though there was no easy way to get through this maze. Stan had been gone for twenty minutes and he thought it was time to get back to the others to see if they had had any luck.

He crawled upward through an opening into a small alcove, but there were no holes leading on; this was not the way out. He dropped back down and chose a different hole. This route twisted downward to yet another room with numerous holes leading out of it. Stan was confused; normally, he could depend on his excellent sense of direction, but the route he had taken was too convoluted. Every hole looked the same, and the solid, crystalline floor was too hard to show any marks, so he could not tell if he had been there before. He began to get worried and started to check every hole systematically, leaving a small pile of rocks to mark each entrance. To his great relief, after several more wrong turns, he found his way back to the others. He had been, as many others would be later, overwhelmed by the complexity of the Tinsel Town maze.

"Boy, I was completely lost," Stan said as he popped out of one of the holes. "We're probably going to have to survey everything to find a route through."

"I couldn't find a way through either," Ron said. "But let's give it one more try."

A few feet into the maze, Stan dropped down a different hole and came into a narrow, slanting fissure passage. This time, he marked the route. Following this larger passage, he came to the edge of a void. His thoughts rushed back to the day before. He was anxious to experience again the feeling of running down a huge passage as fast as his legs would carry him.

He peered over the ledge, looking for an easy way into the passage, but it was too overhung to climb. Nevertheless, he had to find a way down. If he could not find a way into the room, somebody else would return the next day with a rope and get the pleasure of exploring the new passage. Frantically, Stan looked around for another route. The only hope was a small chimney a few feet back up the passage. He scrambled down the chimney and after some fancy climbing, emerged in the room he had seen from above. The sound of footsteps overhead announced the arrival of Ron, who had found another way to the balcony.

"Come on down Ron, there's a chimney right behind you."

They stood on the edge of a big oval room. The smoothly curving ceiling arched down to a floor covered with large square boulders stacked at odd angles. The walls, ceiling, and boulder-covered floor were coated with a layer of white gypsum snow that made everything look soft like cotton candy. Near the edge of the room, a slender, twelve-foot-tall, pure-white column of gypsum stood boldly against the blackness of the cave beyond. They called it the Wizard's Staff.

Beside the column was a rare formation the cavers called a crystal chandelier. A thick growth of gypsum in the form of selenite crystals branched from a central stalk into a bloom of sparkling crystal over three feet long. They agreed that this aged, wizened growth of crystals looked like the Wizard himself, the owner of the staff.

"I guess we finally did find the Land of Oz," Ron said.

Stan laughed, "Considering how beautiful this room is, we should call it the Land of Awes."

Swept up in the excitement of exploring virgin passage, they decided to go a little farther. There were half a dozen holes exiting the Land of Awes. They chose the largest and explored through two more rooms, each one bigger than the last. The final room was actually large enough for Stan to run through. The place was named Darktown because the walls were coated with patches of black calcite. The floor was covered with mounds of calcite rafts, but the most striking feature was the crystalline gypsum hairs hanging from the walls. They were twenty feet long and so delicate that they twisted and floated on the tiny breezes generated by the cavers' movements.

"We should get back," Stan said.

"Yeah, they're probably starting to get worried."

They rushed back to get Dave and Calvin and then started to map through the Tinsel Town maze. By the time they had finished the survey, they had been underground for more than twenty-four hours. Exhausted and hungry, they packed their gear and turned to leave.

On the way out, they met a fresh group of explorers coming into the area. Stan excitedly described the new discoveries. He even tore a page out of the survey book and scrawled directions to the best leads. Then he watched jealously as the new team vanished into the cave to push Darktown and the passage beyond.

Stan, Calvin, Dave, and Ron slowly trudged back to the entrance, dreaming of a good meal, a hot shower, and a cozy sleeping bag. But most of all, they wanted to type their data into the computer to see how far they had pushed the boundaries of the cave. When they reached the huts, Stan pulled open the screen door, its old hinges creaking loudly in the cold, clear night. Cavers were huddled around the latest line plot spread out on the wooden picnic table in the center of the small room.

Word of their discovery had already reached the surface and the group was mobbed as they came through the door. Ron held court to a large audience in the main room, while Stan talked to Steve in the kitchen. Steve interrupted with many questions. How much had they surveyed? Where was the passage going? Were there any good leads left? Stan answered the questions with as much detail as he could remember and then went to take a shower. He was pleased to find that there was still some hot water left.

By the time Stan had showered, dressed, and returned to the main room, the new survey data had been plotted. Stan joined Calvin, Dave, and Ron in pointing out the rooms and where the best leads were. Although the passages around Darktown were large, most of the survey plot looked like a tangle of small passages. Rick came in the front door. He had been eating in his trailer, which he had brought down to avoid staying in the cabins, and had not heard about the latest finds. Stan and the rest of his team described their discoveries to him, and especially stressed how promising the area seemed.

"Any passages going down?" Rick asked.

"Nothing that looked very good, but there's a lot of cave there," Stan said.

Much to their surprise, Rick did not find the discoveries in the Southwest very exciting. His goals were to push the cave deeper and to surpass the number of feet surveyed on the previous expedition. With large, unending passage still being pushed deeper in the Eastern Mega Maze and with dozens of unchecked side passages in the Western Borehole, there seemed to be no need to send groups into the Lebarge area to map small, mazy passages. The tight passages and short survey shots would make it nearly impossible to reach his goals.

Pat Kambesis had just returned from a twenty-four-hour push trip to the end of the Western Borehole but she was too restless to get any sleep. After dinner and a shower, she began to go through the survey notes from the previous two days. Calvin Woods, also just out of the cave, handed her the notes from the Tinsel Town maze and the area beyond.

Pat looked over the notes carefully and noticed numerous leads marked along the walls.

"How did you find your way through the maze?" she asked.

Calvin smiled. "We just followed the air."

The restless feeling gave way to excitement. Pat began to make a hand-drawn map of the leads Calvin had marked at the end of his survey. She wrote down the important survey stations, knowing that the previous team had marked their location in the cave with blue flagging tape. With this information, she would be able to find the end of the mapped passage. Now the only problem was to find a team to go in the next day. Most of the people in the cabins had just left the cave and wanted a day off. With some coaxing and the promise of exciting new passage, she was able to persuade Terry Bolger, Warren Anderson, and Kris Green to go into the cave early the next morning.

Kris' internal clock was still on Eastern Time, forcing him to get up before most of the other cavers. The rest of the team did not mind getting up early, so they decided to work on Eastern Time, getting up two hours before anyone else in the cabin. This way they could get into the cave and past Boulder Falls, one of the main places of traffic congestion, before any other group.

Long after Pat's team had left for the cave, Steve Sims checked the sign-out board, and asked several people in the cabin where Pat was. He was infuriated to discover they had already gone.

"What? What do you mean they've already left for the cave? Our group was supposed to go in first."

"I don't know. They just said they didn't want to wait."

Sims stomped out the door and onto the porch, letting the door slam loudly. "Where's Ray and Neil?" he asked Stan, who was stuffing the last of his gear into one of the two dirty green cave packs at his feet.

"Ray's over in the other cabin, and I think Neil is up at his car getting his gear."

Sims half walked, half ran to the parking lot to find Neil Backstrom. The other group was going to get the best leads if they did not hurry.

"Neil, Pat's group is already in the cave. Get your stuff and let's go."

Neil shoved the last of his gear into his already overstuffed pack. Sims ran back down the hill to get Ray Keeler. Stan and Ray were talking casually on the porch.

"Got your stuff together yet?" Sims said.

"Yeah, it's in the car. We're ready to go."

With wheels spinning and dust flying, they raced down the gravel road to the Lechuguilla parking lot. Sims knew that Pat was in no hurry, so if they went fast enough, they should be able to catch up with her.

Sims and Neil jumped out of the car.

"Pat's kinda small and not as strong as some of the guys on the trip so they can't be past the entrance pit yet," Sims said. They shouldered their packs and began to jog along the trail.

Ray locked the car doors while Sims, Neil, and Stan followed the path out of sight into the shallow ravine. Stan was not particularly concerned with whether or not they caught up with the other group, but he was enjoying the fast pace of the hike.

Sims allowed Stan to take the lead but forced himself to stay ahead of Neil. Behind them, Ray moved steadily up the trail, not wanting to wear himself out before reaching the cave.

"They're not here," Stan called back when he reached the entrance. He had already pulled on his seat harness and was taking a long drink from the water bottle that would stay on the surface.

Ray arrived at the entrance just as Stan landed on the bottom of the pit.

"Off rope."

Sims attached himself to the rope, pushed away from the side and dropped into the hole. Neil followed, and as he hit the bottom, Ray shouldered his pack and clipped onto the rope.

"Hurry up. You're taking too long." Sims' voice rose from the chimney where he was just beginning to drop into the culvert. When they arrived at the start of the Rift, Sims said, "They must have left really early or we would have caught them by now."

They moved on without stopping, but Sims was still frustrated with their slow pace.

"Come on, you don't need to clip onto that. It's just a handline for people who can't climb. You're a climber, aren't you Stan?"

While Sims pushed his group forward through the Rift, Pat brought her team to a halt not far ahead. She looked at her carefully-drawn map and said, "Keep an eye out for F-21; that's our first turn off."

Pat located the station and led her group up into a short tube. Here the passage description was somewhat confusing but a rope dropping into a narrow hole in the floor told them they were on the right track. Just as they prepared to drop down the short pit, they heard the pounding of fast-moving footsteps and saw the lights flickering back down the passage.

"Where are you guys headed?" Pat called to Sims as he and the rest of his team jogged to a stop just short of the hole.

"Oh, just to some lead Stan saw on his last trip," Sims answered casually.

"Do you want to go ahead of us?" Pat asked. Pat knew from looking at the notes that there were plenty of leads in the area, more than enough for two teams.

"Sure," Sims said.

He immediately stepped ahead and clipped onto the rope. After everyone in the party had descended, Stan led them through the new discoveries, pausing only for a short drink from Lake Chandelar. At the Wizard's Staff in the Land of Awes, they left a note for Pat's team. They said they planned to start surveying just a few hundred feet from the junction and in closing, "We plan to head out at 3 or 4 a.m. Perhaps we can meet you here."

Pat laughed as she read the note and handed it to Kris. "That's the last we'll see of them today."

The group began to check the small holes leading out of the Land of Awes. Warren climbed down a narrow slot in the floor and reported good news.

"I can feel good air and I don't think this passage has been checked."

Pat took out her survey book and began to prepare the pages for note-taking. The others broke out the survey tape, flagging, and instruments.

Meanwhile, Sims' team had already mapped several hundred feet of walking passage with no end in sight. Steve, Stan, and Neil were nearly out of control with excitement. There was a real potential that they could break the record for mapping the most footage by one team in one day. Shot after shot, they mapped through the biggest leads available, ignoring all the side passages and giving only a cursory glance at the crawlways. Ray was sketching and they were moving so fast that he was starting to get behind. The passage was large and hard to represent on paper. The walls were over thirty feet apart in some places and they were honeycombed with smaller holes leading off in every direction.

"Would you guys slow down so I can catch up with the sketch," Ray said.

Stan skidded to a halt. "Hey, I see flagging tape up ahead!"

"Maybe Pat's team surveyed through here from another direction," Sims said. He could not hear any other

Terry Bolger (left) and Neil Backstrom in the
Chandelier Ballroom the day it was discovered.

voices but knew he had to act fast if his team was going to get the good stuff. Stan ran up to the station and read the number. It was one of their own. Ray had lost track of their direction and they had done what was to become common in this maze: they had mapped in a complete circle. They stopped to let Ray catch up and to think about what to do next.

In Pat's group, Terry and Warren had taken over the job of measuring the distance between the stations while Kris read the compass. Warren had just pulled the tape into a narrow constriction, when the echoing of his voice caught their attention.

"Borehole!" Warren's words boomed out of the constriction ahead. When Pat and Kris caught up, Terry and Warren were anxiously waiting on a gypsum balcony overlooking the darkness ahead. Pat could sense their urgent need to explore virgin passage. "Go check out the room and see if there's a way out. I need to finish my sketch."

In a heartbeat, they were gone.

"It goes!" A distant shout from Warren reverberated through the corridor.

Pat took a few moments to enjoy the solitude as she finished the sketch and poked around the room. Beyond the soft glow of her carbide light, the 120-foot-wide room gave way to utter darkness a short distance ahead. The others were far out of sight. As she moved deeper into the room, she noticed strange shadows twisting along the wall. Grotesque arms unfolded into the passage extending their gypsum claws into the darkness. She moved closer.

Thick gypsum stalks over fifteen feet long hung from the ceiling. Their tips were faceted with stunning selenite crystals. Drops of water hung on the ends of the delicate crystals. Pat was astounded. Had the others even seen these? As her eyes grew accustomed to the dimness of her carbide lamp in the large room, she saw another cluster, then another. Just one of these displays would be enough to make the room a legend, but there were dozens here.

She moved carefully from display to display, contemplating each glistening arm as if it extended from another world. The approaching voices of the others forced her back to reality. Kris announced that there was more passage ahead.

Pat knew they were impatient to push on, but a room with formations this rare required a complete survey. She broke the bad news to them. "We need to do a full-perimeter survey of this room."

"But there's even bigger passage up ahead, we can't stop here."

"I didn't say stop. I said survey."

Warren took stock of the chandeliers, and pulling out his camera said "She's right, we need to document this."

It took over two hours to complete the meticulous task of mapping the beautiful room they called the Chandelier Ballroom. When they finished, Pat suggested that they continue the survey out of the Ballroom and into the room the others had seen ahead. They picked their way up a steep slope of boulders into a passage even larger than the one they had left. The walls of the huge chamber were 120 feet apart and their voices echoed and reverberated off the ceiling 100 feet overhead. It was a good place to stop to eat, and to give Pat a chance to catch up on her notes. As Pat finished her sketch, she noticed a balcony high above the tunnel they had just come through. "Too bad we can't climb up, there's got to be more passage up there."

Suddenly a light appeared on the balcony and a voice broke through the silence.

"Whoop! There's a big room here."

"Yeah, and it's got people in it." Kris called out.

"Who's there?"

"Us."

"We mapped through a long series of walking passages and ended up here," Stan called down. "I'm going to get Sims and the others," he said. "Are there any leads down there?"

RAY KEELER
Stan Allison in the Prickly Ice Cube Room the day it was discovered.

"I don't know, but it's a pretty big passage," Pat said.

Stan was gone for ten minutes, and then four lights appeared on the balcony.

"How do we get down?" Stan shouted.

"I don't think there is a way down," Warren said. But Neil Backstrom quickly proved him wrong. In a few minutes, they were all standing in the room, sharing stories of their discoveries. Ray pulled Pat to one side. "How much did you survey?" he said, with a hint of pride showing.

"Oh, about two thousand feet," Pat said.

"We beat you! We have close to twenty-eight hundred feet. If we can just survey this room, we'll have more than three thousand. That's a record."

"Well, you may have gotten the footage, but we got the booty."

Ray looked puzzled. He did not understand Pat's remark until later that night when they walked through the Chandelier Ballroom on the way out of the cave.

The new room was so large that they decided to use both teams to survey the passage. They would survey along opposite walls. Sims' team took the right-hand wall and Pat's team took the left and they pushed deeper into the giant passage.

The room was another masterpiece painted in frosty white. The walls were coated with thick, rough crusts of aragonite and gypsum, and the floor along the edges of the room was heaped with mounds of fantastically eroded gypsum. Dripping water had drilled thousands of holes in the soft rock and the jagged edges between the holes textured the floor with razor-sharp spikes. It was like walking in a giant freezer that had never been defrosted so they called it the Prickly Ice Cube Room.

After 500 feet of surveying, they reached the far end. While the others were finishing their sketches, Neil began to scout around for leads. In the ceiling of the room was a deep, rounded groove that led into a deep gash high on the left wall. Neil tried to climb the sandy, crumbling wall below the gash but he stopped seventy feet off the floor, just short of his goal. He could see that the passage kept going, but without a rope it was too dangerous, so he turned back.

It had been an eventful trip. Sims' team had set a record for the most surveyed footage in one day. Pat's team had discovered one of the most beautiful rooms in the cave:

a room that would become the very symbol of Lechuguilla and the centerpiece for every article and book about the cave. But most important of all, there were leads everywhere. The cave was not finished yet.

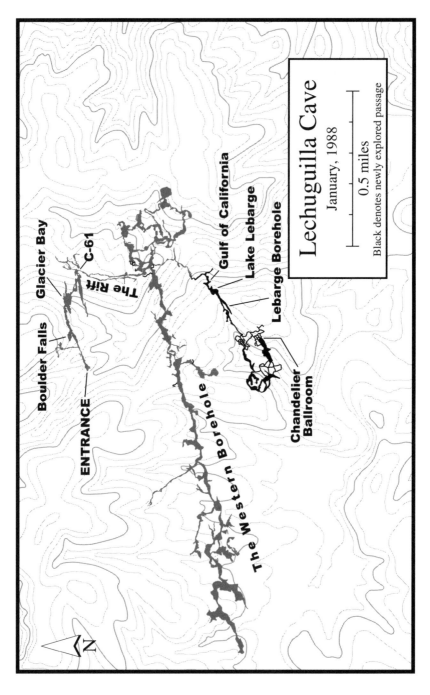

Lechuguilla Cave
January, 1988
0.5 miles
Black denotes newly explored passage

Boulder Falls
Glacier Bay
C-61
The Rift
Gulf of California
Lake Lebarge
Lebarge Borehole
ENTRANCE
The Western Borehole
Chandelier Ballroom

N

➤➤ 10 ⫷⫷

BACK AGAIN

he March wind blew steadily across the Chihuahuan desert. The Guadalupe Mountains blocked
the air, compressing it and driving it up the canyons and over
the ridgetops. The spring winds were well known to the
cavers who came to these mountains. Sometimes, the
ninety-mile-per-hour storms destroyed tents and scattered
campsites. More than one group of cavers had left a cave
after dark, only to be forced to crawl along the trail back to
their car, unable to stand upright against the howling gale.
Now, the last week of March, 1988, sixty cavers descended
upon Carlsbad Caverns National Park to chase a different
kind of wind: the elusive breezes of Lechuguilla Cave.

Ron DeLano was hanging around the cabins, eagerly
awaiting his turn to get back into Lechuguilla. He had
already been in the cave on the first day of the expedition.
It was what he had seen on that trip that made him so anxious to get back underground.

They had been exploring the maze of passages
around the Chandelier Ballroom, mostly large walking passages with walls covered by sparkling gypsum crystals. But

eastward out of the maze, they had found a very different kind of passage. The rock had been dissolved away leaving hundreds of rounded holes. All the holes were connected in a complex honeycomb of twisty little passages. It was like walking around inside a giant sponge. They called it boneyard because it resembled the tiny cavities inside animal bones.

The passage led steeply downward, devoid of the gypsum that was so pervasive in the other corridors. The Swiss-cheese-like boneyard and signs of corrosion on the walls indicated the passage was formed by caustic vapors rising from deep below. In many places the floor was covered a foot deep with a fine gray powder called rock flour. Donald Davis had recognized the significance of these changes; the corridors must have once overlaid an acid lake, probably near the water table. It implied that this part of the cave could go very deep.

So the survey teams plunged downward. At each turn, a dozen leads went in all directions. They consistently chose the ones that led down. They soon found a large room, 100 feet long and 50 feet wide that they named the Land of the Lost. This room was now the hub of exploration in Lechuguilla Cave.

Ron DeLano sat impatiently in the Land of the Lost, drinking from his water bottle and munching on a candy bar. Garry Petrie, Joe Orr, and Dick Larson, the other members of his survey team, were already exhausted. Ron had, in his excitement, dragged them through the cave at almost breakneck speed. As they sat recovering from their five-hour journey into the cave, two other survey teams caught up with them. Together they discussed the nearby leads to decide which one each team would take.

Ron wanted to survey along the Void. Discovered on the last trip into the area, the Void was a large chasm that had stopped further exploration to the east. The explorers could not see the bottom even with the most powerful headlamps and they could see only a faint outline of the far wall. Loose, rock-flour slopes angled down to the edges of the pit, making footing treacherous. The soft, crumbly, dirt floor and the absence of substantial rocks made it impossible for them to anchor a rope. The best anyone had done so far was to survey the passages along the edge of the Void, but no one had found a way around it or a route leading to the bottom.

Ron's team and another group went off in the direction of the Void while the third team started surveying a steeply sloping passage leading out of the room. It took Ron just five minutes to return to one of the promising leads he had found on his previous trip and to begin measuring distances and angles off into the unknown.

Unfortunately, the unknown is not always interesting. The thrill of being the first person to walk through a passage often wears thin as the hours go by. Promising corridors loop back on themselves, leads turn into dead ends, boots fill with rock flour, gypsum crystals grind into tender shoulders under the straps of a cave pack. After many hours underground, the stumbling explorer sometimes wonders what it is about caving that is supposed to be so appealing.

Ron was having his doubts as he recorded the minute details of a hallway in the survey book. They had been at this for hours and had found nothing but more mazy passage. Everything was a dry, dull, dusty-gray color. The reality was that even in Lechuguilla Cave, one of the most impressive cave discoveries ever, most of the trips were routine.

Ron was finishing some boring floor detail on his sketch when Dick came racing back down the passage.

"I found a lake."

Ron looked up from his work.

"How far?"

"Just around the corner. It's neat."

Ron put his pencil and sketch book away as the others went around a bend in the passage. He followed them

CAROL VESELY
Kris Green in the Land of the Lost.

up a sloping ramp. At the end of the corridor, a small window opened into a larger room.

The room was over twenty feet wide and the gentle curves of the domed ceiling stood two dozen feet overhead. Soft mounds of rock flour and small pebbles lay on the sloping floor. At the far end of the room, a pool of deep blue water lay still in the quiet of the cave. Its shoreline, fringed with swirls of white and orange shelfstone, curled and twisted about like the arms of an octopus. A system of small canals crossed beneath large boulders, leading beyond the wall of the room into a small crawlway. To continue would require getting very wet, a prospect that thrilled none of them. Garry Petrie scanned the walls of the chamber and found another crawlway to check.

The passage almost immediately expanded into a stoopway. Turning to the right, Garry found the continuation of the watery canal. Shining his headlamp into the water, he called to the others.

"Can you guys see my light?"

"Yeah! How did you get there?"

"I'm on the other side of the wall. The passage keeps going. Go in the first crawlway to your left."

Garry looked over his shoulder to make sure the others were following him, then he continued on. He was surrounded by terraced pools, some only a few inches deep, others six feet or more. Stepping carefully, he worked his way down the passage. Soon the ceiling rose slightly and the corridor terminated in a beautiful blue pool a dozen feet across. The beam from his headlamp pierced the depths of the pool, but he could not see the bottom.

The others caught up with Garry and found him sitting quietly at the edge of the pool.

"Another survey team is in the room behind us. We could hear their voices as we started into the crawlway."

"I'll go back and show them the way," Ron said. "Besides, I want my camera for this."

It was only a few minutes before the members of the other two survey teams joined them in the small chamber. By odd coincidence, all three teams had surveyed routes that led to the same place. Thirteen cavers squeezed into the now-crowded room.

The fifteen-foot-high chamber measured ten by twenty feet, with the azure pool taking up almost exactly half of that area. Small ledges were visible just beneath the surface of the water on the near side, but at the far end was the deep blue color that comes from depth. On the far wall, there was a small triangular opening at water level, as though it were a portal to a connected lake beyond. The only other exit was a small crawlway halfway up the wall at the midpoint of the room.

Steve Reames, Garry, and Don Kluever climbed up the wall into the hole. The gypsum-lined crawl ran parallel to the lake. After twenty feet and two more turns, the passage was high enough to crouch in, but still no wider than one person. Steve poked his head out of a hole that dropped down into a water-filled room. Anxious to see what was beyond, the other two cavers crawled on top of him, their three heads sticking out over the balcony. They were near the ceiling of a room with the water's surface eight feet below. The ledge on which they were perched was under-cut. Dropping into the watery passage would be a one-way trip, as it would be impossible to climb back up. The water led down a sinuous corridor to turn a corner forty feet away. As they surveyed the scene, a flash of light briefly lit the chamber.

"Hey! Can you guys see our lights?"

Cavers in the other room shouted for quiet several times before they could reply.

"We can hear you. Have you found a way around the pool?"

"No, we can't get through here, but we can see your lights through that triangular hole on the far side of the pool. Do you think you can swim through?"

"Maybe. How long of a swim is it?"

"We can't see the end, and there's no way to get out on this side. You might be swimming for a long time. We're coming back."

They turned around and crawled back to the others. The three teams pieced together what they had seen. It was clear from their survey notes that they had gone beyond the currently known outer limits of the cave. If the passage ahead continued, it could break into an entirely new area.

Ron looked at the water and at the triangular portal on the other side. The water was only sixty-eight degrees.

"I'm going to check it out," he said.

Dick and Joe crawled back to the balcony with their lights in case Ron had a light failure while swimming down the corridor. Ron undressed quickly and then put his helmet and headlamp back on. Neil Markovitz, no longer able to resist the call of the unknown, undressed to go along. Ron lowered himself into the cold, crystal-clear pool. Treading water, he ducked his head only slightly to pass through the triangular portal. As he rounded the first bend he saw the cavers on the balcony overhead. He swam on. Forty feet later the passage turned again, and he disappeared around the corner. Neil followed, gasping as the cold water hit his skin. He ducked through the portal, swam down the corridor, and around the corner. Soon their voices faded, the ripples calmed, and the surface of the water became still once again.

The others in the pool chamber remained silent. There was an occasional faint sound of splashing in the distance. But soon the splashing stopped, and the room was filled with the silence of the underground.

"Five minutes," Garry announced, looking at his watch.

A shout came from the balcony. "Ron's coming back."

The sound of someone swimming became louder, and soon Ron DeLano crawled shivering out of the pool, grabbing his T-shirt to use as a towel. "It's beautiful," he said. "It's the most beautiful place I've seen in the Guadalupe Mountains."

There was a huge lake, snow-white formations, a sequence of perched pools. Garry and Steve stripped down for the swim. They had to see this for themselves.

Garry jumped in, but Steve slowly lowered himself into the water, grimacing. Passing through the portal, they discovered it was easier than it looked. They swam down the forty-foot corridor and turned at the bend in the passage. The walls and ceiling receded to reveal a lake at least a hundred feet across. The light from their headlamps reflected off the waves causing shifting patterns of light on the ceiling high overhead. The water was deep, with the exception of a single submerged rock pinnacle that Garry found with his knee.

The passage on the far shore was ten feet high and only eight feet wide, but continued beyond Neil, who was sitting among a forest of stalactites. Each one had a cluster

of crystals on its end, giving the effect of a collection of bottle brushes. The stalks of the stalactites were brilliant
white in contrast to the yellow and orange crystals on their
tips. As Garry and Steve climbed out of the water, they
could see a passage leading onward, its floor consisting of a
series of stepped pools, each one overflowing into the next.
The rim of each pool was encrusted with shelfstone – thin
crusts of travertine that had built out along the surface of
the water. They were only an inch thick where they
attached to the walls. The pools were of different depths,
giving each one a unique shade of green and blue. The
walls were covered with overlapping layers of flowstone.
Each layer was a slightly different hue of white, pastel yellow, or cream. Here and there, scattered about the flowstone walls, small, sparkling aragonite bushes shone like
miniature Christmas trees.

Over the next two hours, nearly all of the thirteen
cavers made the fifty-yard swim to see the treasures of
Lechuguilla Cave. As each returned, the excitement
encouraged another two or three to take the swim. Ron
made the round-trip three times, the last time treading
water the entire way holding his camera above his head.
Finally, they returned to the amphitheater to discuss the
return trip to the surface. They were six hours from the
entrance, and the long night had taken its toll. Each survey
team adopted a different strategy for leaving the cave.
DeLano's group decided to rush to the surface, Roy's team
decided to sleep for a couple hours and then start out, and
Steve Reames' group decided to travel for a couple hours,
sleep, and then finish the trip.

"What are you going to call this, Ron?" It was his
privilege, being the bookkeeper of the discovery team, to
name what they had found.

"Castrovalva."

"Castro-what?"

"Castrovalva is a place on the TV series *Doctor Who*.
It's a serene and restful planet that he visited. I think

there's no more peaceful and tranquil place in this cave than what we just found."

In another part of the Void, at the same time that Castrovalva was being discovered, Donald Davis stood waiting for the rest of his group. Donald was one of the few cavers who knew the Void area well. He had been on four trips to the region and was just beginning to understand the complex maze of interconnected passages.

The sound of footsteps in the corridor announced the arrival of the rest of the survey team: Pat Kambesis, Kris Green, and Neil Backstrom. They were all there for different reasons. Pat had heard about this newly discovered part of the cave and wanted to learn the intricacies of its mazy passages. Kris was out for an adventure; he knew that, more often than not, trips with Donald led to great discoveries. Neil had just been hanging around the huts, disappointed with the results of his previous trips, when Pat asked if he wanted to come along. It was Donald who was driven to return to this particular place. He had noticed the corrosion, boneyard, and rock flour. There were even yellow sulfur deposits in some of the passages. All these were indications that strong acids had been present here when the cave formed. Even more exciting was the fact that the passages in this area plunged steeply downward. The cave looked like it would go deep here, and deep was exactly where Donald wanted to go.

"Where's that lead you wanted to check out?" Kris asked.

"This way," Donald said as he turned and walked down the corridor.

They made their way along a broad ledge at the edge of the Void. Donald led them through a long sequence of twists and turns only he could have remembered, until they reached a large room. He escorted the group past several large boulders to the opposite side of the chamber.

"There," Donald said, pointing down an irregularly shaped hole in the floor. They could see the bottom of the pit about ten feet down and it was clear that the passage continued. Although Donald had been the leader up to this point, Pat now took over by right of being the sketcher. She took out her survey book and handed the reel of survey tape to Donald. He anchored the free end to a rock and began climbing down the pit, paying out the tape as he went. They began the laborious process of surveying point to point through the cave.

The passage spiraled downward, constantly turning to the left as the explorers corkscrewed their way into the depths. At first, the passage was a stoopway about four feet wide and five feet high, but it soon turned into a large fissure that resembled a miniature version of the Rift. It was about two feet wide and thirty feet high and large breakdown boulders were wedged precariously between the walls. The boulders made the fissure look like a set of stairs for someone with a giant's stride so they called it the Grand Staircase. They worked their way down the rift, testing each boulder before climbing past.

At the bottom of the fissure was a narrow room with a level floor. It was a good place to rest, so they took a short break. Pat sat down on the floor and continued to work on her sketch. She had been keeping a running profile of the passage to track the depth of the cave. Since the profile had been drawn to scale, all she had to do to find the depth was count the squares on the graph paper.

"We're at minus twelve fifty," she announced suddenly.

"Isn't the record depth for the cave twelve hundred and four feet?" Donald said. "If you're right, we've just set a new record."

Pat laughed. "That was easy. Everybody has been telling me that the cave has reached base level and couldn't go any deeper."

"Yes," Donald said. "And I don't think we're done yet."

Donald set off down the passage looking for a way to go deeper. In a few minutes, they heard him shouting. When they caught up, he was peering down a small hole in the floor.

"It doesn't end yet," Donald said pointing down the hole.

They could see another fissure, smaller than before, angling steeply downward. The walls were narrow and pitted from corrosion, and as the cavers forced their way deeper into the darkness, sharp fingers of limestone tore at their clothing. Twenty feet, forty feet, sixty feet, the passage continued down, getting smaller with every foot. Then the fissure opened again to just over four feet high and twenty feet wide. Small raft cones littered the floor, indicating that a lake had once been here. They needed a name for the record-setting fissure, so even though it was early in the morning of April second, they decided to call it the April Fools Passage.

"This is very interesting," Donald said as he stopped and aimed his headlamp at a strange formation on the wall. There were hundreds of thin parallel ridges running horizontally along the sides of the passage. They were made of creamy white calcite and the edge of each ridge was thin and rippled. The formations resembled the edges of a huge stack of pancakes.

"What is it?" Pat said.

"They're called folia and they're very rare. They're formed by water rising and falling in the passage."

Donald pointed at the edge of one of the ridges. "We think the ridges are formed right at the surface of the water. When the water rises or falls, a new ridge is deposited."

He thought for a moment and then added. "It means we're getting close to the water table. It also probably means that the passage will end soon."

Donald was right. He pushed into every small crawlway leading out of the room, but even he could not find a route leading deeper.

Pat sat on a small rock and finished the sketch while the other three rested. "Thirteen hundred and eighty," she announced. "Including the high point that's twenty-six feet above the entrance, this puts the cave at just over four-teen hundred feet deep. I could be off by plus or minus ten feet or so, but that's as close as we're going to get until we enter these notes into the computer."

They had been in the cave for over fifteen hours, but the thought of putting the data into the computer and announcing a new depth record gave them plenty of energy for the six-hour trip to the surface. The computer showed that the cave now measured 1,415 feet deep, making it the second deepest cave in the United States.

With the new depth record, Lechuguilla was begin-ning to attract world-wide attention. European cavers have a special fondness for deep caves, and while Lechu-guilla was not as deep as many of the cave systems in Mex-ico or Europe, cavers across the Atlantic were beginning to show an interest. Six of the best Swiss cavers – Urs Wid-mar, Jasmin Ustundag, Pierre-Yves Jeannin, Ursula Som-mer, Phillipe Roullier, and Sura Ballmann – flew to the United States to visit Lechuguilla. Although they were impressed by the shear beauty of the cave, they were disap-pointed by the lack of maps. Reams and reams of line plots had been generated, but there were no maps showing the passage walls and floor detail.

The Swiss cavers also ran week-long expeditions in Europe, but they concentrated on one part of a cave until all new discoveries had been drawn onto the map. That way, they could find survey errors and fix them before leav-ing. It also meant that they always had up-to-date maps to help them decide where to explore.

Even though the Lechuguilla Cave Project had been going strong for over a year, the only real map was still the one that Rick had presented to the park. Cartographers had been assigned to work on maps for the new parts of the cave, but the Project was discovering passages so quickly that no one could keep up. With no central person in charge, each cartographer had to sort through piles of survey notes to find and organize all the data for a particular part of the cave. The Swiss suggested that the solution to the problem would be to stop exploring until the maps were up to date. The members of the project were too excited by all the new discoveries even to consider such an option.

The project had much bigger problems than the lack of maps. Over the last few expeditions, the park was starting to receive complaints about the behavior of some of the cavers. It was understandable that the large expeditions would cause some difficulties, but the problems were getting worse.

There had been complaints about people changing their clothes in view of tourists, drinking in public, driving too fast in the park, and being rude to visitors and rangers. These problems were straining LCP's relationship with the park. They were also straining the relationships among the project leaders. In March, 1988, there was a major flare-up between Rick Bridges and Roy Glaser. Normally, Rick and Roy were in the cave on alternate days. This was one of the few days when both of them were on the surface at the same time.

"You've got to go down Apricot Pit on your next trip," Rick shouted.

"I'm going back to the Western Borehole. We left a bunch of good leads on our last trip," Roy said.

"You've gone to the Western Borehole on your last two trips; now you have to go east."

"Why?" Roy was tired of being ordered around by Rick.

"We've gone over that a dozen times. Before this expedition we agreed that everyone would alternate trips between the east and west arms of the cave."

"Why? If there are leads in the Western Borehole, why are we ignoring them just to follow some stupid rule?"

"Because that's what we agreed on!"

"Well then we should change what we agreed on."

"No!" Rick yelled. "I know this cave better than anyone here. I know how to explore this cave with maximum efficiency."

"I don't care about your efficiency," Roy said. "I'm here to have fun."

The arguing continued at full intensity for over an hour as Rick and Roy wandered in and out of the hut. The other cavers were embarrassed to see the project leaders in open conflict. Although some of them may have had their opinions, they did not interfere. They just found that it was a good time to go for a hike or to drive into town to buy groceries. Soon the cabins were empty except for Roy and Rick.

$\Rightarrow$ 11 $\Leftarrow$

Lost!

arly the next morning, Pat Kambesis, Kris Green, and Steve Davis stopped at the end of a short corridor deep in the Western Borehole. The passage they were surveying had quickly degenerated into a maze of fissures and crawlways. It was time for a short food break. Pat, Kris, and Steve scanned the walls with their headlamps while they ate. Although they had been mapping this new area for hours, it was so incredibly complex that they still did not understand it. Which of the leads would take them to bigger passage? They agreed to split up, each one searching in a different direction for the elusive way onward. They would check each lead for a hundred feet. If large, going passage was found, then they would all continue the survey in that direction.

Steve selected a small hands-and-knees crawlway. Dropping his pack, he started into the convoluted passage. He quickly crawled a dozen feet, then paused. He looked over his shoulder at his pack lying on the floor behind him. A voice in his head said, "A caver always takes his pack." But the passage ahead looked small, and it would be a nuisance to drag his pack along with him. "I won't be going far," he thought. He continued forward and quickly covered a hundred feet, finding numerous branches. He was not content. "A hundred feet is nothing," he thought. "What if the next great discovery is just around the corner?" He pushed further into the cave; up, down, and around.

Out of the corner of his eye, he saw darkness. And darkness was exactly what he was looking for. Quickly covering the dozen feet between him and the looming blackness at the end of the passage, he stood up. A huge room lay before him, floored with large blocks of gypsum. Steve ran to the center of a chamber and looked around. It was over a hundred feet long and at least fifty feet high. This was it; he had found the route onward. He turned around, took two steps and froze. The wall before him looked like Swiss cheese. There were dozens of holes leading out of the room. "Which one did I come out of?" he said. There was no reply.

Six hours later on the surface, it was another beautiful, cloudless desert morning. Just past nine, the main cabin was packed with three dozen cavers cooking breakfast and preparing to go underground. Steve Reames had risen early to enter survey data in the computer. It was a rest day for Steve, and he intended to do nothing more strenuous than typing, reading, and eating. To stretch his legs for a moment, he walked across the room to the wall map. He had just started to examine one corner of the map when Ron Kerbo strode through the doorway. Kerbo was wearing his serious look; it was clear he was not happy. Steve waited for the bad news. What stupid thing had one of the cavers done this time? Had someone parked in the superintendent's parking spot, walked between the huts in his underwear, or urinated on the wall of the visitor center? Kris Green and Pat Kambesis were right behind Kerbo, and obviously had something to do with the problem.

Kerbo stopped in the corner of the main room and spoke in a loud and clear voice. "May I have your attention, please."

The ruckus in the main room subsided somewhat, but the kitchen was still noisy.

"May I have your attention, please. We have someone lost in Lechuguilla. Steve Davis disappeared from the Chandelier Graveyard area several hours ago and has not been seen since. The group he was with spent more than an hour looking for him. Pat came out to organize a rescue. Patty, could you describe where this area is?"

Pat Kambesis quickly described where the new area was in relation to the known cave.

"Does anyone here know this area of the cave?" Kerbo asked.

Steve Reames and Buddy Lane raised their hands and looked around. They were the only two. With the exception of Kerbo, Steve and Buddy were also the only two present who had cave rescue training.

"Steve and Buddy, get your gear together, you'll be the initial response team. There'll be a mandatory meeting for everyone in ten minutes at the chapel. All other trips to the cave are canceled." Kerbo turned and walked out the front door of the hut. He had ten minutes to plan the rescue.

Steve Davis was still kicking himself for leaving his pack behind. It had taken several minutes before it sank in. He was now separated from Pat and Kris by a maze of passages over a thousand feet underground. But the pack was the most frustrating part. He knew better than to leave his pack. It had food, water, a space blanket, and spare lights. Now all he had was what he was wearing. A helmet with one main light and one backup, a survey tape, and a roll of flagging tape. Quickly, he started checking the holes, trying to find the one through which he had entered the big room. He put blue flagging tape at the entrances of those he knew were wrong. He would have to check every hole until he found his way back.

After a time, Steve took a short break and stared at the maze of holes. The unmarked holes still greatly outnumbered the marked ones. He knew he had to continue. It would take hours before a rescue effort could be mustered. There could not be more than half a dozen people who knew their way to this section of the cave. He shouted, only to hear the deafening silence in return. Picking a likely candidate, he started down yet another crawlway.

Steve Reames hurried to collect his gear for the rescue. His heart sank when he looked at his headlamp. Now he remembered: he had returned from the cave late last night, completely exhausted. Normally he would have put his battery on the charger immediately so it would be ready in case of an emergency, but this time he had been too tired to bother. The battery needed fourteen hours to recharge, hours he did not have right now. Rummaging through his duffel bag of cave gear, he discovered that all three of his backup battery packs were charged, good for nearly thirty hours of light. He put the new batteries in his cave pack and plugged the used ones into the charger.

Gathering together food, water, spare lights, and other caving gear, Steve considered the problem at hand. Search and rescue involves three simple steps. Find the person, administer first aid, and then transport. In the worst case, the victim or body must be strapped into a litter and carried out of the cave.

Steve thought back to all the practice rescues he had participated in. The crucial thing in cave rescue is time. It takes time to get someone out of a cave, lots of time. He remembered the last real rescue he had been on. A member of Steve's party had fallen in a Colorado cave, bruising his spinal cord and paralyzing a leg. He was only 800 feet from the entrance of the cave but it took twenty-two hours to get him out. Steve Davis was lost in Lechuguilla Cave, over a mile from the only entrance. It took five hours of normal travel just to reach the place where he had last been seen.

CAROL VESELY
Steve Davis rappelling into a boneyard pit.

Pat was waiting in the chapel with every available caver when Kerbo entered. He walked straight to the front of the room.

"Pat, explain what happened."

"We were checking leads. I don't know which one Steve went down. We yelled for him for over an hour, but got no response. Warren Anderson and his survey team came by, so they stayed and waited for Steve while we came for help."

There were hazards. The area they had been surveying was over 150 feet above the floor of the Western Borehole. Pits were everywhere, and most of them connected
with the borehole below. A fall down any one of them would
be fatal. There were numerous gypsum bridges spanning
these pits, most of which would not hold the weight of a
human being. It was entirely possible that Steve had fallen
down one of the many pits and was unconscious or dead.

"Who was the trip leader? Why did you let him go off
by himself?" someone asked from the back of the room.

"It doesn't matter," Kerbo said. "We have someone
lost in the cave. We need to find him. Any more questions?
OK, then, I want everyone to get their gear ready and
report to the main hut." He abruptly left the room.

Steve Davis' carbide lamp flickered one last time and
finally went out. Reaching for his helmet, he turned on his
electric backup light, the second of three light sources.
"Four more hours," he thought. "Four more hours of
light." Once his light was gone, he would really be lost. In
total darkness, he would be unable to move without getting
more lost or falling down a pit. It was frustrating to think
that he had carbide good for twenty-for hours in his pack,
only a couple of hundred feet away. It might as well have
been a couple hundred miles for all the good it did him now.
The crawlway ahead opened into another room. Carefully
marking his route with flagging tape, he entered the room.
One wall opened into a void below. Steve knew he was high
above the Western Borehole. If he were lucky, the void
would connect to the borehole below or to the passage they
had been surveying earlier. Someone below might hear him
and could tell him where he was.

"Hello! Is anyone there?"

Silence.

He shouted again, then he retraced his steps to the
first room and marked the crawlway as checked.

Buddy Lane opened the closet and could not believe his
eyes. This was supposed to be a rescue cache? The contents of

PLATE 1

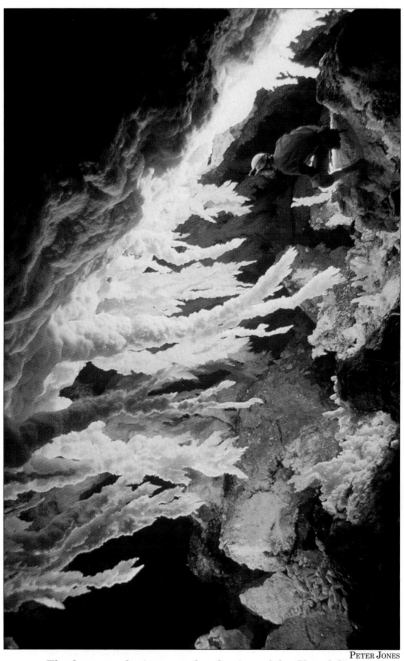

PETER JONES
The famous selenite crystal stalactites of the Chandelier
Ballroom are one of the hallmarks of Lechuguilla Cave.

PLATE 2

The Pearlsian Gulf is named for the large
number of cave pearls found in the room.

PLATE 3

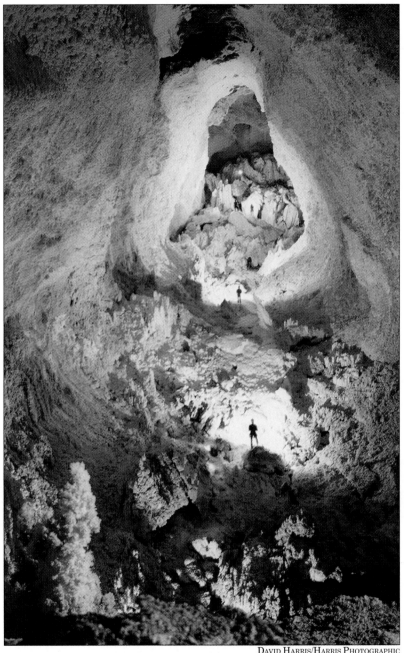

DAVID HARRIS/HARRIS PHOTOGRAPHIC
Six cavers make their way through
the enormous Prickly Ice Cube room.

PLATE 4

DAVID HARRIS/HARRIS PHOTOGRAPHIC
Bill Allen climbs onto the flowstone
of Ultra Primo in the High Hopes area.

PLATE 5

A caver pauses next to a collection
of 15-foot-long soda straw stalactites.

PLATE 6

David Harris/Harris Photographic
Bill Allen looks into the Red Lakes
Passage in the Western Borehole.

PLATE 7

PETER JONES

The Leaning Tower of Lechuguilla is located
along the main passage of the Western Borehole.

PLATE 8

DAVID HARRIS/HARRIS PHOTORAPHIC

Chris McKay and Larry Lemke
share a meal in the Deep Seas camp.

PLATE 9

PETER JONES

Hudson Bay is a well-decorated, large
side-chamber off the Western Borehole.

PLATE 10

NORM THOMPSON

Three cavers marvel at the formation
room in the Lakes of Castrovalva.

PLATE 11

NORM THOMPSON

The Emperors Throne Room is one of many
large chambers in the Eastern Mega Maze.

PLATE 12

DAVE BUNNELL
The Huapache Highway section of the Western Borehole
is one of the largest passages in the cave.

PLATE 13

DAVE BUNNELL
The Oasis is near the far end of the Western Borehole.
The water line of an ancient lake is readily visible.

PLATE 14

DAVE BUNNELL

Above the Pearlsian Gulf is a heavily
decorated region known as Yo Acres.

PLATE 15

DAVE BUNNELL
A caver pauses at the edge of Lake of the Blue Giants.
This lake has been dived to a depth of 80 feet.

PLATE 16

PETER JONES

This 18-inch-tall stalagmite in the Emperors
Throne Room resembles a miniature Buddha.

the small storage closet were in total disarray. Clearly no one had been in here for quite some time. There was no shortage of equipment, but just finding what he was looking for would be a problem. "At least we have plenty of rope," Buddy noted as he sorted through the gear. He looked at the ends of several of the ropes. They should have had tags to indicate the length of the rope and its purchase date, but he found none. Buddy would have to measure and mark the coils later. He needed to find locking carabiners first. The inventory list clearly stated that there were fifteen somewhere in this mess.

But something was not right. Holding the inventory list in the bright light of the doorway, he scanned the sheet from top to bottom. "Not here," he mumbled. The rescue cache had no field telephones or wire. Conventional radios can penetrate only a few feet through solid rock. Cave rescuers always string temporary phone lines through the cave. But now if Davis was hurt, someone would have to return to the surface, get the needed supplies, and go back, wasting ten hours in the process.

Steve Reames was almost ready. Don Kluever entered the small hut. He was packed and ready to go.

"Kerbo told me to go with you. Since you and Buddy are the only ones with rescue experience, he didn't want both of you in the cave at the same time."

"Sounds good. Are you ready?"

"Yeah. You know where this place is?" Don asked.

"Pretty much, I haven't been to the exact spot, but I know where the lead is."

John Roth, the assistant cave specialist came in with a walkie-talkie in his hand.

"You guys ready?"

"All set."

Steve and Don walked rapidly along the trail to the cave. John had not hiked this trail as many times as the Lechuguilla veterans had, so his pace was slow and it took a conscious effort by Steve and Don not to leave him behind. The silence along the trail was broken only by the occasional crackle of John's park-service radio.

At the entrance to the cave, Steve and Don put on their rappelling gear. John's job was entrance control. He sat on the lip of the pit, his feet dangling over the edge, ready to supervise the rappel. Don went down first and Steve followed.

"Make sure no one gets in too much of a hurry down there," John said.

"Will do," Steve said.

Don waited for Steve's feet to touch the cave floor before disappearing down the next fissure. Steve and Don would remain just within earshot of each other. Steve would reach the top of each rope drop just as Don completed it. Neither would wait unnecessarily for the other.

Back in the maze, Steve Davis was down to three hours of light, and he was sweating profusely. He had been lost for five hours and he had shouted down into the darkness of three more rooms, only to have his words swallowed up in the emptiness below. He knew a rescue was underway by now. Crawling through another passage, he froze. Was that a sound he heard? Lying motionless, he strained to hear the slightest sound over the noise of his own heavy breathing. Nothing. He kept crawling. He was beginning to hear things. Another room appeared ahead of him. For the fourth time, he emerged from a crawlway and carefully marked it with a small cairn of rocks. Entering the center of the room he scanned the walls looking for an opening to the passages below. Finding one, he hurried over to it and shouted into the darkness.

"Hello!"

"Who's up there?"

Steve almost fell into the hole.

"It's me, Steve Davis."

"Are you the one that's lost?"

Davis paused at the inane question. How many other people did they think were wandering around in the mazes above the Western Borehole?

"Yeah, that's me. Who are you?"

"It's Warren Anderson, Kevin Komisarick, and Shari Lydy. Pat asked us to wait here while she went for help."

"How do I get down from here?"

Kevin moved to the bottom of the fissure Davis was staring down. For the first time in hours, Steve saw the headlamp of another human being – thirty feet below. The fissure was overhung. There was no way anyone could free climb down to the level below. He had to get down there, but how? Warren's team had a section of rope about fifty feet long. If they could get the end of the rope up to Steve, he could secure it and rappel down.

They tied a rock to the end of the rope and attempted to throw it up the three-story height to Steve. The rock bounced off the walls repeatedly, always a dozen feet short of its goal. Fifteen minutes and several sore arms later, they gave up. There was no way they could get the rope up to him. If only he had some way to pull it up. Suddenly, Steve had an idea. He took out a spool of flagging tape, unrolled it, and lowered the end down to the others. They tied the end of the rope onto the tape. Steve hauled up the rope, tied it to a projection and rappelled down to safety.

The rescue team of Don and Steve Reames arrived at the top of Boulder Falls. Don held up his hand as a sign to remain quiet. Someone was at the bottom, but too out of breath to shout a clear message. The echoes off the cave walls made it impossible to discern its meaning.

"I think he wants to come up," Don said.

"Sorry," Steve said. "This time, I think we take priority. Yell 'On rope' and go."

Steve waited the standard two minutes that most people took for the rappel and listened for the "Off rope" signal. Instead, a slow, deliberate message returned from below, every syllable bouncing off the cavern walls.

"Davis . . . is . . . here . . . stop . . . rescue."

⇛ 12 ⇚

FIRE AND BRIMSTONE

t was now April of 1988. Trips to Lechuguilla Cave had been regularly scheduled every other month for the last eight months. As the cave and the number of people visiting it grew, the amount of pre- and post-expedition planning increased accordingly. It was taking more and more time to enter the survey data into the computer, photocopy the trip reports, make line plots, write expedition reports, and prepare lead lists for the next expedition.

Even with a lot of help from other project members, it was surprising that Rick had been able to keep up for as long as he had. Lechuguilla had grown exponentially for the first few months, doubling in length with each expedition. After the first expedition, the cave was just over 7,400 feet. By the end of the second it was 17,000 feet, after the third it was 37,000 feet and after the fourth it was 67,000 feet. Now Lechuguilla Cave was 84,000 feet, over sixteen miles long, having been explored faster than any other cave in history. The Lechuguilla Cave Project had done an amazing job of keeping up with all the exploration, but with the May expedition only five weeks away, the workload was overwhelming Rick.

Ron Kerbo was also having difficulty keeping up with the frequent expeditions. The park had less planning to do before the event, but still it was not trivial. The big problems for the park came during the expeditions themselves when the cavers required almost continuous attention. Kerbo had a mandatory group meeting on the first day and meetings with Rick every day thereafter. There were frequent requests by the participants for access to the copying machine or to park files. Finally, there was a continuous stream of minor infractions, ranging from vehicles improperly parked along the road to cavers tracking mud into the visitor center. During these ten days all other activities in the cave resources office ceased. There were more than eighty other caves in the park that also needed Kerbo's attention. So in the interest of letting everyone catch up, he canceled the May expedition.

Pat Kambesis was not content to let the month of May slip by without a trip to Lechuguilla. She had been actively exploring the caves of the Guadalupe Mountains for years. A few quick phone calls to friends in Georgia, Texas, and California confirmed what she already knew: she would have no problem putting together a team. The next step would be to get a permit from the park.

Kerbo and Pat were longtime friends. Pat had been on every expedition since the breakthrough dig, and Kerbo knew that she was well qualified to lead a trip into Lechuguilla. He thought about the proposal. It would be for only a few days and involve just one team that would remain underground the entire time. This would require his attention only on the first and last days. He decided that the small group could be admitted to Lechuguilla without undue strain on the cave resources office. Kerbo gave his approval, but on the condition that Pat work under LCP. He issued a four-day permit that encompassed Memorial Day weekend.

Rick was taken aback when Pat called to tell him she had a permit for Lechuguilla. Although Pat's trip would be technically under the auspices of LCP, Rick was concerned that it would set a bad precedent. If Pat's trip was successful, then other cavers would get ideas. They might try to bypass LCP entirely to run their own expeditions. Rick was determined not to let that happen. He amiably discussed the upcoming trip with Pat. "Oh, by the way," he began, "there are just a couple things I'd like you to do in preparation for the LCP expedition in August." Pat cheerfully accepted the tasks that Rick suggested. She had benefited from the previous work of LCP, so it was only right that she contribute in return.

By the last week in May, however, Pat's expedition was overloaded with work. Every day or two, Rick called to add another seemingly trivial task to the list, which was now much too long to be completed in only four days. But Pat also knew that she had no choice. If she declined to do even one of the tasks Rick had assigned, he would report to Kerbo that she was not acting in the spirit of LCP. That could be used as grounds to cancel her permit.

Pat had invited four close friends to come on her trip. Carol Vesely and Bill Farr came from California, Kris Green from Atlanta, and Terry Bolger drove up from Texas. As they gathered in the park, they were all uneasy. They were prepared for some kind of last-minute change that would unravel all their plans. But when they got to the cave specialist's office, they found the office locked and a handwritten note on the door: "Pat, have fun. Kerbo."

Many hours later, they were deep in the southwestern branch of Lechuguilla Cave on their way to the Chandelier Ballroom. Their packs were immense − each of them had brought enough gear to camp for four days. Rick had repeatedly refused to let anyone camp in the cave during project expeditions, so Pat had de-emphasized the camping aspect. But with the huge list of things to do and only four days to do them in, Pat knew it would be most efficient to stay in the cave. They were just going to take cat naps, she insisted. It was only a detail that the cat naps included sleeping bags, stoves, and four days worth of food.

During a marathon survey trip on the January expedition, Neil Backstrom had found a promising lead off the Prickly Ice Cube Room. He had climbed the first seventy feet, decided that they would need a rope to continue safely, and turned back. This time Pat's team had come with enough rope and equipment to finish the climb. Their plan was to complete all the tasks Rick had given them in two or three days, leaving the rest of the time to push the climbing lead.

They settled into camp and ate a short meal. The first task on the list was to flag several of the main routes through the Chandelier Maze and Mouses Delight. They traveled the routes, placing small strips of orange flagging tape as they went. Hours later, they returned to camp and decided that they had done enough for one day.

The next day, they re-sketched, marked leads, and flagged routes. By the third day, it was clear that they would not have time to do the climb they had planned, but they were happy. They had the cave to themselves, and they were doing what they loved most. Besides, these were all jobs that needed to be done even if no one wanted to do them on LCP expeditions.

Pat closed her survey book and looked down a passage she recognized. "Hey you guys, let's go check out the deep point."

"You were there just a couple months ago," Bill said.

"There are still some side leads that haven't been checked. We might be able to make the cave a little deeper."

"Sure, why not?" Bill said. "I haven't been to the deep point."

They retraced the route Pat had surveyed on the previous expedition. Although several side leads were marked on the notes, Pat knew that most of them just looped around in the maze of crawlways near the deep point. Still, every lead needed to be checked. They hurried onward with Pat and Kris leading the way. Down the maze of descending walking passage, down the sloping fissure, down the smaller tubes, and into the April Fools Passage.

Pat and Bill pushed the final crawl at the end of the room to see if they could eke out another five feet of depth. Near the top of the chamber, there were several horizontal tubes leading down, but none seemed to go deeper than the April Fools Passage. Kris forced his way into one unpromising lead that was slightly larger than his body.

"I see water." he shouted back, his muffled voice barely audible. The other cavers stopped.

CAROL VESELY

Pat Kambesis taking notes just above
Sulfur Shores. Note the folia on the upper wall.

"Water?" Pat asked.

"Yeah," Kris said. "There's a fissure leading down. It's not very big, but I think I can see water at the bottom."

"Don't go down," Pat commanded. "Do you smell anything, like sulfur?" Kris wriggled his way back out of the opening and sat upright in the room with the others.

"No," he said. "Why?"

"I was talking with Gerry Atkinson last week," Pat said. "Have you heard the latest on how the cave may have been formed?"

"Something about sulfuric acid?" Kris guessed.

"Right. There's a lot of evidence to support the theory that Lechuguilla, and many of the other caves in the Guadalupes, were formed by sulfuric acid rather than carbonic acid like most other caves. Rising hydrogen sulfide from the nearby oil fields mixed with oxygen-laden water from the surface to create sulfuric acid. The acid ate away the limestone, forming Lechuguilla Cave."

"So?"

"I asked if it was possible that hydrogen sulfide was still rising and collecting in the cave. Gerry said that it was quite possible, and since hydrogen sulfide is heavier than air, it would be concentrated in the deepest parts of the cave."

"What does hydrogen sulfide do to you?" Kris asked.

"If the concentration is above five hundred parts per million, you die. But you can smell much smaller amounts. It smells like rotten eggs."

"Then we should be able to smell it and stay away," Kris said.

"Well, not exactly," Pat explained. "In concentrations above 100 parts per million it overloads your sense of smell so you can't tell it's there."

"So if someone were rappelling into a pit, they could drop right into the lethal zone . . . ."

"And die before they ever smelled anything," Pat said.

"Antidotes?"

"None."

Kris leaned back against the wall and let out a long sigh. "That's just dandy, I feel so much better now."

"It's not likely there's any gas here," Pat said. "But I just wanted to let you guys know before we started surveying."

They started the survey down Kris' lead. During all their years of caving they had felt safe. Caving is not dangerous if one uses common sense. Pits can be dropped with ropes. Darkness can be conquered with lights. Loose rock can be avoided. For the first time, they had an objective danger that could not be easily circumvented.

Kris took the survey tape and started to work his way back through the hole. Pat recorded the numbers, plotted the data, and sketched the shape of the walls. Forty minutes later they had reached a small pool of water at the base of the fissure.

"I think I smell sulfur," Pat said.

The others froze and carefully sniffed the air around them.

"I think I smell it too," Carol said, "but it doesn't smell like rotten eggs."

"It could just be small sulfur deposits around here," Bill said.

"Let me stir up the pool a little and see if it gets stronger," Kris suggested. He cautiously dipped one finger in the milky pool and swirled it about. "Does it smell any stronger now?" he asked.

"Could be," Bill replied.

"I'm not sure," Carol said.

"Pat, are you finished with the sketch?" Kris asked.

"I'm done," Pat said. "Let's go."

They started back out of the passage at a fast pace, not slowing until they cleared the small crawlways and fissures that made up the deep maze. Soon they were hiking along the large walking passages back to camp, laughing at their haste.

"We need a name," Carol said.

"Sulfur Shores," Pat said. "A grand name for a puddle at the base of a nasty fissure."

It was not until they were back at camp that Pat confirmed their hopes – they had added sixty-seven feet of depth to the cave and set a new record for Lechuguilla. Lechuguilla was still only the second deepest cave in the United States, but with 1,476 feet of vertical extent it was now only seventy-four feet away from first place. Even though they never got to the lead in the Prickly Ice Cube Room, they were still pleased. They had re-sketched hundreds of feet of passage, flagged over forty new leads, and set a new depth record.

⚜   ⚜   ⚜

In August, 1988, cavers returned to a changed landscape. A fire started by lightning had burned hundreds of acres along the north edge of the park. The hills around Lechuguilla Cave had been transformed. The dry grasses had burned instantly, leaving almost no trace of their previous existence. A faint smell of smoke still hung in the air even though the fire had burned out two months earlier. Only the lechuguilla plants seemed to have escaped unscathed.

By great luck, or perhaps because of the cool, damp air exhaling from the cave, the fire had missed the large scrub oak trees by the entrance of Lechuguilla Cave. These trees were the only convenient anchor points for the entrance pit ropes. The hillsides nearby were already beginning to show signs of recovery. Small patches of grass were starting to sprout, green against the jet black soil. Occasional sotol stumps, almost unrecognizable without their leafy fronds, were sending out small green shoots.

The August expedition was also the first anniversary of the Lechuguilla Cave Project. The legend of Lechuguilla Cave had traveled far and wide. Seventy-six cavers from eighteen states and three foreign countries were converging on Carlsbad Caverns National Park to explore the discovery of the century.

For over twenty years, cavers had wondered why there was only one large cave in the Guadalupe Mountains. Carlsbad Cavern, at 20.8 miles, was many times longer than all the others. Out of over a hundred nearby caves, the longest were only two or three miles long. The second-longest cave was less than five. For years, cavers had hiked the ridge tops and the valleys searching for another big cave. Many new caves were found, but most were small and insignificant. Despite the setbacks and frustrations, there was always the hope that somewhere out there was another big cave that would rival Carlsbad Cavern. Now, after two decades of searching, the dream was coming true.

Every Lechuguilla expedition had a theme. At the beginning of the week, Lechuguilla Cave was the twenty-fourth longest cave in the United States. Carlsbad Cavern was twenty-second on the list. In the back of everyone's mind was the magic number five; they needed five more miles to surpass Carlsbad Cavern. When each team returned, the survey data was entered in the computer and added to the total length. As the week wore on, they watched the length of Lechuguilla increase to seventeen miles, eighteen miles, nineteen miles.

While the cavers methodically explored and surveyed in the cool darkness below, on the surface everything was in chaos. With only twenty explorers underground at a time, forty to fifty cavers were left on the surface in cabins designed to shelter twenty-four. Returning cavers dumped dirty clothing and cave gear on the floor. There was little or no coordination of meals, so food preparation was anarchy. Three times a day, the kitchen was pandemonium. Cleanup was usually postponed for hours or even days. Some cavers ate in town just to escape the madness.

To add to the difficulty, the Chihuahuan desert is always unbearably hot in August. The endless string of ninety-degree days was interrupted only by the days that hit 100 degrees. The windows and doors of the small huts were open twenty-four hours a day in an attempt to keep the cabins as cool as possible, but this let in swarms of flies, gnats, and worse. Some teams in the cave delayed their return until early morning in an attempt to avoid the desert heat. But despite the heat and discomfort, everyone was happy. They knew that in their lifetimes they would never have another opportunity like this.

Roy Glaser, Steve Sims, and Cyndie Walck were making the long hike out from the depths of the Southwest branch. It had not been a terribly productive trip; they had surveyed only a few hundred feet of small, tiring passage around the Chandelier Ballroom. Steve and Cyndie were only slightly tired, but Roy was nearly exhausted. He had switched teams in the middle of his trip so he could stay in the cave longer and explore more passage and had been underground for more than thirty-six hours.

They paused briefly at the edge of Lake Chandelar for a short rest and to drink from the deep blue pool. A dozen feet away, a wall of rock divided the passage. The route back led through an archway lined with delicate aragonite crystals. The centerpiece was a large aragonite bush that clung to the roof of the archway, forcing each caver to pass through on hands and knees.

Roy hated crawling, especially when he was not feeling well. He stood with his pack in his hand and approached the archway. Once before he had used a trick to get through. By pressing his back against one wall he could squeeze past the aragonite bush with a quarter-inch to spare. This way he only had to bend his knees a little and he did not have to crawl.

Steve and Cyndie stared wide-eyed at Roy's maneuver and began to shout. Roy muttered under his breath as he squeezed past the aragonite bush and popped out on the other side of the archway. Steve and Cyndie quickly followed, crawling under the arch, and joined Roy on the other side.

"What did you think you were doing?" Cyndie shouted. "You destroyed that aragonite bush!"

NORM THOMPSON

Typical chaos in the cabins.

"I did not. I've done that move before – I missed the bush by a quarter-inch."

"Look at all the aragonite needles on the ground!" Cyndie pointed at dozens of aragonite clusters lying on the trail.

"Those were there before," Roy said. "People have been brushing off a few crystals at a time ever since this passage was discovered."

"There's a lot more now."

"Look," Roy said, "I've been in this cave at least thirty times. You've been in here only once or twice. I know what I'm doing."

"What's going on here?" Rick Bridges said as he came around the corner. Rick was leading a group of Russian cavers to the Chandelier Ballroom. He was trying to impress these visitors, and did not want them to see his cavers arguing.

Roy, Cyndie, and Steve told three different versions of the events. Rick agreed to discuss the matter further on the surface, then continued to lead his party into the cave. Roy, Cyndie, and Steve had little to say to each other as they proceeded out of the cave.

Before their data from the Chandelier Ballroom had even been entered, Lechuguilla Cave had already become the longest cave in the Guadalupe Mountains. By the end of the expedition, the score was Lechuguilla: 21.3 miles, Carlsbad: 20.8. A computer plot of the new champion was posted on the wall. The cavers were excited and happy.

⚜   ⚜   ⚜

In spite of all the accomplishments of the project, not everybody was happy with LCP. After only four expeditions of the new Lechuguilla Cave Project, the paperwork and number of rules had grown faster than the cave. Many of the cavers bemoaned the increasing bureaucracy of the project. There were rules requiring participants to alternate their trips between the east and west halves of the cave, rules forbidding two sketchers from being on the

SANDRA SVOBODA

Rocky Mountain Caving cartoon lampooning the growing bureaucratic similarities between LCP and the Cave Research Foundation.

same survey team, and rules requiring that the computer data be kept secret. Every participant was required to sign a release giving LCP ownership of all the work they did in the cave. Even photographs had to be turned into the project so they could be copied and added to the files.

In early 1988, the controversy began to surface in public. A flurry of letters appeared in *Rocky Mountain*

Caving criticizing the management of the project. To add fuel to the fire, there were editorials condemning the publicity surrounding the project. Finally, *Rocky Mountain Caving* printed an anonymous cartoon that lampooned LCP by comparing it to CRF, an organization known for its bureaucracy.

Rick had always been sensitive to any criticism of LCP and he was especially sensitive when that criticism appeared in print. *Rocky Mountain Caving* had ridden the rising tide of new discoveries to become one of the premier caving publications in the country. Each big discovery in Lechuguilla was followed by a flurry of articles in *Rocky Mountain Caving*. The magazine was now the authoritative reference on Lechuguilla Cave and was also the focal point for those critical of Rick's management style. It galled Rick that a magazine that had made its reputation on Lechuguilla was now criticizing LCP. He decided to deal with *Rocky Mountain Caving* by curtailing the source of its articles. Since he controlled access to Lechuguilla Cave, he could use his influence to make sure no new articles came from LCP cavers. There was just one problem, and that problem was Donald Davis.

Donald was a prolific writer. He had been on every expedition and he documented all of his trips with detailed articles in *Rocky Mountain Caving*. Everyone looked forward to Donald's articles because they were both exciting and scholarly, and because Donald had a real knack for being where the action was. So when Donald asked Rick for a list of participants on the last expedition, Rick balked.

"What do want that list for?" Rick asked.

"I need the correct spelling of the names for my article," Donald said.

"We talked about that before. You're not publishing any *RMC* articles until the *NSS News* issue comes out," Rick said, his face turning red.

"You did talk about that on the drive down," Donald replied calmly. "I don't recall that I agreed."

"You'll be scooping the article coming up in the *NSS News*," Rick said. "You can't do that."

"I don't believe that the editors of the *News* will care, but I intend to confirm it with them when I return," Donald said. He picked up his notebook and pencil and walked out of the hut. Rick was only one step behind.

"If you publish that in *Rocky Mountain Caving*," Rick said, "I'll expel you from the project. You'll never be allowed into Lechuguilla Cave again."

Donald paused. He had half expected that this would happen. "I believe you have neither the right nor the authority to prevent me from entering Lechuguilla Cave."

Rick was outraged. He thought his threat would solve this problem with Donald. "Donald, I'm warning you," he said. "You'll have to choose between Lechuguilla and *Rocky Mountain Caving*."

Donald was as stubborn as Rick and also knew he could call Rick's bluff.

"Lechuguilla Cave is on National Park property," Donald said. "Only the superintendent and the cave specialist have the authority to keep me out. You don't have that power, and I suspect that if this issue was brought before Kerbo, he'd agree that I have the right to publish whatever I like wherever I want."

Donald turned and walked off. Rick stormed back to the hut.

≫13≪

THE
ALTERNATE EXPEDITION

he white Toyota pickup sped steadily across the New Mexico desert. The sun had set on the short November day hours ago. It was another long drive from Colorado. Paul Burger and Steve Reames were on their way to Carlsbad for the first Lechuguilla expedition completely independent of LCP. A dozen veteran cavers were going to survey, explore, and conduct wind studies. Steve had never been more miserable.

In the beginning it seemed like a good idea. Steve was one of the growing number of cavers who felt they could no longer work within LCP. Rick's domineering personality had driven away many cavers, but he was still able to fill every expedition because so many others were drawn by Lechuguilla's siren song. Steve decided to try another way. Ron Kerbo had often declared that the cave was public property; it belonged to the American people and any qualified group of cavers could apply for a permit to enter the cave.

Pat had been allowed to run her own trip into the cave a couple months before, but it was still an LCP project. Steve had decided to run a completely independent expedition that would encourage other groups besides LCP to work in the cave. He wrote a proposal and submitted it to the National Park Service. Even though he knew Kerbo's frequently-stated policy, Steve was surprised and delighted when a permit for Lechuguilla Cave arrived by return mail.

For Ron Kerbo, Steve's request could not have come at a worse time. Ever since Lechuguilla had passed Carlsbad Cavern in length, there had been increasing attention from the general public. Local businessmen in Carlsbad wanted the park service to develop the cave. To them, the great wonders of Lechuguilla meant money. A second great show cave in the park could double the number of visitors to the area. But the very idea of lighted walkways and handrails in Lechuguilla Cave gave Ron Kerbo fits. He knew that commercial development would inevitably destroy the wildness and beauty of the cave and he was determined to save Lechuguilla from this fate.

Kerbo was afraid that any conflicts among the cavers would give the business interests in Carlsbad the opportunity to criticize the park and to push for commercial development of the cave. Although there had been a few complaints about Rick and the way expeditions had been run, the park was satisfied with the result. For sixteen months, exploration had been running smoothly. Every two months there was an expedition that increased the length of Lechuguilla by miles. Under the leadership of Rick Bridges, Lechuguilla Cave had become the second deepest cave in the United States, and caving groups were mobilizing support for legislation to make it the world's first officially designated underground wilderness.

Kerbo believed it would be best if there was only one group of explorers, the Lechuguilla Cave Project led by Rick, and he was concerned that Steve's expedition would trigger a wave of conflict and competition among the cavers. Nevertheless, the park had to allow any qualified group to explore the cave.

Steve began organizing his expedition immediately, and he quickly assembled a team of a dozen strong cavers. Don Doucette, Art Wiggins, and Donald Davis – some of the most experienced Lechuguilla cavers – agreed to come.

The trouble began two days before the expedition. Kerbo called Steve at work to ask what the purpose of the expedition was. Steve was momentarily confused. Kerbo had signed the permit; surely he had read the proposal for the expedition. Still, Steve explained in detail how he planned to do wind studies and exploration in Lechuguilla Cave. Kerbo asked a few more questions and then hung up.

Over the next two days, Kerbo called a half-dozen times, asking more and more detailed questions about Steve's expedition plans. He wanted the correct spelling of the participants' names, more details on the purpose of the expedition, and a promise from Steve that all the survey notes had to be turned over to the park. By the last day, the questions felt like an inquisition and Steve was a nervous wreck. He fully expected to arrive in Carlsbad to find that his expedition had been canceled.

As the white pickup truck rolled to a stop in front of the familiar huts, Steve and Paul could see the shadowy outline of a large, brown passenger van. The climbers from Colorado Springs had already arrived. As Steve and Paul walked into the main hut, Don Doucette looked up from his guitar. "Steve," he said, grinning. "Glad you made it."

Art Wiggins appeared from the back room, followed by Bryan Becker, Harvey Miller, and Phil Hurst. Steve shook hands and smiled weakly.

"I hope you guys didn't waste a trip down here."

"You knew we'd come," Don said.

"We may not get to go in," Steve said. "Kerbo seems dubious."

"Kerbo was by here an hour ago," Don said. "He was quite friendly. He did say he wanted to talk to you first thing in the morning in his office."

This was routine, but Steve was worried anyway. Paul walked back to the pickup truck as the guitar music inside started again. Steve stood alone for a moment on the front porch, gazing at a sky alive with stars. As he looked across the small arroyo toward the entrance of Carlsbad Cavern, he wanted to be happy.

Early the next morning, Ron Kerbo marched through the back door of the hut with short, brisk strides, throwing out quick good mornings to everyone he saw. Steve looked up from the maps and computer plots strewn about on the table. "I'd like to see you in my office before anyone goes into the cave," Kerbo said. He disappeared out the front door as quickly as he had arrived.

Steve glanced at Don and quickly followed Kerbo out the door. "Before anyone goes into the cave," Steve repeated, afraid to get his hopes too high.

Ron Kerbo's office was in one of the stone buildings near the cavers' huts. In the tradition of the National Park Service, a brown wooden sign with carved lettering stood over the doorway: Cave Resources. The floor plan was the same as the other huts, but the kitchen had been converted into an office and there were desks in the living room.

Kerbo's large desk sat in the center of the converted bedroom. A leather chair stood behind the desk, three small chairs in front. The walls were lined with file cabinets whose labels were so old that the ink was nearly unreadable. The future of every cave in Carlsbad Caverns National Park was decided here.

Steve sat stiffly in the unfamiliar room. Usually, only Rick went into Kerbo's office. Kerbo shuffled through the papers Steve had submitted.

"What's this 'wind measuring device' your permit talks about? Did you design it yourself?"

This was Steve's area of expertise and he felt a surge of confidence. "It's a balanced bridge configuration with a self-heating thermistor matched against a reference resistance. I can demonstrate it for you if you like."

"No, that won't be necessary."

"How many of the people in your group have been in Lechuguilla before?"

Steve bristled slightly, having been asked the same question only two days before.

"All but two."

"Which two?" Kerbo asked.

Steve replied with the names and a detailed resume of the two cavers who were new to Lechuguilla. What was the problem? The Lechuguilla Cave Project conducted expeditions with forty people, half of them having never been to Lechuguilla before.

Kerbo produced a sheet of paper from the pile on his desk. "Before you go to the places you have planned, I have a list of tasks that Rick has given me that need to be done first. The old entrance portion of the cave needs to be re-surveyed, the back portion of Wooden Lettuce needs to be surveyed, and the entrance culvert needs to be repaired. I may also come up with some additional tasks as the week progresses."

Steve nodded obediently, but inside he was fuming. The tasks that Rick and Kerbo had given him were tedious and time consuming. There was no doubt that they all needed to be done, but LCP had been running for over a year and they had never taken the time to do them.

Steve and Kerbo rose from their chairs and shook hands formally. As Steve turned to the door, Kerbo offered a final word of advice. "Keep an eye on that new kid you have on your trip, Paul Burger. I hear that he's abandoned party members on some of the trips he's been on."

"I'll watch him," Steve said as he left the office and the Cave Resources building, allowing the screen door to slam behind him.

"Watch Paul!" Paul was one of Steve's best friends and there was no person in the world he trusted more than Paul. He was the kind of person who would carry another caver's pack if he was having trouble. Rick must have invented a story about Paul to feed to Kerbo. Steve would put up with being ordered to do dog work, but not with lies.

"How'd it go?" Don asked, looking up from his guitar.

"We have to do this shit work before we can explore." Steve threw the sheet of paper on the table. He swore so infrequently that it caught the others off guard.

"What do we have to do?" Don asked. He looked at the list. "Hmmm. Entrance area, Wooden Lettuce, culvert. We can do it."

"Sure, it'll take us all week," Steve said.

"No, I think we can do it in two or three days," Don said.

"Then Kerbo will just add more things to the list."

"Maybe, but then again, maybe not."

"How do you figure two days?" Steve said. He looked at the list again.

"Well," Don started, "Phil, Harvey, Art, and I can survey the high leads in the entrance area while you, Paul, and Donald finish the survey of Wooden Lettuce. Then we can do what we want." Don was always optimistic.

They completed all the work Kerbo had laid out for them on Saturday and Sunday. To their surprise, Kerbo said they could now work on their own projects.

Donald Davis had the perfect project in mind. He reminded them about a tube above the Moby Dick Room at the far eastern end of the cave. The lead had been examined by several parties, but everyone agreed that only skilled rock climbers had any hope of exploring it. The computer-generated line plots showed that the lead was at the far eastern extent of exploration. A breakthrough here would lead cavers into a large expanse of empty space on the map.

The Moby Dick Room was a five-hour journey from the entrance. This would be another thirty-hour trip. Steve much preferred sixteen- to eighteen-hour trips, but there was no way they could get all the way to the Moby Dick Room, do some useful work, and return in less than thirty hours.

Three hours later, they were at the entrance of the cave. By force of habit, Steve took up his position at the end of the team. He traveled down the entrance rope, down the ten-foot climb and through the culvert. He continued alone, knowing that his teammates were only 100 or 200 feet ahead. The warm, moist air bathed him as he continued down the entrance corridor and through the three constrictions to the top of the Flowstone Slope. Steve felt better the further he went into the cave. He was beyond the reach of Kerbo and Rick. It was just him and seven of his best friends exploring one of the most fantastic caves ever discovered.

The trip past Glacier Bay, EF Junction, Apricot Pit, and Nirvana was uneventful. Four hours after entering the cave, they stopped just past the Rusticles formation.

"Where's the turn-off?" Paul asked.

"We're not sure," Don said. "Donald's checking out the passage over there to see if it looks familiar."

"Isn't the route marked?"

"No, there haven't been many trips back here."

"There will be once we break through." Art said.

They laughed, dreaming of huge corridors and vast chambers.

"This is the way." The muffled sound of Donald's voice came from the nearby passage. Paul removed some orange flagging tape and a felt marker from his pack.

"I'll mark this so we don't miss it again," he said. "To Moby Dick Room," he wrote in bold letters. He added an arrow and a symbol at the end of the tape.

"What's that?" Steve asked.

"It's a whale," Paul said.

"It looks like a fish."

"It's hard to be artistic with a blunt felt pen."

Steve and Paul followed the others through the fissure pointed to by the newly placed flagging tape.

The hour and a half journey took them through a maze of short corridors and crawlways. The trip was tedious

CAROL VESELY
The Moby Dick Room is over 200 feet long.

since each person was frequently required to remove his pack and pass it on to the person ahead. They sometimes lost the route, but eventually they arrived at the margin of an immense room.

"This is it," Donald said.

The chamber was 200 feet long and 120 feet wide. The large arched ceiling rose to fifty feet in the center of the room and it sloped gently to meet the floor at the ends. The floor was strewn with six-foot boulders covered with flowstone and sharp calcite crystals. Level areas were few and far between; sleeping here would be a challenge. Donald walked to the center of the room, dropped his pack, and continued up the slope at the far end to a large hole in the ceiling. The rest of the cavers dropped their packs at the same spot and began to set up camp.

Don Doucette took a small camp stove from his pack and began to assemble it on a slightly sloping rock.

"I don't feel any air here," he said.

"It's unlikely you ever would," Steve said. "The passage is too large. When the air is confined in a small crawlway, its speed increases so you can feel it. But the same volume of air moving in a large room like this goes only one or two miles per hour, much too slow to feel."

"I should have brought some incense or a cigarette," Don said, lighting his stove. "Then we might have been able to see the smoke move." He started making coffee.

"That's a good idea," Steve said. "Maybe I should put together a little air tracing kit and bring it . . ."

"Stop drinking that stuff and get up here!" Donald yelled from across the chamber. Don and Steve looked at each other quizzically. A large boulder blocked the direct view between them and Donald. How did he know that Don was making coffee? Suddenly they came to the obvious conclusion. "Wind!"

"How long from the time you opened the coffee to the time Donald smelled it?" Steve said.

"Thirty, maybe sixty seconds."

Steve glanced at the size of the room surrounding them. "That's impossible," he said. Steve shouted back to Donald.

"How did you know what we were drinking?"

"I can smell the coffee from here," Donald answered. "We don't have time for that. There's a lead to be climbed over here."

Steve reached for his pack. "Whatever is up there must be huge to move this kind of air," he said.

They worked their way across the room and began climbing a steep rubble slope into an alcove along one wall. Soon all eight of them had gathered around Donald.

"What did you find?" Steve said.

"All the air is funneling into this chimney," Donald said as he pointed straight up.

A circular tube ten feet in diameter rose vertically above them, the far end beyond the reach of even the combined illumination of their headlamps. Its walls glistened with white crystals of gypsum. Clusters of delicate aragonite bushes clung to the walls and completely covered large areas.

Don shook his head slowly as he looked at the walls above. "This one's going to be tough. Bryan, what do you think?"

Bryan Becker was one of the best climbers in the country. He was in his early thirties and his five-foot-six-inch frame appeared unsuited for rock climbing, a sport where long arms and long legs are an advantage. But he had broad, strong shoulders and arms of steel. Bryan had scaled many of the major climbing routes in both North and South America, and was well known in Colorado climbing circles. He had once single-handedly carried an injured partner down from the summit of Mt. McKinley.

"You want to lead?" Don asked.

"Sure, I'll try it," Bryan said.

Phil started looking for a belay anchor, Don uncoiled the rope, and Harvey dumped out the climbing equipment as Bryan changed into his climbing shoes. Donald, Paul, and Steve watched the well-rehearsed team prepare. It took them twenty minutes to get ready.

"On belay," Bryan said.

"Belay on," Phil said.

Everyone stopped talking. Every headlamp was focused on the wall above Bryan.

"Climbing."

"Climb."

Several swift movements put Bryan fifteen feet off the ground and made the climb seem deceptively simple. But now he slowed and searched for each handhold carefully and deliberately. The chimney's shape had changed. From below, it appeared to be circular, but from Bryan's elevated vantage point he could see that it was actually a fissure that was now about twenty feet long and between five and ten feet in width. The climb was looking better. By moving toward the inner part of the fissure where it narrowed, Bryan would be able to chimney between the opposite walls. He climbed a few feet higher and reached across, pushing against the white crystals of gypsum. They compressed beneath the force of his hand, like freshly fallen snowflakes. His hand sunk four inches into the soft wall and stopped. Carefully, Bryan shifted his weight to his newly formed handhold. Small crystals of gypsum fell softly to the floor below, but his position held.

Above him, Bryan saw a small rock protrusion the size of a silver dollar. He raised his right foot and placed it on the wall at the level of his waist. Pushing off with that foot, he let go of the gypsum handhold and quickly stepped up into it with his left foot as he grabbed the rock protrusion with his right hand. He stopped, now four feet higher than he had been a moment ago. The climbing gear attached to his shoulder-sling gently clanked like some odd-sounding wind chime. He looked down at the others. They were sweating as much as he was.

"That was a pretty radical move," he said.

"Nice," Don said. "Think you should put in some protection?"

Bryan looked at the rock around him and then at the floor below. "Yeah, you're probably right. I really wouldn't enjoy falling from here." He laughed as he took a sling from his shoulder and threaded it through a slot in the wall. He attached a carabiner to the loop of webbing and hooked his belay rope into it. Bryan looked at the route ahead. There was no sign of the top, or of a ledge to rest on. He climbed more slowly now and gained only a foot or two with each move. He was careful not to damage the aragonite bushes that lined the walls.

A long hour passed, followed by another. Harvey took over belaying from Phil who was worn out from the tension. Always being on the alert to stop a fall is as tiring as climbing. The others had moved out from under the base of the climb, away from the danger of rockfall. They no longer pointed their headlamps upward; Bryan was too high for their lights to be of any use. A third hour passed. The exertion and psychological stress were beginning to wear Bryan down, but he continued. He had left food and water behind; it was easier to climb without the weight of a pack. As the night wore on, Don took over the belay from Harvey.

After more than four hours, Bryan realized that he would not make it to the top. He was over sixty feet above the floor and the end was still nowhere in sight. But where should he stop? There was a small rock bridge spanning the fissure above him. It was still another ten feet up. He continued wearily, determined to make the bridge before turning back. It took twenty minutes to cover the final ten feet. Bryan stepped across onto the bridge and relaxed. As he did so, the rock shifted. He scrambled for a handhold as the rock fell away from his feet.

"Rock!" he shouted.

"Rock!" Don repeated.

The comatose cavers sprang to life as fist-sized missiles crashed down.

Bryan regained his footing on the solid dirt- and rock-covered core of the bridge.

"I hope I didn't break any of the aragonite bushes," he said to himself.

"You OK?" Don shouted.

"I'm all right," Bryan said.

He looked up. The route looked slightly easier from here on up, but he had no energy left. As he looked around, the sparkling reflections of dozens of aragonite bushes flashed in the beam of his headlamp. It was a most difficult climb in a most beautiful corridor. He then knew what he would name the route: the Aragonitemare. Tying the rope around the bridge, Bryan clipped his figure-8 to the rope. In just a couple of minutes he was down.

The lead was still going, and with that much airflow, it could go big.

Harvey went up the rope. Half an hour later he returned. Not only did he fail to see any way of continuing, he had no clue how Bryan had climbed as far as he did. They would have to let it go. They left the rope hanging, gathered up their equipment, and returned to the Moby Dick Room to sleep.

But Bryan could not sleep despite his fatigue. He got out his recorder and blew a long, sweet note that resonated through the chamber. The lyrical notes echoed through the emptiness of the Moby Dick room. Slowly each caver collapsed into his sleeping bag and slipped from consciousness. Sometime after the others had drifted off, Bryan lay down his recorder and fell into a deep and long sleep.

The occasional tossing and turning of cavers was the only sound that penetrated the vast chamber. It was totally black, yet the frequency of rustling from every corner slowly increased. Soon a single light snapped on. A groggy voice croaked from nearby. "What time is it?"

"10:00 a.m."

"We gotta get up."

Don, having prepared the night before, reached toward the stove near his head. He had a pot of coffee started before he left his sleeping bag. Steve put drops in his eyes to re-wet his contact lenses while Paul started eating a breakfast of granola bars. Soon everyone in camp was making breakfast and packing gear. Everyone but Bryan.

Phil climbed across the boulders over to Bryan's sleeping bag.

"C'mon Bryan," he said, nudging him gently. "It's time to get up."

"Ahhgrumph," Bryan said.

"I can't imagine why you're still tired," Phil said.

Don and Steve started working on logistics. "We're supposed to be out by 6:30 tonight," Steve said. "We're still five hours from the entrance, and another hour back to the cabins."

"I was hoping to take the long route back, past the Orange Bowl and Stud Lake," Don said.

"You could do that if we send out one group to let them know the others will be late," Steve said.

They decided that Paul, Phil, and Steve would head directly for the surface, while the rest of the crew would take the longer, scenic route.

"Besides," Don said, "I think Bryan could use another hour of sleep."

They looked across the room at the still-motionless sleeping bag.

Paul, Phil, and Steve soon shouldered their packs and started off across the Moby Dick Room. They traveled rapidly through the Giant Chiclets Room, down through the maze, and back to the flagging-tape marker with a whale drawn on it. They turned without pausing and continued past the Rusticles, through Nirvana, and back to the bottom of Apricot Pit. The ascent up the sequence of ropes in Apricot Pit was tiring, but once they reached the

top the remainder of the trip would be easy. At the top of
the pit they rested, then continued through EF Junction,
the Rift, Glacier Bay, and Boulder Falls. It was after 9:00
p.m. when the last member of the team reached the cool
night air of the desert.

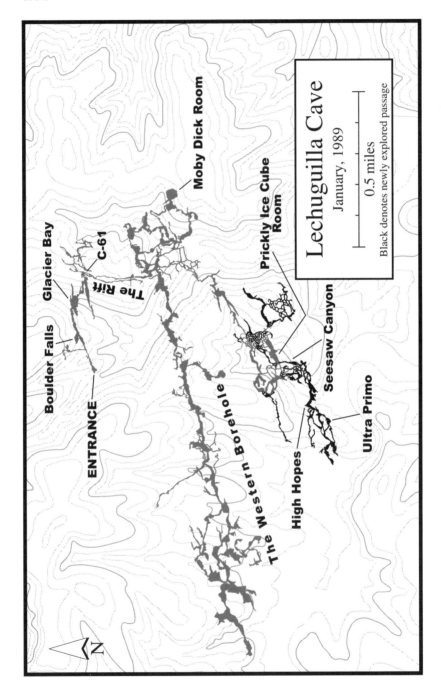

Lechuguilla Cave
January, 1989

0.5 miles

Black denotes newly explored passage

Moby Dick Room

Glacier Bay

C-61

The Rift

Boulder Falls

ENTRANCE

Prickly Ice Cube Room

Seesaw Canyon

The Western Borehole

High Hopes

Ultra Primo

N

⇛ 14 ⇚

LIGHTS, CAMERA, CHAOS

n October, 1988, Rick finally put together a plan to make the Lechuguilla Cave Project a non-profit corporation. To complete the board of directors, Rick had recently appointed Pat Kambesis as one of the project directors. She was well known in the caving community and well respected by the park service for the high quality of her survey work and for her finished maps. Rick would be president of the corporation, and John Patterson would be secretary.

Rick called Pat at her home. They discussed some of the preparations for the next expedition, and then Rick brought up his plans for incorporation. Pat agreed that incorporation was needed. Many of the Lechuguilla cavers worked for large companies and could get funding from their employers. As a legal entity, the project would have an easier time obtaining donations. Rick and Pat discussed the various ramifications of incorporating for half an hour before Pat asked the inevitable question.

"What about Roy?" she said.

"Roy's been a bit of a problem lately," Rick said. "He's been breaking project rules, he hasn't been carrying his share of the work, and he destroyed a whole wall of aragonite bushes in the F-survey."

"That's a pretty harsh accusation," Pat said. "I heard that he just brushed by some bushes in a tight spot and knocked off some needles."

"I was there," Rick said. "Sims and Walck were yelling at him the whole time. He just walked right through them like he didn't care."

"Hmmm," Pat said, just a little unsure of herself. "If that's true, then it's pretty serious."

"Yes. The park wants us to get rid of him."

"Who said that?" Pat said.

"Kerbo said we should remove him from the board."

Pat thought about this for a moment. She had known Kerbo for years, and it seemed unlikely that he would meddle in the politics of LCP. In fact, just a year ago Kerbo had encouraged Dave, John, Roy, and Rick to reconcile.

"I think we should talk to Roy about this," Pat said.

"No! I've already been talking to him about this. We're going to incorporate without him."

"You talked to him about incorporation?" Pat asked.

"Look," Rick said. "We don't have forever to get this done. We've already drawn up the paperwork and Patterson is going to send it in this week. Roy hasn't been acting in the spirit of the project, so we've decided not to make him part of the corporation. Do you want to be listed as an officer or not?"

Pat had been a director for only a month and did not particularly want to rock the boat over issues she did not fully understand. "OK. Go ahead and file the papers. But I don't want anything done behind people's backs. I want you to promise that you'll talk to Roy and explain why we did this."

"I'll talk to him."

A week later, an envelope came back from the Secretary of State. The Lechuguilla Cave Project was incorporated in the state of Colorado as of November 7, 1988. The constitution and bylaws of the newly formed corporation contained a provision that directors were appointed for life. There was no mention of membership for any of the cavers who had contributed hundreds of hours of work to LCP. Rick wrote a letter to the project leadership explaining why he felt it was important to incorporate and he included copies of the certificate of incorporation. Copies were sent to Kerbo and Pat, but not to Roy.

✤   ✤   ✤

One month later, Ted Lappin, Paul Burger, and Stan Allison were back at Carlsbad Caverns National Park. They had driven down for the Thanksgiving CRF expedition expecting to spend a relaxing weekend of easy trips into Carlsbad Cavern. Surveying in Carlsbad was fun and there was the added bonus of coming out of the cave on Thursday to a huge turkey dinner.

When they arrived, however, the CRF cavers asked them for help with a project in Lechuguilla Cave. CRF was working on a precision laser survey of the front part of Lechuguilla, but there was no one in their group who knew how to rig the ropes for the entrance pit and Boulder Falls. Ted, Paul, and Stan leaped at the opportunity to get back into Lechuguilla. They hoped that after they rigged the ropes for CRF, they would be able to check out a tantalizing lead that had been left after the last expedition.

The high climb at the end of the Prickly Ice Cube Room had finally been completed and beyond was another climb so promising that it was called High Hopes. On the last expedition, Donald Davis and Joe Oliphant had free-climbed 120 feet above the floor, but they were reluctant to continue without climbing gear. Stan was an experienced climber and he wanted to make a quick inspection trip to determine how much equipment would be needed to complete the climb. Kerbo gave them permission, provided they did nothing more than check the lead.

A local caver, Dave Logan, volunteered to come along to help carry the ropes. The next morning the four cavers were at the edge of the entrance pit to Lechuguilla Cave.

"Yo!" Ted yelled, as he tossed the rope down to the dirt below.

"Yo?" Stan said.

"Well, I had to make sure that no one's down there." Ted pulled the rest of his gear on as Stan clipped into the rope.

"Yo, on rope!" Stan yelled as he backed smoothly over the edge.

The tattered edges of the plastic seal on the gate buzzed in the wind coming out of the cave. Paul struggled with the lock. He shielded his eyes from the blinding sand as he opened the gate. Rocks rattled down the metal tube and sent a new wave of dirt into the air. Stan went first. He backed into the pipe and squinted as bits of gravel clanged down the sides and dirt sandblasted his bare arms. Ted and Dave arrived at the top of the culvert just as Stan called a faint, "Clear!"

"Watch the loose rocks, I'm going down," Paul said as he backed slowly into the culvert. He felt with his feet for the rungs. The wind pulled his heavy cave packs upward and they bounced and banged against culvert walls above his head.

"The cave's really blowing today." he shouted over the roar. Halfway down the culvert Paul noticed that even his ten-pound pack of vertical gear was being lifted by the wind.

"Hey, look at this!"

Ted and Dave moved to the edge of the culvert and knocked down a handful of dirt as they looked in. The heavier stones rained down on Paul, while the lighter sand blew back into their faces.

"I don't think I've ever seen it this windy before," Dave said.

Paul dropped to the floor below and ducked into the crawl. The roar quickly faded as he moved away from the culvert. There was just as much wind, but without the culvert to focus the airflow it was not nearly as loud. He caught up with Stan who was waiting on the far side of the crawl and they followed the well-worn path into the cave. Without thinking, they automatically reached for holds they knew would be there and stepped in well-worn footprints. They had followed the same path so many times that traveling through the cave had become a well-known routine for them. They rigged the rope for the Flowstone Slope and made their way deeper into the cave, where they stopped to wait at the top of Boulder Falls for Ted and Dave.

They rappelled down Boulder Falls. As they continued onward they reveled at being the only people in the cave. There would be no waiting at the drops, no murmur of approaching voices, and no one to tell them the latest news. There was also no pool of experienced Lechuguilla cavers on the surface in case they got in trouble, just a handful of CRF cavers, most of whom did not know the cave.

They pushed on, passing EF Junction and Lake Lebarge. Five hours later they arrived at the FLI Room at the base of the High Hopes climb. With only a verbal description to guide them, they spent another hour searching for the lead before Stan found it on the far side of the room.

Ted, Paul, and Dave made their way through the aragonite jungle to the bottom of the High Hopes climb, where they strained to see through the gloom above. The lead was just as reported: a high, obvious fissure with a rope hanging from it.

The rope was anchored to a small ledge just out of sight above them. From where they stood there was no way to tell how difficult the upper part of the fissure was. Stan decided to take a look. He put on his ascending gear and began to climb the rope. He soon disappeared into the fissure overhead. From the floor of the room, the others could see only the light from Stan's headlamp. After what seemed like an eternity, he called, "Off rope." His call was punctuated by bits of falling rock. "I'll see how it looks and tell you whether to come up or not." More rocks fell into the room.

The others turned off their lights and looked up to watch Stan. Paul paced back and forth impatiently, anxious to follow. Stan called down something unintelligible followed by another barrage of rock. Then silence. They could hear their own breathing.

A shaft of light flickered across the ceiling. Stan yelled something that was lost in the echoes of the pit.

"What?" Paul yelled, staring almost straight up to where Stan's light seemed to float in midair.

"Borehole!" Stan said.

Before the echo had even faded away, Paul had his ascenders clipped onto the rope.

"Are you guys coming?" he said to Ted and Dave.

"I don't know," Ted said. "We shouldn't go too far."

Stan called down again to see if anyone was going to follow.

"Just a minute." Paul called back. He turned to Ted. "Don't worry, we won't get in trouble. We'll just check it out a little way to see where it goes."

Ted rolled his eyes. He had heard those words before, usually just before the speaker set off in a frenzy of exploration through many intricate passages that took three trips just to map.

"Don't worry so much." Paul was already on his way up.

Stan was waiting on the ledge when Paul arrived. Paul stared at the seemingly unscalable wall in front of him and wondered how he was going to climb it. To Paul's surprise, instead of climbing up, Stan traversed horizontally along the edge of the pit, placing his feet in a series of holes cut long ago by dripping water. He reached upward and pulled himself into a shallow, narrow chute and chimneyed to a higher ledge. Looking back to check on Paul, he disappeared behind a wall of seemingly solid rock.

Paul yelled "All clear," to Ted and Dave, and followed Stan. He was not as graceful a climber as Stan, but he moved carefully and deliberately. Then he looked down. He was 120 feet above the floor and Ted and Dave's headlamps were tiny pinpoints of light far below. He had a sudden queasy feeling in his stomach and the room seemed to spin slightly. He snapped his attention back up to the climb and concentrated on the rock in front of him. Beads of sweat dripped from his brow. Methodically, he put his hands and feet in the same holds he had seen Stan use, and continued the climb. His heart was pounding when he reached the safety of the ledge. He had never liked heights.

The ledge funneled into a tight crawlway that corkscrewed upward and opened into a large chamber that swallowed Paul's light. The two cavers grinned and exchanged a high five. Paul followed Stan as he picked his way along the tops of large, smooth boulders.

The room narrowed into a long tube twenty feet in diameter. Several aragonite stalagmites stood over ten feet tall along the right side of the passage. Stan stopped at the junction between the room and the borehole.

"This is as far as I went."

"Should we keep going?" Paul asked.

They could see that the tunnel turned a corner about a hundred feet ahead and disappeared out of sight. There was still no sign of Ted or Dave so they decided to explore at least as far as the bend in the passage.

The floor ahead was strewn with needle-like aragonite crystals and as they walked down the huge borehole, they tried to choose a path that would cause the least damage. There was a line on the wall that divided the passage horizontally. The lower half of the corridor was well decorated with aragonite and crystalline gypsum. The upper half, everything more than six feet above the floor, had been scoured clean to the bedrock by warm, moist air. The distinct scour line and a hint of airflow told them that this could be the Big One, the passage that would go on and on.

They neared the corner, dreading the sight that had
dashed their hopes so many times before: a blank wall.
Instead, the tube narrowed to fifteen feet in diameter and
continued onward as far as they could see. With great
reluctance they turned back.

✦   ✦   ✦

One week later, the Denver Museum of Natural History held an opening gala for their latest video production:
Lechuguilla Cave – The Hidden Giant. For over a year the
museum had been working on this documentary. Now,
after months of editing, the general public was about to
discover Lechuguilla Cave. Over a hundred and fifty PBS
stations across the country broadcasted the production.

Rick Bridges already had bigger plans in the works.
The filming for the museum had been completed ten
months earlier and dozens of new discoveries had been
made since then. Rick had visions of an hour-long special
on a major network, a program that would reveal the challenge and adventure of world-class caving. He pictured a
program that would be so beautiful and spectacular that
Lechuguilla would become a household word. He also
thought that royalties from the program could support his
caving activities for years to come.

Several months earlier, Tom Zannes had contacted
Rick about doing some filming in Lechuguilla. Tom was a
freelance videographer with years of experience filming
and producing outdoor adventure programs. He was technically competent with ropework and had the stamina and
caving experience to handle the rigors of Lechuguilla Cave.
After months of negotiation he had secured the support of
NBC.

Rick approached a handful of select cavers he thought
would be interested in the project. There was no denying
the amount of work involved. Hundreds of pounds of cam-
eras, tripods, and electrical equipment had to be trans-
ported deep into the cave. Battery packs would have to be
taken back to the surface every other day for recharging.

Filming itself is a tedious process often requiring the patience of a saint. Some cavers flatly refused. They were not interested in shuttling gear "simply to inflate the egos of a handful of prima donnas." Some agreed to carry batteries on their way into or out of the cave, but they had no interest in the actual filming. Other cavers, however, viewed the project differently. Like hundreds of people that flock to California every year, they had been captured by the lure of Hollywood and each of them wanted to be a star.

Thus, the stage was set for the January, 1989 expedition. The High Hopes discovery made the previous Thanksgiving would be the highlight of the film. It would provide an opportunity to do something never before achieved in any major video production – film virgin passage as it was being discovered.

Tom's plan was to start at the entrance and work his way into the southern branch of the cave. The first few days were spent shuttling gear and filming the well-worn hiking trail from the parking lot to the cave entrance. By the fourth day of the expedition, Tom had documented most of the route from the entrance pit, through the Rift, past the Chandelier Ballroom, to the Prickly Ice Cube Room. They still had to climb out of the Prickly Ice Cube Room and work their way through Seesaw Canyon, before they would reach their destination, the High Hopes climb.

Tom was now just below the climb in the Prickly Ice Cube Room, ready to film the next scene. He positioned his assistants with spotlights at strategic locations throughout the room. The cavers waited impatiently as Tom moved about the chamber making last minute adjustments. They were not as interested in the filming as they were eager for Tom to turn on the lights. The high-intensity video lights were a hundred times brighter than the best headlamp and would provide a rare opportunity to check leads high in the ceiling overhead. A signal from Tom brought artificial daylight into the cave.

The camera was focused on the base of the climb, where Neil Backstrom, Steve Sims, and Donald Davis sat looking haggard from a long week of exploration. They discussed the discoveries leading up to this point. At first they were uncomfortable in front of the camera and needed prompting from Tom, but they soon relaxed and the story unfolded. Neil described his first ascent into the new passage they called Seesaw Canyon.

"That's great guys," Tom said as he motioned for the lights to be doused. "Let's move on and set up for the climbing shots."

Tom lifted the camera to his shoulder and filmed Neil climbing the first twenty feet of the route to Seesaw Canyon. To get the footage Tom wanted, Neil had to repeat the climb four times. Tom then climbed above Neil to film Neil's fifth and sixth ascent. Each step of the way was recorded from different angles and with different cavers. The crew of a dozen cavers slowly made their way deeper into the cave. Ten hours later they arrived at the base of the High Hopes climb.

Paul Burger and Pat Kambesis worked in the background where they moved gear and held lights. They were helping the video crew primarily so they would be first in line to explore High Hopes when the filming was finished. They had been patient for the last twelve hours, but they could wait no longer. Anxious to escape the constant din of the camera crew, they quickly climbed the rope into High Hopes. It was like stepping out of a crowded room into a sound-proof chamber. The silence of the cave enveloped them as they waited for the others to catch up. Paul took Pat down the corridor to the farthest extent of exploration.

"I have only one question," Pat said. "Why didn't you keep going?"

"We were a long ways in and figured we'd get in trouble for scooping this much as it was. So we just went far enough to make sure it kept going."

"Do you want to go ahead a little more?" Pat said.

Paul grinned at the foolish question and the two of them followed the corridor another hundred feet. Their

RAY KEELER

One explorer ascends the rope to Seesaw Canyon
while the other dons his seat harness.

consciences stopped them as they remembered their promise to let Tom film the exploration of this passage. They
returned to the chamber at the top of the High Hopes
climb and spent the next hour poking around the room
looking for other leads.

At the base of the High Hopes climb, Tom took the
camera off his shoulder and placed it back in its foam-lined
case. "OK guys, that's enough for today." The assistants
hauled the lights and audio recording equipment across
the room and placed them in a pile next to the camera case.
It had been a long day and they still had an hour's trip back
to base camp in the Chandelier Ballroom.

Tom was tired, but he wanted to plan the next day's
filming. While the rest of the crew made their way back to
camp, Tom and a couple of cavers climbed the rope into the
High Hopes chamber. Paul and Pat greeted them as they
arrived at the top and immediately took Tom to the end of
exploration.

"What's past here?" Tom said.

"We don't know. This is as far as anyone has been."

"We'd like to get started on the survey," Pat said.
"Do you mind?"

"No. Why don't you go until you find something
interesting?"

"Like what?" Paul asked.

"I don't know. Like a pit or something," Tom said.

Donald Davis and Kris Green stayed to survey with
Paul and Pat, while everyone else returned with Tom for a
much-needed night of sleep. Tom agreed to meet the surveyors at this spot the next morning at 9:00 a.m.

After Tom left, the four cavers discussed their
options. They too had had a long day, so they decided to
take a short nap before starting the survey. They found
level spots on the floor and quickly fell asleep. Paul slept
fitfully with images of grotesque formations and endless
passages filling his dreams.

Four hours later they woke up, chilled but ready to
explore. They located the last station marker at the top of

the High Hopes climb and then surveyed around the perimeter of the room. Now, at last, they could survey into the borehole that had entranced them ever since they had first seen it. The corridor started as an elliptical tube fifteen feet high and twenty feet wide. Like much of the cave in this area, the walls showed typical acid corrosion features. There were dozens of shallow holes etched in the ceiling that gave the passage a pock-marked, sponge-like appearance. Everywhere they looked, thick mounds of snow-white gypsum and bizarre, crusted stalagmites towered over their heads. They named the passage Shangri-La, after the fictional Tibetan land of eternal youth.

At 9:00 a.m., they returned to the meeting place, but there was no sign of Tom. They decided to continue surveying and to check back again later. Through the long morning hours they explored and surveyed nearly 1,000 feet of passage.

Donald was in the lead, scouting the route down the passage.

"Hey, look at this," he shouted, pointing down a dark pit to the right. They had arrived at the junction of several passages. To the left and straight ahead, passages branched and curved out of sight. To the right, the pit plunged down into the darkness. The walls of the abyss were etched with deep corrosion grooves and smeared around the mouth was a black coating of gorilla shit that stood out in stark contrast to the snow-white gypsum in the rest of the passage.

The cavers examined all the leads looking for a way to climb down the pit. Donald and Kris followed the center passage down to the edge of a beautiful room they called Ultra Primo. Shouts of excitement echoed through the passages with each new discovery.

Pat called the three wild-eyed cavers back for a quick pow-wow. Although it was clear the route continued, they had promised to let the video crew film virgin passage. Tom was several hours overdue. They suspected that some kind of problem had forced him to return to the surface. They had been underground for over twenty hours; it was time to go back. Pat assured them that they would have the first chance to explore the new passage when they returned the next day. The others reluctantly agreed. They opened their packs and finished the last of their food in anticipation of the long trip back to the surface.

They walked quickly back down the Shangri-La passage. As they reached the High Hopes chamber, Tom appeared at the top of the climb looking as though he had just showered and shaved. The sounds from below indicated that the entire video crew was right behind him. They had overslept, but now they were full of energy and raring to go.

The tired surveyors glanced at each other, turned around, and led the crew back to the pit they had just discovered. Tom was excited. He took numerous shots of Shangri-La, filmed the newly named Conniption Pit, and began scouting the new Ultra Primo room.

RAY KEELER

Donald Davis in Ultra Primo.

Tom pointed one of the camera lights into the room. Thick cascades of white and caramel-colored flowstone covered the walls. It swirled across the sloping floor like a broad river of rock that flowed around the corner and disappeared in the distance eighty feet away. Tiny rimstone dams dotted the floor and dozens of small pools of crystal-clear water sparkled in the movie lights. The twenty-foot-high ceiling was festooned with yellow, white, and gray stalactites. Across the room, thin ribbons of flowstone guarded a dark opening leading up to the left. This was much better than Tom had expected.

"OK, let's get some shots of you surveying into this and then we'll get some virgin exploration shots."

The camera crew began setting up their equipment in Ultra Primo. Everyone was impressed by the awesome beauty. The excitement was palpable as the filming began.

A shout came from the far end of the chamber, "Hey, there's a lake down here." Everyone had to have a look. The Ultra Primo passage sloped down to the shores of a clear, blue lake fifteen feet wide. The smooth flowstone floor was punctuated with small cones of razor-sharp aragonite. Beyond lay the inviting darkness of unexplored passage.

As the others gathered at the newly named Blue Velvet Lake, Paul whispered to Pat that he wanted to be the first person to cross the lake. He felt that since they had done the work of surveying the passage, one of them should be first, regardless of the wants of the film crew.

"Paul will go first," Pat announced loudly.

Pat's commanding voice left no room for argument. In seconds Paul was undressed and walking down the steep slope to the margin of the lake. The lights were turned on and the camera started before anyone realized what was happening. Almost immediately Paul slipped on the slope and fell into the water, ungracefully becoming the first person to enter the lake.

"Don't turn around," Tom coached. "Keep your back to the camera."

"My God! I'm bleeding," Donald said.

He had undressed to follow, slipped on the flowstone floor and had torn loose a toenail. His bleeding foot was now reddening the flowstone and threatening to pollute the lake. The camera panned to the left and zoomed in on the injury. Kris rummaged through his pack looking for the first aid kit.

Pat raised her voice above the commotion. "Paul, does it go?"

The bright lights turned from Donald's foot to the helmeted figure crossing the lake. On the other side, a tall fissure led off into the darkness.

"I think so," Paul said. "Yes, to the left, the right, and straight ahead."

"Stop!" Pat said. "I have to take a survey shot before anybody else goes across." She sighted through the compass and quickly scratched the numbers into the survey book. "OK," she said as she reeled in the measuring tape.

Most of the camera crew was already undressed and in the water. Tom stopped filming long enough to remove his clothes and follow them across the lake, camera held high over his head.

Once on the far side, the cavers stepped gingerly down the passages. Pat smiled at the yelps of barefoot cavers attempting to negotiate the gypsum- and aragonite-covered floors. When the thrill of discovery had worn off and the cavers regrouped, they agreed that each of the passages went for at least a hundred feet without any sign of stopping. They would either have to continue surveying or call it quits for the day.

For Paul, Pat, Donald, and Kris, the answer was obvious. They had been underground for over thirty hours. The rest of the cavers concurred. There was no reason to push beyond the point of exhaustion. The cave would still be waiting for them tomorrow.

⚜   ⚜   ⚜

Several weeks later, Rick summoned Roy to a special meeting at his house in Denver. When Roy arrived he was surprised to see that John Patterson was there. John had been all but inactive for the last year. Obviously, Rick had something important to say.

The people in the room were ominously quiet as Rick began. "There are going to be some changes in the way we do things," he said. Rick outlined a number of changes that would, for the most part, put him in complete control of the project. For forty-five minutes he went on with no comment from Roy or John.

When Rick was finished, Roy took the floor. He voiced his concerns and those of other cavers in the project. He wanted an independent third-party to handle the project funds and he did not think it was appropriate for Rick's girlfriend, JoAnn Hall, to be treasurer. Finally, he wanted a newsletter and more people elected to the board to share power and authority. He continued for a half-hour, explaining his views.

Once Roy was finished, Rick spoke again. He repeated his original plan almost word-for-word. After five minutes Roy interrupted him.

"You didn't listen to what I said."

"I'm explaining how things are going to be done."

"You're missing the point," Roy said, his face red with anger. "You seem to have already decided how the project is going to be run and you don't seem to be interested in my opinion."

"John and I have already decided what changes need to be made." Once again, Rick recited the changes he intended to make.

Roy stood up from the table and moved toward the front door. "Well, I don't see that we're going to make much progress here," he said. He had argued with Rick enough times to know when resistance was futile.

"If you leave now, you're off the project," Rick said.

Roy turned his back and walked out the front door. The screen door slammed behind him. Rick nodded. It would no longer be necessary to tell Roy that they had incorporated the project without him three months before.

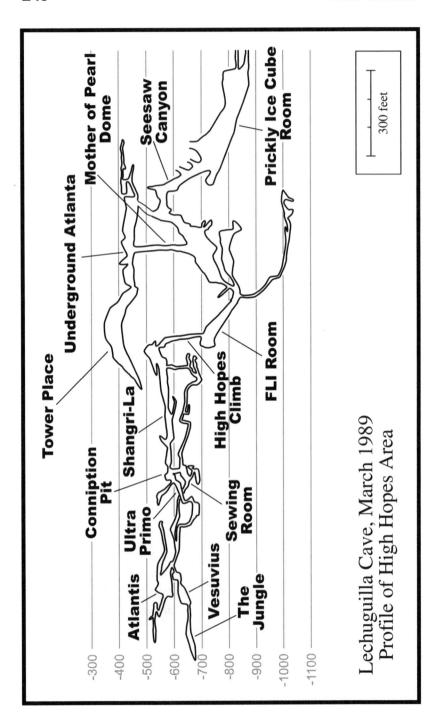

Lechuguilla Cave, March 1989
Profile of High Hopes Area

After the meeting, Roy drifted away from the project. Although he still made an occasional trip to the cave, Roy was never again in a position of leadership.

⇒»15«⇐

THE FAR EAST

y May, 1989, almost every caver in the country wanted to visit Lechuguilla. Originally, the explorers had been some of the most experienced diggers, climbers, and surveyors in the country. But now after just over two years of rapid exploration, cavers of every stripe attended the expeditions.

Rick brought many cavers into the fold with promises of the fame and recognition that came to everyone associated with Lechuguilla Cave. The concept of tag-team caving had been lost in the rush to make the next big discovery. Cooperation and sharing had been replaced with secrecy and individualism. No one openly lied or sent other teams to dead-end passages, but if a survey ended in a large walking passage, the members of the survey team would neglect to mention it in the trip report. They would check it themselves on their next trip.

Lechuguilla Cave had hit the big-time. Articles had been published in *National Geographic*, *Smithsonian*, and numerous newspapers. There was also a video in the works for *National Geographic*. This high profile was continuously fueled by Rick and his hand-picked directors. The frequent portral of Rick as the driving force behind the exploration of Lechuguilla ignored dozens of other people who had worked long hours mapping, entering survey data, and seeing to the day-to-day operations of the project. Although the publicity repelled some cavers, the intense spotlight of the press attracted many more. Cavers who openly spoke out against the publicity were strongly encouraged to step aside to make room for others who were willing to support the project. Some of the most experienced cavers stayed with the Lechuguilla Cave Project, but many left to avoid the increasing competition, convoluted politics, and favoritism.

The project, however, had an even bigger problem than the dissatisfaction of some of the cavers; the cave was not cooperating. Although wonderful discoveries were still being made, the cave did not significantly expand during the second year. No longer could explorers pick a compass direction at random and walk into virgin borehole. Cavers who came to Lechuguilla expecting to explore walking passages and decorated galleries were pressed into service to inspect the vast number of untouched crawlways. What the project needed was another big breakthrough.

Lyle Moss had an inkling where the next discovery might lie, but he felt no particular obligation to reveal his ideas to anyone else. Lyle was a climber and he had found a niche for his skills. Where everyone else could explore horizontally or drop pits on ropes, only climbers could go up. He had already enjoyed several successes – and many failures. Climbing into high leads was always a long shot. Many difficult hours could be invested only to arrive at a blind dome or impenetrable crack. Despite the odds, there was one lead that Lyle was certain about: the Aragonitemare.

Rick thought the Aragonitemare was a waste of time, so he encouraged Lyle to look at other climbs in the cave, but Lyle persisted. He knew that Bryan Becker had simply run out of time before he could complete the climb. Lyle had been to the Moby Dick Room and ascended the rope left by Bryan. The climb ahead was well beyond his abilities. He did not possess the incredible skill of Bryan, but brute force could often be used as a substitute for skill. The thought that the original explorers might want to return someday to complete their climb never entered Lyle's mind. This was Lechuguilla, where no one had a claim on any passage, and here was a promising lead just waiting to be pushed.

Lyle recruited two other experienced Lechuguilla explorers, Don Kluever and Dan Clardy, and during the May, 1989, expedition they quietly set off for the cave. They paused briefly at the Rift, continued past EF Junction, and worked their way down Apricot Pit. Several more hours of caving took them past the Rusticles, through the rough maze of sharp chimneys and small tubes, to a fork in the trail where an indistinct path led off to the left. A piece of orange flagging tape lay on the floor before them.

"This is where we turn," Lyle said. "The whale on the tape points the way to the Moby Dick Room."

"It looks like a fish," Don said.

They climbed and crawled through the tortuous passages and finally arrived at the base of the Aragonitemare. Long overdue for a rest, they dropped their packs in a heap on the floor and collapsed next to them. It had taken them over six hours just to reach this point. As they ate and drank, they gazed up at the high dome-shaped passage. The real work would begin a hundred feet above their heads. After a few minutes rest, they put on their vertical gear to ascend the rope that hung free in the chimney. Another hour passed before all three of them were on the small ledge where the rope was anchored, 150 feet above the floor.

Lyle opened his pack and took out a Bosch electric hammer-drill. With the Bosch, he could drill quarter-inch holes four inches deep in solid rock. Once a hole had been drilled, he could drive an expansion bolt into it, attach a

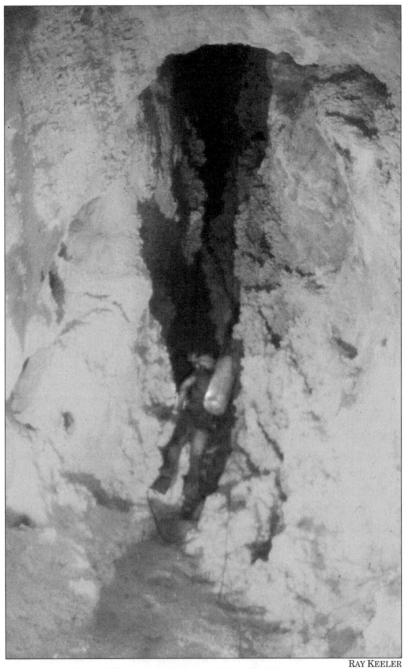

Stan Allison at the base of the Aragonitemare.

sling to stand in and drill another hole six feet higher. In this way, any climb, no matter how sheer or overhung, could be conquered. A single battery pack provided enough power to drill six holes and Lyle had two battery packs. Don and Dan were properly impressed. The Bosch with two battery packs cost more than all the rest of the caving gear combined.

Lyle was following a narrow crack that ran up one wall of the twenty-foot-wide chimney. This was the same crack that Bryan had climbed months before. After Lyle had gained another fifty feet, he noticed that the chimney was getting wider and appeared to end in a large dome. As he climbed to get a better view of the dome, he noticed a subtle breeze issuing from a large opening above and to his right.

"Hey, I can feel a breeze," Lyle shouted down to his companions on the ledge. He was surprised to hear the sound of his voice echoing back from the passage above. The sound reverberated for several seconds before fading away.

CAROL VESELY

Stan Allison near the Land of Enchantment.

"Wow, there must be one hell of a room up there to produce that kind of echo."

Lyle was dying to check out the passage, but it was going to be tricky to reach. The opening was on the other side of the dome and the intervening wall was overhung and smooth. He might be able to bolt across the gap in a couple of hours. But Lyle had another idea. Maybe he could swing across the gap.

He climbed up the wall about twenty feet, set a bolt in the rock, and anchored the rope. Then he climbed back down until he was even with the opening and tied himself into the rope. Finally, he leaned on the rope and pushed out with his feet, swinging across the void in a long smooth arc. As he pendulumed toward the opening, he looked for a rock or a knob, anything to hang on to. He grabbed instinctively for the nearest handhold and, with all his strength, pulled himself into the passage.

A high, wide tunnel stretched far beyond Lyle's light. He could feel a cool breeze drifting past him. This was definitely the way on. He decided to call it the Land of Enchantment, a special name he had been saving for a new discovery like this. The next task was to help Dan and Don get up. He rigged a permanent rope to replace his climbing rope, and by 4:00 a.m. all three explorers were at the top of the pit. Urged on by the long and distant echoes of their voices, they walked to the edge of a highly-decorated chamber. They could see that the passage continued, so they did what any other caver would have done in the same situation: they lay down on the damp, rocky floor and instantly fell sound asleep.

In a cave, morning is when you happen to wake up. For the three cavers at the top of the Aragonitemare, morning came after five hours of sleep. They ate breakfast and then began their survey.

Starting from the tip of a prominent rock, Don stretched out the measuring tape and began surveying through the Land of Enchantment. After a few hundred feet, the

passage narrowed slightly. Don stopped and stared in
amazement at the path ahead. They were about to explore
another of the exquisitely beautiful passages that Lechuguilla had become so famous for. Forests of pure white stalactites hung from the ceiling and the walls were covered
with a thick coating of frost-like calcite and gypsum crystals. The floor was heaped with ridges and towers of
sparkling, pristine aragonite six feet high. Don could not
find a way to cross the room without damaging the formations.

"Lyle, which way should we go? The floor looks
pretty delicate," he said.

"Just make a path. We'll keep all of the damage to
one trail," Lyle said.

Don stepped down into a narrow valley between two
mounds of crystal. The floor crunched and tinkled with

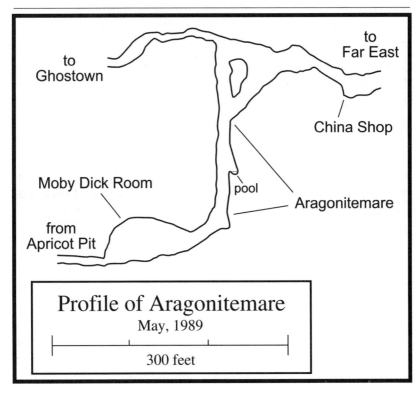

Profile of Aragonitemare
May, 1989

300 feet

each step. He picked his way across the room and set a survey station.

The crystal-lined tunnel continued as an oval passage about thirty feet across. The floor slanted steeply to the left and several dark crawlways angled down along the edge of the passage. Lyle and Dan finished the shot across the room and followed Don. Even though Don had already crossed the passage, Lyle and Dan winced as they heard the crunching sound of tiny crystals being ground under the soles of their boots. They felt like bulls in a china shop, so they named the room the China Shop.

Beyond the China Shop, the crystal aragonite thinned out and the tunnel angled up a slope of loose rocks and boulders. Here the passage expanded into a large room about a hundred feet across with a shallow pool in the center. It was a good place to replenish their water and to take a short rest.

To the right, leading away into the darkness, was a narrow, slanting fissure they called the East Rift. To the left, on the opposite wall of the room, was a similar fissure they called the West Rift. Although the fissures looked promising, the main passage was larger. Ahead they could see the base of a gypsum glacier similar to the ones at Glacier Bay and the Prickly Ice Cube Room. In the past, other gypsum glaciers had led the way to major extensions of the cave. They decided to climb the glacier and see what was on the other side. When they got to the top, there was nothing but a blank wall. The main trend of the room they called the Land of Fire and Ice had ended, but there were still many leads. There was the West Rift, and several pits that would require a rope to descend. But most of the air seemed to funnel into the fissure passage on the right, so they decided to map into the East Rift.

They were beginning to feel tired, but the cool breeze and the lure of new passage drew them down the fissure. It was a typical Lechuguilla fissure with deep dark holes in the floor and boneyard mazes vanishing into the ceiling above. They surveyed to a room where large broken stalagmites covered the floor. Lyle thought they looked like artillery shells so he decided to call it the Silver Bullet Passage.

By now they were exhausted. Lyle decided it was time to leave. He made a few final notes in his survey book recording the fact that the aragonite was growing horizontally and the crystals pointed into the cave. He also noted that the last strip of flagging tape was twisting in the breeze. The cavers were just too tired to follow the wind any further.

As they approached the Aragonitemare on the way out, they heard a cacophony of voices echoing through the China Shop. At the top of the drop, a group of cavers were milling around. Lyle and his team looked at each other, surprised to see so many people at the top of the new climb.

"What are you doing here?" Lyle said.

"You've been gone for more than forty hours, so we figured you must have finished the climb and broken into something really big. We didn't want to miss out on exploring the new passage, so we brought two teams and just climbed your ropes. Does it go?"

Lyle laughed. "Does it go? It doesn't stop going!" Lyle, Dan, and Don told them where the most promising leads were, then began the long journey out of the cave.

✤　　✤　　✤

Two days later, Pat Kambesis sat at the large central table examining survey notes. She always looked over the notes from returning teams to see what they had found. There were several promising leads listed on the notes from Lyle's trip.

"Look, it says 'survey tape is moved around by wind,'" she said to Miles Hecker, who was looking over her shoulder.

"Do they mean flagging tape or measuring tape?" Kris Green asked.

"Who cares?" Pat said. "Either way, it means big cave." As she looked back at the scrawled notes the words

Bob Montgomery in the China Shop.

"directional aragonite" jumped out at her. Aragonite crystals always grow pointing toward the source of drier air. If all the aragonite was pointing in one direction, it meant that there had to be a constant breeze in the passage. She knew where she was going on her next trip. Pat went into the back room to look for Carol Vesely. It took Carol only an instant to understand the meaning of the notes. Together they started searching for any of the discovery team members who might be awake. Pat and Carol looked around the cabins and found two cavers who had followed Lyle's group up the Aragonitemare.

"Too late," Bob said. "There are some pits we didn't check, but the rest looks like mop-up."

Pat and Carol glanced at each other. They had heard this before, usually just before a big discovery in a heavily-worked area. As they walked outside, Dan Clardy followed. He had been on the climbing team with Lyle and was eager to return. Pat and Carol agreed that Dan would be their sixth person, making enough for two survey teams.

As Pat, Kris, Carol, Miles, Dan, and Bob Montgomery were getting ready, Stan Allison came into the room.

"Where are you guys headed off to?" he asked.

"The Far East," Pat said. "There are some good leads that move a lot of air in that area."

"Wow," Stan said. "Can I come?"

"We already have two teams."

"Please," Stan said. "I'll carry the ropes."

"Done," Pat said. "We have a three-hundred-foot rope we are going to use to re-rig the Aragonitemare."

Despite his heavy load, Stan led the way through the cave. They stopped briefly at the top of Apricot Pit, again for water in Nirvana, and then at the junction beyond the Rusticles. The tell-tale strip of orange flagging tape lay draped across the floor and pointed the way on.

"This is the turnoff," he said. "There's a piece of flagging tape here with a whale on it."

"Looks like a fish," Kris said.

Stan took the lead again, guiding the party east into the fissure ahead. An hour and a half later, they arrived at the base of the Aragonitemare.

Lyle had not surveyed up the Aragonitemare, so the new discoveries were not tied into the rest of the map. Pat took out her gear and prepared to complete the survey.

The other problem they had to deal with was re-rigging the drop. One of the last teams coming down the Aragonitemare had discovered that six inches of the rope's protective sheath had been worn away by the sharp aragonite. They had repaired the rope by cutting out the worn section and tying another rope to the end, but now there was a knot halfway up.

Bob and Miles began the task of replacing the damaged rope. When they examined the old rope, they were surprised to find that the new section below the knot was already beginning to wear through. The rock was cutting through the rope amazingly fast.

It was several hours before the survey was complete, the rope replaced, and everyone had ascended the 200 feet

CAROL VESELY

The Eastern Borehole beyond the Silver Bullet Crawl.

to the Land of Enchantment. They filed through the China Shop and into the gypsum-floored passage beyond. When they reached the Land of Fire and Ice, Pat suggested splitting into two survey teams. Carol, Stan, and Dan turned left and headed into the West Rift to check each pit and side lead along the way. Pat, Kris, Bob, and Miles turned right into the East Rift to look for a small lake that had been reported by one of the previous teams. They wanted to replenish their dwindling water supply and survey a stoopway that was supposed to be on the other side of the lake.

Pat's team searched for over an hour but could locate neither the survey nor the lake. They gave up and turned their attention to the lead in the Silver Bullet Passage where Lyle had noticed the flagging tape twisting in the wind. They followed the flagged survey route to the eastern limit of exploration. The passage got smaller and smaller, eventually becoming a narrow hallway.

When they reached the end of Lyle's survey they understood why he had stopped. Several small leads twisted away from the end of the survey, but none of them looked as though it would lead to larger passage. The air was blowing into the cave and they could feel a slight breeze, but it was hard to tell which of the many passages it flowed into. Miles took out a stick of incense and lit the end. A pungent smell filled the room and a thin wisp of white smoke curled toward the ceiling and drifted into a narrow fissure to the left.

Pat climbed into the opening, followed the cool breeze to the end of the fissure and squeezed into a small crawlway leading to the right. The passage continued so she hurried back to get the others.

"Directional aragonite," she said, pointing into the fissure as she took out her survey gear.

They surveyed down the fissure and into the crawlway. They stopped at the junction of several small passages.

"Hey, look at this," Pat said. She was pointing at a small opening near the floor of the passage. The perimeter of the hole was encrusted with small aragonite bushes whose branches were completely folded over, pointing down the passage.

"Wow, that's the most directional aragonite I've ever seen."

Miles was in the lead so he wormed his way through the opening, followed by Bob and Kris. Pat was in the rear, sketching the passage.

"Borehole!" Miles shouted from ahead.

When Pat caught up with the rest of the group, they were standing on a gypsum block, staring into the blackness beyond. They had come into the side of an immense passage. The ceiling arched twenty feet overhead, and the far wall was eighty feet away. The floor, an irregular surface of boulders and deep brown dirt, stretched away in both directions. They put down their survey gear and walked to the center of the room. They turned left and followed the passage north, quickly covering 300 feet. The borehole continued into the darkness. They turned around and headed back south, covering another 300 feet of virgin passage before coming to a junction. Before them the ceiling rose and the passage split again. Each branch was over a hundred feet wide. They called the place the Grand Guadalupe Junction.

"You know," Pat said, "we're going to have to survey all the passage we just scooped."

They re-traced their steps back to their survey gear.

"I wonder how the other group is doing?" Pat said.

Stan Allison was wondering the same thing. Carol and Dan were resting, but Stan was not tired, even though they had been underground for over twenty-four hours. They had finished surveying an uninteresting side passage near the Land of Fire and Ice and were now working their way through the East Rift. Stan was wondering why he had not seen the other team for so long. He decided to check up on them while Carol and Dan slept.

Picking up his pack, Stan followed the survey markers down the passage. The small strips of blue flagging tape guided him to the end of the main corridor and into the fissure. Stan stopped to consider his options. An assortment of small passages and crawlways branched in all directions. He looked for footprints in the floor. A trail of faint scuff marks led across the hard, calcite-cemented floor and into a seemly blank wall. Stan got down on his hands and knees and saw that the dirt had been disturbed in one of the small crawlways. The light from his headlamp illuminated a piece of blue plastic tape flapping and twisting in the cave breeze. This was definitely the route Pat's team had taken.

A few minutes later Stan stopped. He had reached a huge chamber with passages leading to the left and right. He stared into the black void. Now he knew what had kept the others. Somewhere in the vast chamber before him they were surveying. He took a step forward and sank ankle-deep in the soft dirt floor. Footprints led in both directions but Stan took a guess and turned right. He started jogging down the corridor, shouting to get the other team's attention.

The size of the passage and the number of leads had almost overwhelmed Pat's team. To keep the task manageable, she made an arbitrary decision: they would survey in one direction until they could no longer make 100-foot shots. Then they would return to the last large side passage and repeat the process. They had surveyed over 1,000 feet of passage before they heard sounds in the darkness behind them.

"Over here," Pat shouted. The pinprick of light was too far away to identify the caver. Stan sprinted across the room and joined the surveyors.

"Wow," Stan said, sweat dripping from his forehead.

"Impressive, isn't it?" Pat said.

"Is there more to survey?" Stan asked.

The others laughed. "Stan," Pat said, "there are side passages the size of buses that we haven't even looked at. There's enough here to keep us surveying for a week."

"Wow."

"Where's Carol and Dan?" Kris asked.

"They're resting back in the East Rift," Stan said.

"Maybe you should go wake them up and tell them to come up here."

"Yeah," Stan said. "They won't believe this." He turned around and hurried back down the passage. He jogged past several of the large leads Pat had described and suddenly discovered that the only footprint in the passage were his.

The passage was virgin in front of him. He traced his footprints back and found two fresh trails in the soft dirt. He looked to the left and the right, trying to figure out which way he had come in.

"Guys?" Stan asked.

Bob had been watching Stan. He laughed.

"Wrong way Stan. You picked the wrong borehole."

Pat's team continued to survey, shooting 100-foot shots into virgin passage. It was another hour before Stan, Carol, and Dan returned.

When the two teams got back together, they took a short meal break. Carol examined Pat's survey notes to look for the most promising area to survey. The main passage had forked a few hundred feet back and Pat's team had surveyed down the left branch. Carol decided to take the right branch while Pat continued in the left.

Pat's team surveyed into a wide, gypsum-lined maze of walking passages. The cave looped around pillars with more leads branching off in all directions. After several hundred feet, the character of the passage changed. The gypsum gave way to flowstone-covered floors that led down into an old, dry pool. Thick orange-colored calcite deposits marked a distinct water line against the soft, white gypsum. The cavers ducked underneath a low arch and climbed back up to the gypsum level. Soon there was another dry pool. They were now following a chain of dry pools through the labyrinth of tunnels.

As her team surveyed down the corridor beneath the vaulted ceilings, Pat occasionally thought she could hear running water. She would pause and listen every few seconds, but she convinced herself that it was merely the sound of air moving through a constriction, or the echoes of her teammates' footsteps distorted by the passage walls. Water appeared infrequently in Lechuguilla, and when it did it was always in small, quiet pools. Although running water is common in eastern caves, the Chihuahuan desert above delivered very little moisture to Lechuguilla Cave below.

The explorers climbed out of another dry pool and ducked beneath a low ceiling as they climbed back to the upper level. Around the corner, unbelievably, was a flowing stream. It was small and would not get a second look on the surface, but in the dry underground chambers it was liquid gold.

A tall, wide canyon stretched to the left. A dark-red river of stone covered the width of the passage and vanished into the murk beyond the reach of the cavers' lights. A thin sheen of water flowed across the floor and dropped noisily into a small basin. This basin fed another, and the water flowed across a narrow ribbon of flowstone to drain into the two-foot-deep, ten-foot wide pool at their feet. To the right, the water drained through a chain of shallow pools into the dark maze of passages behind them. They christened the stream the Lost Pecos River after the famous Pecos River that crosses New Mexico and winds through the town of Carlsbad.

Pat's team surveyed up the canyon, continuing in their bare feet. The walls were covered with narrow ribbons of calcite. Cascades of red and yellow flowstone streamed down sides of the passage from holes high in the ceiling. They followed the stream up to a wall covered by thick formations where the water issued from a thin crack in the rock. This was a good place to stop.

Pat, Kris, Bob, and Miles retraced their steps and met Carol, Stan, and Dan back at Grand Guadalupe Junction,

RAY KEELER
Stan Allison at the Lost Pecos River.

the spot where Stan had gotten lost. Both teams had been in the cave for over forty hours, and the strain was beginning to show. They compared notes and added up the survey footage – over 6,100 feet in an area they had been told was pushed out. It was clear that they had discovered not just a large chamber or passage, they had discovered a whole new area of the cave.

As the tired cavers reached the Rift, they could hear the voices of another team on the way in. Steve Davis soon appeared, leading a trip to the Western Borehole.

"Hi, guys," Steve said. "Are you just now getting out?" He had last seen them a day and a half earlier at the Aragonitemare. The two teams could not have been gone for such a long time if there was nothing left to survey.

"You found it, didn't you?" he said.

"Yeah," Pat said. "We sure did."

⚜   ⚜   ⚜

The September, 1989 expedition was a feeding frenzy. Seventy-one cavers from all over the United States gathered, eager to explore in Lechuguilla Cave. Nearly all of them had heard about the new discoveries in the Far East. The now-familiar sequence of events had occurred several times before – after each significant discovery, everyone made plans to go to the new area. The Lechuguilla cavers called this behavior "lemming runs." It was clear there was about to be a lemming run to the Far East.

On the first day of the expedition, Ann and Peter Bosted, Pat Seiser, Garry Petrie, and members of two other teams all went down Apricot Pit, past Nirvana, and up the Aragonitemare. Their packs were laden with the extra gear needed to bivouac in the cave – the Far East was now deemed too far away for day trips. It took over eight hours to reach the Grand Guadalupe Junction from the entrance. But the rewards were worth the effort. Large walking passages branched in nearly every direction and room after room was filled with crystal clear pools and exquisite formations. The flowstone on the walls was colored with shades of red, orange, and yellow. The names of the new discoveries were just as colorful: Wild Black Yonder, The Ruby Chamber, Firefall Hall.

Two days later, Ann and her team were on their way back to the surface. They had just completed surveying several hundred feet of virgin passage. Although excited about the wonders they had seen, all four were tired from the long trip. They rested at the top of the Aragonitemare, still a long way from the surface.

Pat Seiser rappelled down the 200-foot pit first, followed by Garry, and then Peter. Ann sat alone at the top, glad for the chance to rest, listening for a signal from below. Soon she heard the faint call of "Off rope." Ann gathered her gear and attached her figure-8 to the rope. "On rope," she called down the pit, although she knew they could not hear her; the rest of the team would be sitting safely in the Moby Dick Room out of range of the falling debris. The deep shaft below acted as a funnel for small rocks that might be knocked loose, and after a 200-foot fall, even the tiniest pebble was a lethal missile.

Ann loosened her grip on the rope, which slid smoothly through her figure-8 as she began to inch her way

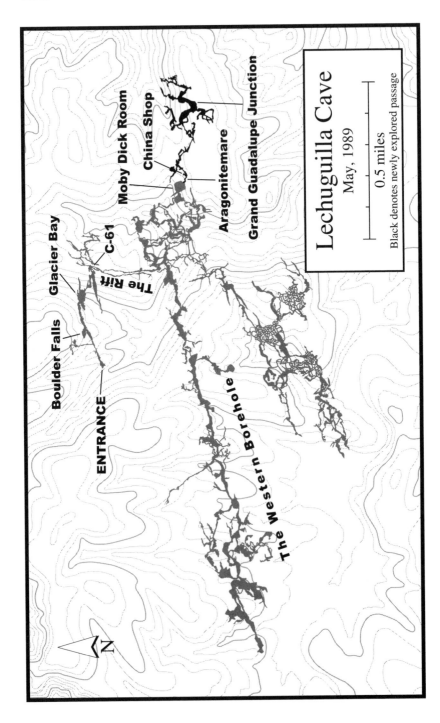

Lechuguilla Cave
May, 1989

0.5 miles

Black denotes newly explored passage

Moby Dick Room
China Shop
Aragonitemare
Grand Guadalupe Junction
Glacier Bay
C-61
The Rift
Boulder Falls
ENTRANCE
The Western Borehole

N

down the pit. She stepped carefully but still could not avoid knocking dozens of small rocks down the pit. They bounced and ricocheted off the walls, making soft tinkling sounds as they rained down the vertical shaft.

The cliff was slightly overhung and the rope dangled free a few inches away from the razor-sharp aragonite bushes. As she continued her descent, she tried to keep the rope from rubbing against the wall. She knew that a nylon rope is very vulnerable when it has weight on it and something as sharp as aragonite could slice right through it.

The rope was dirty and was coated with tiny grains of aragonite that made it a struggle to descend. She was trying to feed the rope smoothly through her figure-8, when something caught her eye. She looked down at the rope below her and froze in horror. The braided outer sheath of the rope was cut completely around its circumference exposing nearly a foot of the thin, white fibers at the core. The mutilated rope was on the verge of failure. As she watched, another tiny thread of the core snapped, its ends hanging free in the cool air of the pit.

Frantically, she thought through her options. She could see a prominent ledge where she could take her weight off the rope, but she would have to cross the damaged section to get there. It seemed to be her only option, so she let the bare strands of the rope core slide slowly through her figure-8 until her feet touched the ledge.

"Peter!" she screamed at the top of her voice. "Peter!"

Peter, Pat, and Garry, were talking quietly in the vastness of the Moby Dick Room. Garry looked at his watch.

"I wonder what's taking Ann so long? She should be . . . ."

"Shhhh," Pat said. "Listen."

They heard Ann's distant voice calling down the pit. The sound was garbled and faint, but she seemed to be asking for Peter. Peter moved quickly across the boulders to the bottom of the Aragonitemare.

As Ann saw the pinpoint of light below, an involuntary shiver went up her spine. She was still well over a hundred feet above the floor.

"Peter, the rope is shot. I can't rappel any more. It's about to break!"

Peter stood helplessly at the bottom of the pit. "Can you tie it off?"

Ann looked desperately around her at the walls of the fissure. The glistening white walls were nearly featureless, except for the coating of razor-sharp aragonite. She saw a small bridge of rock about four inches in diameter that she thought she could anchor the rope to.

"I think so."

Ann was an experienced caver, but she was unfamiliar with the knots and rigging used for anchoring ropes. Still, if she could find a way to attach the rope, she might be able to get down.

She began by pulling up all the slack rope below her. This gave her about eight feet of rope below the frayed spot to work with. She doubled it, fed it through the natural bridge and tied a simple knot. If the anchor held, all the weight would be taken off the damaged part of the rope. If it failed, Ann would fall just a short distance, but the sudden stop would put a huge load on the frayed section of rope.

With adrenaline flooding through her body and her hands trembling, Ann attached her figure-8 to the rope below the knot. Slowly she shifted her weight to the rope. The knot tightened and loops of rope bit into the rock. The inevitable shower of aragonite rained down the pit sending Peter running for cover. The anchor held. Ann rappelled slowly all the way to the bottom.

Sliding off the end of the rope, she felt a surge of relief. She staggered to the Moby Dick Room where she collapsed on the floor, sobbing uncontrollably. Peter put his arms around her. Pat and Garry offered food and water from their packs. Ann shook her head and held onto Peter.

"What about the others?" Ann asked. They knew that another team led by Pat Kambesis was only an hour or two behind them. Would they notice the damaged rope before they rappelled into trouble?

"I wouldn't trust that knot any more than necessary and the rock I tied to is so thin it could break," Ann said. "If anything happened, it would be my fault."

"Maybe we should go back up and try to re-anchor the rope," Garry said.

The four cavers looked at each other. They were neither physically nor mentally capable of climbing back up the Aragonitemare.

"Look," Pat Seiser said, "it's too dangerous for us to try to go back up and even if we tried to warn them, they'd never hear us. Pat Kambesis' team will most likely send their strongest person first, since the most experienced is usually the first to rappel. They'll probably see the break before they get to it, so they can fix it properly from above. There's nothing we can do from here."

The others nodded in agreement.

The journey back to the surface was a long one. The four cavers were exhausted when they finally reached the huts. Pat Seiser unpacked her gear, cleaned it, and then repacked it without saying anything to the others. There was the real possibility that there would soon be a rescue, or more likely a body recovery. The four cavers paced the huts, waiting to hear word from Kambesis' party.

Seiser looked at the clock again. The other team was four hours overdue. They spoke little, each expecting the worst. Suddenly, they heard the sound of voices outside the hut and the creak of the kitchen door. The four of them jumped up to see Pat Kambesis walk through the door. Ann rushed across the room and hugged Pat with all her might.

"You're all right! You're all right!" She broke out into tears again.

Kris Green told his story as the others in the room listened. He had been the first down the pit and found the frayed rope. He untied the rope from the rock anchor and tied a butterfly knot across the damaged section. He then tied the rope to a prominent projection that protruded a foot from the wall. This way, he hoped, the rope would stay off of the sharp rocks. Luckily, there was a small ledge to make it easier for the rest of his team and the others in the Far East to cross the knot. With some difficulty, they were able to reach the bottom. The rope would definitely have to be replaced and re-rigged again before the next trip.

⇛ 16 ⇚

ADVENTURE
IN THE OUTBACK

O ver the next year, caving in Lechuguilla changed drastically. The cave had grown to the point where extended day trips were no longer sufficient to reach the farthest frontiers of unexplored passages. Over time, the cavers developed a new style of caving specially adapted to the warm temperatures and big passage of Lechuguilla.

Paul Burger was a twenty-year-old geology student from Colorado. He was tall and strong with curly red hair and light blue eyes. Everyone knew Paul for his quick wit and cynical sense of humor, but he was also a very determined caver. Even though he was big, Paul seemed to relish the tightest crawlways and he was never completely happy until he was freezing in some cold, wet, miserable passage.

It had been more than a year since Paul had been to Lechuguilla, and he was starting to realize how much things had changed. He and Stan Allison were standing in front of one of the CRF cabins. Paul walked to the back of his truck and began unloading some white shopping bags, taking an inventory of the items he needed for a five-day trip underground.

"Is all that going to fit in your pack?" Stan asked.

"It better; it's the only pack I've got other than my side packs. Are you bringing a stove?"

"Yeah, do you want to share?"

"Yes, I don't even own one."

"If you carry the fuel, I'll carry the stove. I'll go get the bottle."

It was another pound he had to add to his overloaded pack.

Paul carefully stuffed his equipment into the pack. He started with the items he would not need until he got to camp. He did not tell anyone that his doctor had forbidden him to go caving for another three weeks, because he had broken his hand a month ago and the cast had just been removed.

He put the large space blanket that would act both as a ground cloth and blanket at the bottom of the pack, then packets of freeze-dried food. Paul had never camped in Lechuguilla before. The last time he had been to the cave, exploration was still being done on day-long trips. He knew he was not going to like the jump to five-day camping trips with a thirty-pound pack.

Stan had returned with a shiny red bottle of fuel.

"You'll never get all that in your pack."

"Sure I will. I just hope it doesn't explode going over Boulder Falls."

"Are those straps going to be strong enough?"

The standard method of hauling a pack during rope work is to attach it with webbing to your seat harness.

"I hadn't thought of that," Paul said. "Maybe I'll just keep it on my back the whole time."

"It'll be pretty uncomfortable on your lower back, especially while ascending."

Stan spoke from experience. He had spent over a month last spring exploring deep caves in Mexico where they carried heavy packs to a camp over a day's travel from the entrance.

Paul looked at the pack straps. They were probably too weak to hold his heavy pack, but he would worry about that when he got in the cave. He checked the lighting system on his helmet, and his battery supply. He was relieved to find that he had enough for ten days on his primary lights and his two secondary systems were probably good for five more.

The pack bulged as he tightened the compression straps. He heaved it from the bed of the truck and slid the straps over his shoulders. A hard metal corner poked into his lower back.

He dropped the pack to the ground and stomped on the sharp area. Satisfied that the lump had been subdued, he pushed the heavy load onto the truck bed and closed the tailgate. Stan came over to stow his giant nylon pack.

"Pat and Kris are on their way down to the cave to rig the entrance. They'll meet us there. I told them to go on into the cave when they got the rigging done. That way we can move as two groups of two instead of one big group of four."

"Sounds good to me. I just need to drink some more water and make one more visit to the little caver's room and then I'll be ready to go."

Pat Kambesis and Kris Green were just reaching Boulder Falls when Paul and Stan caught up with them.

"Why don't you two go ahead and pass us," Pat said. "Stan knows the route and you guys move faster than us. We'll meet you in camp."

Pat backed away from the rope and put her pack down. Paul was amazed at the size of Pat's pack. Not only was it bigger than his, but against Pat's small frame it appeared larger than her whole body.

Paul rappelled down Boulder Falls and waited for Stan at the bottom. Little had changed in the cave in the year since Paul had been there. Memories of the passages came flooding back as he and Stan walked quickly through the corridors. In almost no time they passed Rim City, Glacier Bay, Windy City, and Sugarlands to reach the edge of the Rift.

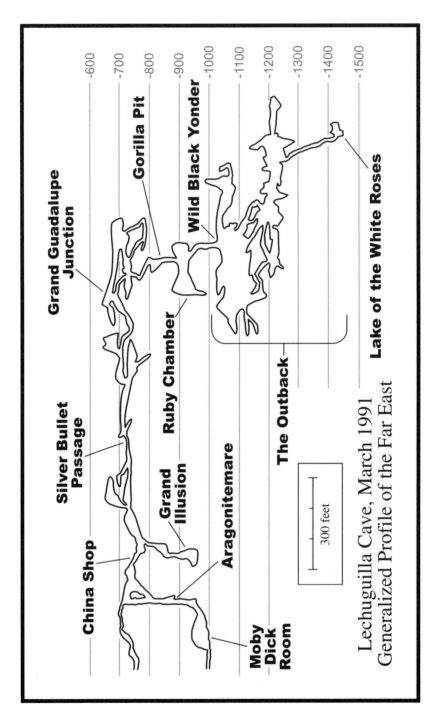

Lechuguilla Cave, March 1991
Generalized Profile of the Far East

"Damn, I'd forgotten how hot this cave is." Paul wiped the sweat away from his eyes and sat down near C-61. He grumbled to himself when he saw that Stan was not sweating at all. "That's what I get for caving with a long-distance runner."

Stan's heavy pack did not seem to affect him at all. Paul's pack had not been particularly unwieldy through the first part of the cave. For the most part, it was like backpacking at night. The Rift was a different story. The passage tilted to the left and Paul's pack kept throwing him off balance. In several places, small rock protrusions grabbed the straps and held him back. Grit worked its way under the pack straps and mixed with his sweat forming a gritty mess that ground against the bare skin of his back.

They moved across the first of the roped traverses in the Overpass. Stan climbed across the rough rock face, unclipped from the rope, and went on. Paul put his boot out on the first foot hold and shifted his weight. The pack pulled his center of balance backward and he began to pivot off the rock. He grabbed at the far wall and braced his arm against the rock, stopping the swing. Awkwardly, he worked his way to the far side, very glad he was attached to the rope. Paul caught up just as Stan was unclipping from another traverse.

"Off rope," he said, and waited for Paul to clip in.

Paul stared at the traverse and then at the passage around him; there was something unfamiliar about this passage.

"Did they change the route through here?"

"No, this is the way we've always gone."

"Does this one have a name?" Paul asked.

Stan gave him a quizzical look, "This is Freakout Traverse, where the boulder moved while Roy was traversing the pit."

"What happened to the Freakout rock?"

"Down at the bottom of the pit."

"When did that happen?"

"Last year sometime."

"Did it fall while someone was crossing it?"

"Not exactly. Let's just say it had a little persuasion."

They continued through the Overpass and stopped for a break at EF Junction.

"Has anyone been doing anything in the Southwest?" Paul asked. He stared down the familiar tunnel into the F-branch.

"Not really. Almost all the action has been in the Far East and a little in the West."

"Are they finding anything new or is it just mopping up?"

"Mostly mop up and some re-survey. They've found quite a bit of bad data and sketches that need fixing, but no one really likes doing work trips."

"Man, the trail sure has changed a lot since the last time I was in this branch; the footing is almost good," Paul said as they reached the top of Apricot Pit.

"Yeah, the pits aren't as slick as they used to be either; all of the trips have really scraped off the gorilla shit."

Stan clipped onto the first rope and began to rappel. "I'll wait for you at the traverse line."

Stan vanished over the edge. Paul called down, "What traverse line?"

There was no response, but a few minutes later Stan called, "Off rope."

Paul began rappelling down Apricot Pit. The ropes were still dirty and stiff but Stan was right about the pit being cleaner. The sticky black slime that had coated everything and made footing impossible in the past had been scraped away to reveal the stained and corroded limestone beneath.

Paul crawled backward down the steeply inclined ramp of the second drop, his pack scraping and dragging on the low ceiling. He worked his way down through the rocks to the start of the third drop. In the past, they had been forced to go down an obnoxiously tight and awkward crack.

But now there was a twenty-foot horizontal rope that allowed them to traverse across the fissure and bypass the tight spot. Stan was out in the fissure sliding across the traverse line using a short piece of rope tied at his waist called a cow's-tail. The carabiner tied to the end of the cow's-tail made it easy to attach to a traverse line and slide from point to point.

"You can either use a cow's-tail or an ascender on this traverse. It doesn't matter on the way in, but you'll want to use an ascender on the way back up because the rope slopes up to where you are. Do you have a second cow's-tail?"

"No, why?"

"Just around the corner from where you are, there's a knot where the rope's anchored to the wall. If you have a second cow's-tail, you don't have to disconnect the first one from the rope when you move past the knot."

"Now you tell me." Paul clipped his one-and-only cow's-tail onto the rope. He reached the knot and wedged himself sideways into the fissure with his pack against the floor and his feet against the ceiling. This would keep him from falling while he carefully disconnected the cow's-tail and clipped it on the other side of the knot.

With this obstacle behind them, they soon reached the bottom of the pit and stopped for lunch. Paul peeled his pack off and looked at the raw marks across his shoulders. It was going to be a long, painful trip to the campsite.

After fifteen minutes, Stan was pacing back and forth on the large flat rock where they had stopped. Paul finished putting his water away, re-shouldered his pack, and followed Stan into the small hole at the end of the room. Too soon, Paul was sweating and breathing heavily again.

They traveled quickly through the old familiar route. The Low Tide Room passed in a blur as they quickly moved into Nirvana and stopped for water. A small, laminated sign marked the watering spot. On it was written: "Use the pitcher to fill your bottles. Do not drink directly from either the pool or the measuring cup."

The last time he was here, Paul remembered that it was standard procedure just to dip your bottle into the pool to fill it up.

"What's this for?" Paul said.

"Oh, they don't want bacteria contaminating the pools."

They continued on through the Rusticles and past the turnoff to the Orange Bowl where Stan examined the small directional marker.

"Hey, why is there a fish on the tape?" Stan asked.

"Very funny."

They maneuvered through the small fissures and climbed into the Moby Dick Room at the base of the Arago-nitemare. Paul recognized the spot where he had slept during his first trip to this climb. He could almost hear Bryan Becker's recorder in the darkness.

Stan climbed the slope on the far side of the room, donned his ascenders, and was soon climbing quickly up the rope. Paul had not seen the pit since that first climbing trip and knew it only by its reputation. He could not help but think about the number of near accidents that had occurred on this series of ropes. Paul did not like ropework anyway, and especially not difficult or complicated rope-work.

Stan called down that he was off rope and Paul went to the base of the climb. He attached his ascenders, took a deep breath, and began to climb up the rope with smooth and steady strokes.

The top of the first rope was a rebelay, a spot where the rope had been tied off and redirected to keep it from touching the abrasive rock. Struggling with his pack and vertical gear, Paul transferred to the next section of rope and climbed to the ledge where Stan was waiting. Stan was already clipped onto the next rope and began to ascend as Paul heaved himself onto the ledge.

Paul detached from the lower rope and moved beneath an overhang to wait for Stan's next signal. Pieces of rock and aragonite rained down. Paul wondered what those rocks were doing to the rope below.

"Off rope."

Paul climbed to the top, sweating and panting.

"Looks like you made it," Stan said.

"Just barely. Can I throw up now?"

"Not yet, we still have a ways until camp."

"How much is 'a ways?'"

"About two hours from here, but most of it's pretty easy."

Paul groaned and took another long drink of water. From here on in he would be traveling through unfamiliar passage and that would make it hard for them to move fast.

"Remember, Stan, you have to give me the Grand Tour since I haven't been up here before and you were in on all the big booty."

"I wasn't on every trip."

"Close enough."

"This is the Land of Enchantment," Stan said pointing down the beautiful crystal-lined passage.

"How did they ever pick a route through all this stuff?" Paul asked as they reached the far end of the room.

"I don't know, but I'm glad I didn't have to do it."

The passage was over twenty feet wide with numerous holes along the left wall.

"Stan, how much of this has been checked? There are an awful lot of holes in the floor."

"Actually most of them have been looked at, at least a little bit. The second team up checked all of the larger pits along this passage."

"Do any of them do anything?"

"One of them goes down to the Grand Illusion, which is a big dead-end room."

They walked past several more pits in the floor as Stan continued his description of the first trips into the Far East. Pausing at the top of a shallow crest, Stan turned to Paul and casually announced, "The passage gets a little strange up ahead."

"What do you mean strange?"

Stan climbed around a small ledge along the side of a pit.

"Oh, by the way," he said, "don't fall here."

Paul came to a small sign written on flagging tape: "Delicate aragonite, don't fall here." Paul looked over the edge into the pit. He could not see the bottom but he could see the walls were lined with razor sharp aragonite all the way down.

Paul worked his way around the pit, being very careful not to violate the instructions, and then followed Stan deeper into the cave. They climbed east up a long breakdown slope. By the time they reached the top, only Stan was still able to speak; Paul was totally out of breath. They finally stopped at a small pool. The main eastward trend continued upward along a fifty-foot-wide gypsum glacier, but a narrow, slanting rift led off to the right.

"This is the Land of Fire and Ice. The main room is up above. We go this way." Stan led the way into the slanting fissure and they followed it until they reached the side of a small pit. Paul could see a narrow ledge angling upward to a large passage above the pit. A short piece of rope dangled down from the ledge. With his heavy pack still on his back, Stan reached up to a small knob on the right wall, put his left foot on the rock and shifted his weight up onto the ledge. His pack swung outward but his momentum carried him up into the passage.

"Here, let me take your pack."

Paul handed Stan his pack, thankful to get it off of his back, and tried to repeat Stan's maneuver. He grabbed the knob that Stan had used, but his recently broken hand did not have the strength to pull him up. He tried to reach around the corner to find a higher hold, but the rock was smooth. After several futile attempts at climbing, he gave up, twisted the rope around his good hand, and muscled himself up into the passage.

"That was graceful," Stan said, handing Paul his pack.

The East Rift was only two feet wide in places and it sloped severely to the left. Paul's partly healed hand was throbbing steadily by the time they reached a small climb. At the top was the beginning of the Silver Bullet Passage. Stan stopped the guided tour long enough to remove his pack and stuff it into a small, popcorn-lined hole near the floor. To keep the straps from catching on the rough opening, he rocked the pack back and forth as he pushed it in. Stan followed his pack into the hole, shoving it ahead of him as he crawled out of sight. When Stan reached the far side, Paul shoved his pack into the hole just as Stan had done. Almost immediately, the straps snagged on the popcorn. The bulging pack filled the entire crawlway and he could not reach past it to free the straps.

"A little help Stan," Paul called.

From the other side of the constriction, Stan leaned back into the crawlway and lifted the front of the pack off the popcorn and pulled it through.

"Thanks. It's amazing how much more difficult a crawl is with one of these monster packs."

"Yeah, it takes some getting used to. Fortunately, this is about the only crawl we have to worry about between here and camp."

They continued moving steadily through the cave. They were now six hours from the entrance and five days from leaving. Even though he had spent hundreds of hours in this cave, Paul had never felt such a sense of isolation and remoteness on any cave trip.

They continued down the passage, alternately walking, stooping, and crawling. Then Paul heard the sound of Stan's feet reverberating in a larger passage. Paul crawled across a small pile of breakdown and followed the trail down a shallow slope to a large room.

"Is this the Grand Guadalupe Junction?"

"Not quite but we're pretty close."

They walked down the large passage for another hundred feet to a place where it intersected an even larger

passage. Two large tunnels stretched out into the darkness
to their right and left. Directly ahead, several smaller passages faded into the distance.

"This is the Grand Guadalupe Junction."

After another hundred feet, they came to a small pile
of moldy ropes. They had been left in case someone found a
pit or dome that could not be safely free-climbed. In many
places throughout the cave, caches of rope had been left to
facilitate exploration. The mold grew on organic matter
that was picked up from the cavers' bodies as they were
carried into the cave. It made the ropes smell bad but had
no effect on their strength.

"Down that slope over there is the designated piss
spot. Luckily, we're the first ones here so we can get the
sleeping spot that's farthest away."

"Does it really get that bad?"

"Yeah, but if we take one of the spots on the far side
of camp, we should be OK."

RAY KEELER

Garry Petrie and Roland Vinyard
at the Grand Guadalupe Junction camp.

The passage sloped down to the right and was about ten feet high at the campsite. A six-foot-wide hollow had been dug into the soft sediment floor to make a flat spot that would accommodate two people.

They dropped their packs. Stan pulled a large, collapsible water bottle out of his pack and set off for the Lost Pecos River, the water source for the area. Paul followed Stan as they trudged away from the Junction, deeper into the cave. Stan led the way, down a boneyard passage, through a series of dry pools and finally into a glistening, flowstone-encrusted canyon. In the distance they could hear the distinct sound of running water. As they approached, they could see a narrow stream of water cascading down a series of terraces. This had to be the Lost Pecos River.

Stan filled his water bag, Paul filled two water bottles, and then they headed back. As they approached the campsite, the room was full of noise and light; Pat and Kris had just arrived and were starting to unpack their gear.

"Hey guys," Pat called as Stan and Paul came into view. "You been here long?"

"Not really. Just long enough to unpack and go for a water run. What time is it?"

"It's only about 9:30."

"What's the plan?"

"We'll probably just make dinner and then crash for the night so we can get a good start tomorrow without throwing off our normal schedule."

"Carol's not that far behind us," Pat said. "They're going to check out some pit leads tonight and then work on this level for the rest of the week. We should have the Outback to ourselves."

Morning came to the camp as the first caver woke up and turned on a light. In almost no time, the smell of freshly brewed coffee was drifting through the low passage. While waiting for a hot breakfast of oatmeal or pasta, each of the cavers packed a small cave pack for the day's work.

During the night, Carol, Bill Farr, and Doug Strait had reached camp. After an hour of busy preparation, both teams were ready to go. At the rope cache they split up, knowing they would not see each other for at least twelve hours. Stan led the way to a small fissure that looked like nothing more than a wide crack in a pillar. The only indication to the contrary was the thick coating of aragonite that lined the edges of the hole and the floor leading up to it.

"Wow, how long did it take before someone decided to push into this?"

"Bob Montgomery went into this hole on the breakthrough trip," Pat said. "He saw all of the aragonite and decided to check it out for a little way. He said it kept going but was too nasty to map on that trip. I mean, we were trying to shoot only one-hundred-foot shots."

"How far did he go?"

"As far as I know, he got down to a point where the gorilla shit really starts getting thick."

Stan climbed into the opening followed closely by Paul. The route dropped steeply down an aragonite-lined oval tube. The passage got smaller, the aragonite disappeared, and the walls showed signs of vigorous corrosion. The footing was beginning to get treacherous.

Stan knew the route and he slid feet-first down into another small tube. In the distance, Paul could hear Stan shouting, "On rope."

"On rope?" Paul thought. "Is there a pit?"

Not knowing what was below, he lowered himself carefully down the hole. On the other side, Paul could see a rope dangling down a steeply sloping fissure. The floor was covered with a thick, slippery coating of gorilla shit, kept constantly wet by condensation from the humid air. Stan was sliding down the fissure on his hands and knees, holding on to the rope, trying to keep from losing control. After a few dozen feet, the ceiling rose abruptly. Stan stood up and continued to work his way downward along a deep groove in the floor.

"Off rope."

Paul followed, not quite as gracefully as Stan. When he reached the bottom, he was stained and streaked with gorilla shit. The sloping fissure opened out onto a broad balcony overlooking a large black void. Stan clipped into the rope and rappelled out of sight over the edge.

"Now is this Gorilla Pit, or is what we just came down the Gorilla Pit?" Paul asked as Pat and Kris caught up.

"I think this whole section is called Gorilla Pit, including this drop into the Ruby Chamber," Pat said, pointing into the darkness ahead.

Paul wove the rope through the bars of his rack and began to back slowly down the dirt slope. He worked his way down about thirty feet until he came to the edge of a crumbling dirt cliff that dropped into the darkness. Paul looked around. He could see a huge room below him. The ceiling stretched far out of sight above the balcony and the farthest wall was barely visible over a hundred feet away.

Paul dropped over the edge and down a few feet to a place where the cliff was overhung and he was dangling free in space. In the darkness below, he could see an immense pile of fallen rock that formed the floor of the big room. Stan's light looked like a small island of yellow floating in the darkness. Just above the mountain of breakdown, there was a distinct line on the walls that continued around the circumference of the chamber. Below this obvious water line, the walls were completely free of the dark corrosion residue that coated everything above. Paul remembered Donald Davis saying something about the cave being flooded toward the end of its development. The elevation of this water line corresponded with several other water marks in various sections of the cave. He would have to ask Donald about this when he saw him back on the surface.

He touched down gently on a large, flat rock and walked over to Stan. Pat and Kris soon arrived at the bottom and led the team across the room to where a pit opened along the wall. They began working their way down through a series of fissures and small passages that allowed them to bypass the steepest part of the pit. The sloping floor at the bottom consisted of a jumble of huge boulders that had obviously rolled down from the room above. Pushing on, they climbed to the top of a large pile of rocks where Paul could see the huge passage beyond called the Wild Black Yonder.

In either direction an enormous, slanting borehole stretched out into the darkness. From their vantage point, the passage appeared to be more than fifty feet wide and at least that high. The far side of the passage was severely overhung and along the wall were numerous holes and openings that led into countless unexplored passages. They had entered the borehole by climbing down a steep wall of huge boulders that had cascaded down from the Ruby Chamber, but they still had not reached the floor of the passage.

Stan led the way between two large boulders and onto a narrow ledge with a safety line strung along its length. With one hand on the safety line, he walked across the ledge. At the far end, he clipped into another rope and rappelled down the face of a large boulder to the floor.

"Off rope," he called. "You need to watch the end of the rope here; it doesn't quite reach the bottom. And stay to the left; the right side drops off pretty good."

Paul, Pat, and Kris followed and soon were walking over the piles of loose rocks that lined the left side of the large passage. The real floor of the passage was out of sight, down the rock slope to the right, but they had a good view of the side passages from here. These side leads consisted of a series of low passages five feet high and thirty to forty feet wide. They were stacked one on top of the other in layers that paralleled the ceiling of the borehole. These pancakes, as Pat called them, were surrounded by Swiss-cheese-like boneyard that formed numerous connections

RAY KEELER

Stan Allison surveying in the Outback.

between the flat passages. This explained why the line plot they had seen back in camp resembled a tangled mass of spaghetti.

"Where are we going to map?" Paul asked, wondering how many of these holes had been checked.

"We'll start up in the pancakes and see how it goes. I don't think it'll do much but I need to fill in some blank spots on my map," Pat said.

They turned off the main trend into a smaller side passage. Pat sat down on a broad, dirt-covered ledge and opened her pack.

"I need to see where our tie-in is. We might as well eat lunch here and get out the survey gear."

As they ate lunch, Paul walked across the passage to a steeply descending tunnel leading away from the main survey. Several strips of orange flagging tape indicated that it was an important route, but there was no writing on the tape to tell where it led.

"Pat, where does this trail go?"

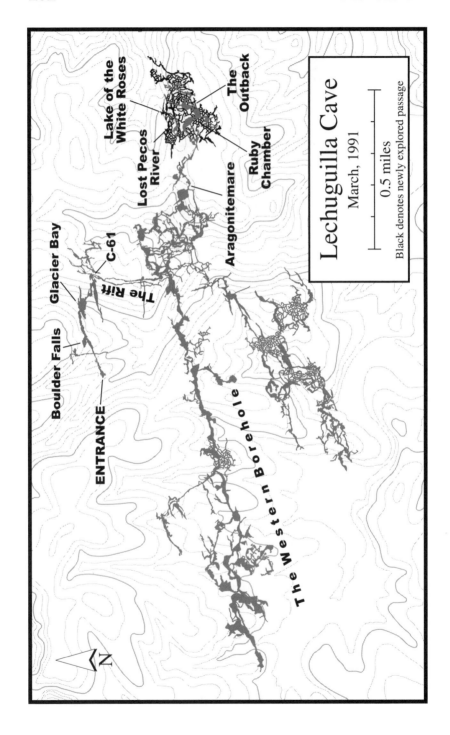

Lechuguilla Cave
March, 1991

0.5 miles

Black denotes newly explored passage

Lake of the White Roses
The Outback
Lost Pecos River
Ruby Chamber
Aragonitemare
Glacier Bay
C-61
The Rift
Boulder Falls
ENTRANCE
The Western Borehole

N

"That goes down to the new deep point. Last December they pushed the cave down to minus fifteen hundred and ten feet. That means that the cave is just forty feet away from being the deepest cave in the country."

Paul started the survey at a nearby station marker and they worked their way into the boneyard. By the end of the day, they had mapped over 500 feet and made several connections between the main passages. But from what they saw, they knew they had mapped only a fraction of the maze.

"I guess it's not quite as easy to find big borehole as it used be," Paul said.

"Yes, most of the big obvious leads have already been pushed. We're doing lots of mop-up surveying in the small side passages that the other teams overlooked," Pat said. "Still, you never know when one of these small crawlways might break through into something big."

After the long trek back to camp they made another water run. While they cooked dinner, each caver tried to get as clean as possible. Water was too scarce to use for cleaning so they wiped the dirt off on the cleaner parts of their clothes and then finished off with baby wipes. After a week of day trips away from camp, there were no more clean spots and everyone had settled into a common state of filth.

By the last day of the expedition, they had mapped several thousand feet of maze passage, but had made no big breakthroughs. Paul sat in the glow of his flickering camp candle and stared up at the large hole in the ceiling above his head.

"Hey, wake up," Stan said, waving his hand back and forth in front of Paul's eyes.

"I was just thinking about this whole camping thing."

"What about it?"

"Well, do you know about the big Crystal Cave expedition in Kentucky in 1953?"

"Yeah, it was one of the first big caving expeditions in the United States."

"Do you realize that we have been underground for almost as long as they spent and they had dozens of people as support teams? I think between our group and Carol's group we've mapped almost as much as they did on their whole expedition. After that expedition, they decided that camping underground was much less efficient than long trips with only a few people. But here we've done it by hauling our own gear."

"I think the difference is in the approach. Back then, they were going under the European expedition mentality with support teams, underground communication, and well-established camps. That doesn't seem to work with the American approach to things," Stan said. "We've adopted the Mexican style of cave camping. Everyone is self-sufficient and carries only what he thinks he'll need. I think that's why it works here. It also has a lot to do with the friendliness of this cave. I mean, most of the passages are big enough so you can carry a pack and it's not like one of those cold, alpine caves. We don't really have to bring much in the way of camping gear."

"I suppose you're right," Paul said. "Even in Mexico, we need sleeping bags to keep warm. Here, you can get away with just some kind of pad and a space blanket. We also have to do a lot more vertical work in Mexico."

They continued talking as they packed. With most of the food gone and the bulky packaging crushed down, everyone's pack was much smaller. They made sure no trash had been left behind and began the long journey out of the cave. Paul looked back at the small alcove that had been home to the eight explorers for the last four days and wondered if this camp would someday be just a stopping point along the way to a deeper camp, hours further into the cave.

It was late afternoon when they finally reached the entrance. Paul scrambled up the slope to the bushes where he had stashed his sunglasses, the brightness nearly blinding him after so many days underground.

They had split into two teams of two to make travel more efficient on the way out, but Paul knew that Pat and Kris were only about half an hour behind them. In no time, they would be back at the cabins, clean, fed, and ready to drop off the survey notes so they could be entered in the computer. In less than two hours, they would see the lines on paper that represented four day's work deep in the cave.

➯➤➤ 17 ⬅⬅⬅

RESCUE!

he last week of March, 1991, sixty cavers gathered for another expedition to Lechuguilla Cave. Trips to the Far East were becoming longer and more arduous and the obvious walking leads had already been explored, leaving only a network of crawlways and tight fissures. There were still many unexplored leads elsewhere, so the first three teams into the cave decided to go west instead.

Mike Mansur was full of energy and eager to go to the Western Borehole. He was a climber, and he had recently learned that one of the climbing leads out of the Reason Room had not been fully explored. He recruited Emily Davis Mobley, a caving veteran in her early forties with over twenty years of experience. Emily made a living running Speleobooks, a store specializing in books about caving. She enjoyed the Western Borehole area and knew it well. She preferred short trips of twenty-four hours or less to the multi-day camping trips required to visit the Far East.

Emily had brought along three longtime caving friends from West Virginia; Steve Mosberg, a family doctor, Bob

Addis, and Bill Bauman. It was their first trip into Lechuguilla.

Saturday morning began as usual with a two-hour
introductory talk by Rick. It was mid-morning before the
cavers started to pack their gear. Mike and Emily worked
with the three newcomers to ensure that they carried neither too much nor too little into the cave. After the short
drive and hike to the entrance, they entered the cave at
two o'clock in the afternoon.

They were in no hurry. Emily explained each obstacle
to the newcomers, making sure that everyone used the
safety lines on the traverses. An experienced team could
have reached Lake Louise in three or four hours, but it
took Emily and Mike's team six hours to reach the popular
resting spot.

They decided to take a two-hour nap before continuing their journey. When they finally reached the beginning
of the Western Borehole at the ABCs Room, they turned
left and climbed up the steep slopes toward the Reason
Room, arriving after midnight. Pat Kambesis had reminded
them about Mike Goar's accident in the room and warned
them about the loose rock in the area. They proceeded
slowly to the spacious Reason Room. Mike was anxious to
start climbing the lead at the far end of the room, but
Emily suggested that Steve, Bob, and Bill might be more
comfortable starting with something easier.

They went to the large, flat rock in the center of the
room, beneath which was an obvious crawlway sloping
down. There were no blue markers indicating that the passage had been surveyed, and it did not appear on their line
plots. Even though it was now early in the morning, they
were full of energy and began surveying down the crawl.

The passage was tight at first, but after a few feet
opened into a three-foot-high fissure that sloped down at a
forty-five-degree angle. They had surveyed only 100 feet
when the floor of the passage dropped off sharply and the
fissure became nearly vertical. Mike and Emily were in the

lead, so they climbed down to take a look. Mindful of the bad reputation of this part of the cave, they tested each hand-hold as they worked their way down past a large chockstone that was wedged in the fissure. Unfortunately, the passage ended just a few feet past the boulder.

Mike climbed over the obstructing chockstone and out of the fissure, calling back to Emily when he had cleared the top of the pit. Emily chimneyed up the fissure and reached for a handhold on the chockstone. As she put her full weight on the rock, the eighty-pound boulder broke loose, dragging Emily to the bottom of the fissure. The noise of crashing rock echoed down the passageway.

Emily sat stunned for a moment. She tried to move but a wave of pain shot up her left leg. She knew what had happened. She had known the instant the boulder bounced off her knee.

Mike and Steve shouted frantically down the pit.

Emily shouted back. "I'm all right, but I think my leg's broken."

Steve climbed down to Emily. Mike turned to call for Bob and Bill, but they had heard the rock fall and were already coming down the crawlway. The three cavers looked through their packs for webbing and padding material.

"Can you move your leg?" Steve asked, very much in a doctor role now.

"Yes, but it's very painful."

"Can you stand?"

"I think so, but I can't put any weight on my left leg."

Steve looked at Emily's knee and shook his head. "I can't tell anything down here. We've got to get you back into the room."

They used a cut-open plastic water bottle for a splint and a mylar space blanket for padding. Steve supported Emily's leg while Mike, Bob, and Bill used a length of webbing for a belay. Sliding on her butt backward up the steep

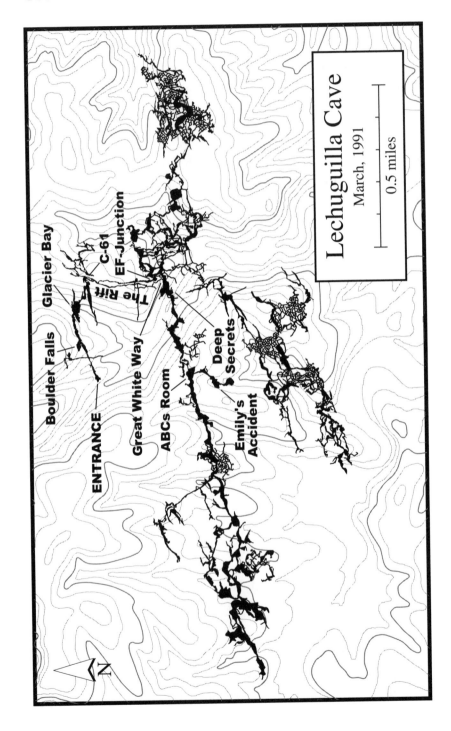

floor of the passage, Emily inched her way upward to the spacious Reason Room. They set up camp on the wide flat rock they had just crawled under.

Steve examined Emily's leg again.

"She has a knee injury. I can't tell for sure whether it's a broken bone, or torn ligaments. I'd need an X-ray to know for certain. Either way, she can't get out of the cave without help."

They were 1,000 feet below the surface and over a mile and a quarter from the entrance. The only way out was to go back down to the ABCs Room and then begin the long and difficult trip to the surface.

Mike and Emily were the only ones who knew the way out. It was obvious that Mike would have to take a message to the surface while the others waited with Emily. Mike emptied his pack and left all the extra food and clothing for Emily. He then started toward the entrance. As his light faded into the distance, the others turned off their headlamps to save their batteries. It would take at least four hours for a message to reach the surface, a few hours to organize a rescue, and at least another four hours for the rescue team to return.

Mike hurried down the passage back to the Western Borehole, but not too fast. He could not risk injuring himself.

At the junction with the main route through the ABCs Room, Mike paused to catch his breath. He knew there were at least two other teams further down the Western Borehole; they might be able to help Emily. Mike left a note in the middle of the trail where it would be seen by any team returning to the surface. Then he continued onward.

Six hours after Emily's accident, in another corner of the cave, Pat Seiser, Garry Petrie, and Mike Taylor walked slowly along the path through the Western Borehole. They had been in the cave for almost twenty-four hours and were still a long way from the entrance. Mike was sick with heat exhaustion, forcing them to travel at half-speed, but their pace picked up as they approached the ABCs Room. The cool water of Lake Louise was only ten minutes away.

Garry stopped abruptly and picked up a scrap of paper.

"What's that?" Pat asked.

"It says, 'Emily broke her leg. She's in the Reason Room, right over there.' "

"When?"

"It's dated 6:30 this morning."

"What should we do?" Garry said.

"We've got to get Mike out of the cave," Pat said. "He's in no shape to help if there's going to be a rescue. Garry, take Mike to Lake Louise. Fill the water bottles, and bring them back to the Reason Room. Then take Mike out of the cave."

Garry and Mike continued down the trail while Pat crossed the room and began the steep climb up to the Reason Room. As she looked around for the route, she realized that other rescuers would be doing the same. She took a few blank pages from her survey book and made signs with the word "Emily" and an arrow. She left one at each turn in the passage to mark the route.

Pat continued along the passage, shouting occasionally until she heard a voice answer her call. She hurried up the final slope into the Reason Room.

"Hi, Pat," Emily said.

Pat was greatly relieved. She had expected to find Emily in pain, stuck in some miserable crawlway. Instead, she was reasonably comfortable and very happy to see a familiar face.

The five of them chatted for a few minutes, and then Bill, Bob, and Steve went to a quieter corner of the room for some much-needed rest. It was clear to Pat that Emily did not need rest, she needed to talk. When the others were out of hearing range, Emily lowered her voice and spoke nervously.

"This is going to ruin the expedition, isn't it," she said.

"Don't be silly. We'll have you out in a day or two and then the expedition will continue as normal."

"We're a long way in the cave," Emily said. "It won't be easy getting me out of here. I just hate to have everyone stop what they're doing just to help me."

"Emily," Pat said, "you'd do the same for anyone else who got hurt in here."

An hour later, Garry returned with several full water bottles and immediately headed back to Lake Louise to take Mike Taylor out of the cave. Since Bob was a novice in Lechuguilla, Garry offered to take Bob along too.

As Garry and Bob hiked back down the passage, the others talked for a bit and then decided to eat dinner. As the hour grew late, they began to accept the fact that a rescue team would not arrive that night. The four cavers assembled makeshift beds, turned off their lights, and fell asleep in the perfect silence of the cave.

⚜   ⚜   ⚜

When word finally reached the surface, one of the first people notified was Jim Goodbar. Jim was a long-time caver who was now the Cave Specialist for the Bureau of Land Management, and he managed many of the caves on the land surrounding Carlsbad Caverns National Park. A quiet and confident person in his early forties, he had decades of caving experience. He also had medical and rescue training. By evening he had assembled a small team and by 3:00 a.m. they had made it as far as the Western Borehole where they stopped to sleep.

At 8:30 the next morning, Jim sent two people back to Lake Louise to get the rescue litter they had left there on their way into the cave. Jim had been concerned that the litter would not fit through the tight passages leading into the ABCs Room. But, after checking them, he was now fairly sure the litter could be used for the entire evacuation. He sent two others to pick up ropes that were stashed further down the Western Borehole, and another two cavers to get some ropes from a nearby passage. When all the gear was assembled, they climbed the last few hundred yards to where Emily was waiting.

Emily and her attendants had been resting patiently. There was only so much Steve could do with limited supplies. He had immobilized Emily's leg with an air-splint and had given her some pain pills. When Jim and his crew rounded the corner carrying the litter, they were greeted with a cheer.

Kneeling down next to Emily, Jim carefully explained to her and everyone else exactly what they were going to do.

Emily looked up from the large flat rock where she had been laying for over a day. "Jim, I'm going to be the best patient you've ever had."

Jim laughed. "We'll take care of you Emily."

He laid out plastic sheets, wool blankets, nylon webbing, and medical supplies. Then he guided his helpers

PETER AND ANN BOSTED
Emily Davis Mobley in a litter ready
to be moved out of the Reason Room.

through the process of making Emily comfortable and safe in the litter.

Jim had never led a major rescue, but he was calm and decisive, and his team responded in kind. In less than thirty minutes, Emily was tied securely into the litter. Just before one o'clock in the afternoon they were ready to start carrying Emily out of the cave.

Steve Mosberg took Jim and his team to one side. "We need to be very careful how we handle her," he said. "If she does have a fracture, any movement of the bones could cause an embolism which could travel to her lungs. An embolism could be fatal. We have to be careful not to jostle her any more than necessary."

Four rescuers lined up on each side of the litter and hoisted it off the ground. They might drop Emily if one of the rescuers stumbled while walking over the rough cave floor. So instead of walking with the litter, they passed it forward from hand-to-hand. As the litter left the hands of the two people in back, they went to the front of the line, ready to receive the litter again. The process was repeated endlessly as they slowly moved Emily through the cave. The risk of someone stumbling increased as the route turned steeply downward. Jim picked a secure rock to use as an anchor and then attached a belay rope to the litter. They passed Emily down the slope while Jim controlled the speed of the descent with the belay. The slope that had taken fifteen minutes on the way in was going to take two hours on the way out.

Emily watched nervously as she was handed down the slope. She could lift her head and look past her toes to the rocks below. She knew that the belay rope would hold her if anything went wrong, but the swaying and occasional lurching of the litter tested her nerves. When she arrived at the next ledge, her rescuers set the litter down and repositioned the belay anchor. Then they lifted her again and repeated the process. Everyone was sweating heavily.

As they made their way down the slope, the ride became
a bit smoother, and Emily began to relax. Three hours passed
before she could see the archway leading into the ABCs
Room. At least the journey across this big room would be
level.

✠   ✠   ✠

While Jim Goodbar was leading the rescue team deep
in the cave, Phil Koepp, the Chief Ranger of Big Bend
National Park, was sitting at his desk. Phil was one of the
regional experts in managing fires. In fact, Phil was an
Incident Commander, which means that he did not actually
put out the fires, but he organized, directed, and managed
operations.

"Panther Junction, Koepp speaking," he said as he
picked up the phone.

"Phil, this is Tim Stubbs over at Carlsbad. We have
an incident over here we'd like you to manage."

Tim briefly summarized the events of the last twenty-
four hours. The cavers had started the rescue process, but
they needed a surface team. Phil had never managed a cave
rescue, but he quickly agreed to go to Carlsbad.

There were now only ten people on the evacuation
team moving Emily through the cave, but it would take
many more than that to get her out. Rick Bridges, Brian
Borton, and Dan Legnini had been up most of the night
organizing logistical support for the rescue. They had to
find equipment and assemble teams to take gear into the
cave. They were calling in cavers from all around the country to help with the rescue. Dan was coordinating the
teams being sent into the cave. By the afternoon of the second day, the three of them had been going non-stop for
almost thirty hours and the strain showed. They were
especially apprehensive about the park service management team arriving that evening. Even though Felix Her-
nandez, the Chief Ranger at Carlsbad, had explained that
the management team was being called in to help, not to
hinder the effort, there was an undercurrent of resentment

among the cavers. They had seen many rescues botched by civil authorities who were unfamiliar with caves. Their greatest fear was that the park service team would come in and take control of the rescue.

Brian stood in front of a pile of gear that he had just assembled on the floor of one of the CRF huts. He checked the items against his equipment list and sorted them into piles. He had been surprised by the lack of equipment in the park service rescue cache, but he was able to borrow more gear from the cavers to fill out his requirements. Much of it had already gone into the cave, and Brian was beginning to wonder where he would find enough for the days ahead. The cave was devouring equipment like a black hole: the more he supplied, the more was requested. And as of that morning they had not even started moving Emily. Rick assured him that Buddy Lane would be arriving on a plane from Chattanooga that evening with lots of gear.

PETER & ANN BOSTED
Hauling team moving Emily through the breakdown.

The door burst open and John charged through the doorway. "Brian! They've set up a command center in the Fire Station. Rick wants you up there right away."

Brian gathered his notes and went out the door.

Later that afternoon, Greg Miller and Steve Reames were racing south from Colorado in Greg's Subaru wagon. The call had gone out for seven more people: five to go into the cave and two for surface support. Greg had participated in several cave rescues and had been the subject of one himself. He had founded the cave rescue group in Colorado and had been its first director. Steve had become director a year later. Steve was less experienced in cave rescue than Greg, but he had spent over 200 hours underground in Lechuguilla and he knew the route from the entrance to the accident site like the back of his hand.

Both of them were trained incident commanders and although they were familiar with all aspects of cave rescue, most of their experience was in rescue management. They had been asked to do surface support, and were anxious to get started. The nine-hour drive to Carlsbad Caverns gave them plenty of time to plan.

"OK, how long do you think it'll take them to get to C-61?" Greg asked.

"Let's see," Steve said, "from the DC-10 squeeze we have about three hundred feet of easy traveling, then another three hundred feet of nasty tight stuff; I'll put down two hours for that part."

"What's that give us?" Greg asked. Steve added up the column of numbers. "Twenty-four hours before Emily starts moving . . . six hours up the Great White Way . . . Wow!"

"How long?" Greg asked.

"Four days," Steve said. "This thing is going to take four days."

Back in the cave, Jim Goodbar's rescue team had been working hard for several hours. They had carried

Emily through the ABCs Room with relative ease, but the tight chimney leading out of the room was another matter. Emily's litter barely fit through the narrow opening at the top and once they passed the tight spot, the rescuers were faced with an awkward forty-five-degree chimney that sloped down for more than forty feet. They tied one rope to the litter and another to Emily as a belay, then lowered her down the chimney. Just as they reached the bottom, Dave Shurtz, a paramedic, Kelly Kellstedt, an Emergency Medical Technician, and Don Coons joined the team bringing the total to thirteen, plus Emily.

"Don Coons! Gosh am I glad to see you here," Jim said. "If I could have asked for one person to help with the rescue it would have been you. What are you doing here?"

"I was on my way back from Mexico and I stopped in at the park."

Jim and Don were old friends. They had caved together in Mexico and the Guadalupe Mountains. At age forty, Don was one of the most experienced cavers in the country and he had been a part of numerous rescues. He was medium height, quiet, and intense. It always surprised other cavers to learn that Don made a living as a farmer in the enormous flat cornfields of Illinois. Jim was relieved to have someone of Don's caliber sharing the responsibilities of the rescue.

They continued along the narrow passage for a short distance until they came to the top of the Cornflakes Climb. Again the litter was connected to ropes and in just a few minutes they had lowered Emily down the fifteen-foot drop. Fifteen minutes later they entered the White Christmas Tree Room where they rested along the shore of Lake Louise. Jim and Don looked at each other and nodded. They had made it through the first run of tough obstacles. Ahead of them was over a thousand feet of walking passage. Jim crossed his fingers and hoped that luck would stay with them.

Emily had been in the litter for over seven hours and she was ready for a break. The rescuers also needed a rest.

They loosened the straps of webbing that held Emily in place, and she sat up and stretched. While the others began to fix dinner, Pat gave Emily a massage. Soon the smells of instant soup and hot tea were drifting across camp.

Jim, Don, and Emily discussed their plans. There were two convenient places to camp for the night in the passages ahead. The first was Deep Seas camp, only an hour away. The next was Little Lake Lechuguilla, about three hours away. Emily suggested that they shoot for Little Lake Lechuguilla. Jim and Don agreed.

The hours passed slowly as Emily was carried through the Deep Seas camp, along the Deep Seas Passage, and into the Fortress of Chaos. A steep slope ahead of them led down into Deep Secrets. Although the day had gone smoothly, Emily and her rescuers were tired. As they inched down the slope, one of the rescuers lost his footing. The litter lurched to the left and as Emily shifted, one of the litter straps caught her across the throat.

"Stop!" Jim shouted. The belayer immediately locked the safety rope.

"We need a hand down here!" Don said as he grabbed the litter and released the strap.

"Are you OK?"

Emily clenched her teeth and nodded her head.

They moved Emily on down the slope into the formation area of Deep Secrets. An hour later they arrived at Little Lake Lechuguilla. Emily's leg was throbbing with pain, and she was tired and angry with herself for not having avoided the rock that caused this whole incident. As they loosened the straps on the litter, Emily could hold back no longer. She broke into tears. Jim and Don moved the rescue team back down the passage while Steve Mosberg talked to Emily and Pat held her hand.

⚜   ⚜   ⚜

Early in the evening on the second day of the rescue, Phil Koepp, Dwayne Alire, and Steve Swanke flew in from Big Bend National Park. They met with Rick shortly after their arrival to learn what actions the Lechuguilla Cave team had already taken. Phil was surprised by how far removed the surface team was from the activity in the cave.

"What was the last communication you had with the rescue team?" Phil asked.

Rick handed him a sheet of paper. "This is the last message we received. It arrived twelve hours ago."

Rick explained to Phil that radio communication was impossible in a cave, and that sending a messenger to the Reason Room and back involved a six-hour trip for a fast caver. To an incident commander used to instant radio communications, the remoteness of the cave was daunting.

Steve Reames and Greg Miller walked into the command center after their long drive to Carlsbad. Phil stood up and approached the new arrivals. One of Phil's responsibilities was to manage rescue personnel. He quizzed Steve and Greg for several minutes. Because of Steve's knowledge of the cave and their rescue experience, Phil assigned them to the understaffed plans section.

Suddenly, someone shouted into the room, "We have communications with the rescue team." Since early that morning, Dave Belski and a team of other cavers had been laying a long string of telephone wire through the cave. Now a person at the entrance, radio in one hand, telephone in the other, could pass messages between the rescuers and park headquarters. Emily and her entourage had just arrived at Little Lake Lechuguilla. After a short exchange of messages, both surface and underground teams turned in for the night.

⚜ ⚜ ⚜

On Tuesday morning, the underground rescue team woke to the insistent beeping of someone's watch. Everyone was stiff from carrying Emily 2,500 feet through the cave. They were now just under a mile from the entrance.

Jim wanted to get to EF Junction by evening, but there were two major obstacles ahead of them. The first was Deep Secrets, one of the largest rooms in the cave. The route through the room went over and under large, haphazardly-piled breakdown blocks. Once across, they would be at the base of the next obstacle: the Great White Way. The 250-foot sloping fissure was no problem for an unburdened caver, but the regular route required squeezing through a short, tight crawlway halfway up the slope. Jim knew the litter would never make it through and they would have to use an alternate route. Their only choice was to haul Emily directly up a little-known vertical pit that bypassed the lower portion of the steep passage. Once they had circumvented the constriction, they could then finish the final fifty feet in the Great White Way. The remaining 300 feet to EF Junction would be easy walking passage.

Jim and Don repackaged Emily into the litter. Emily talked easily now; a good night's sleep was just what she needed.

"How long to cross Deep Secrets?" she asked.

"Six hours," Jim said.

Don assigned people to their tasks. Thirty minutes later they were moving again.

The surface team was at work before dawn on Tuesday. Steve and Greg set up shop in a storage room next to the command center.

"We need to be able to report on the status of the rescue at any given moment," Greg said. "First we need to find out where they are now."

"They should be just starting out from Little Lake Lechuguilla," Steve said. "It'll take them about six hours to cross the boulder field. I'll debrief teams coming out of the cave, and you try to find the communications log and a list of what's been sent into the cave."

Hours later, the rescue team reached the dangling rope that marked the beginning of the Great White Way. Jim was astounded that they had crossed the boulder fields of Deep Secrets in less than two and a half hours.

"Set her down over there," Jim said.

The litter-bearers moved Emily to a large flat area a few dozen feet away from the climb. Emily was grateful for the chance to sit up for awhile and stretch her cramped muscles.

The ceiling rose above them forming a chamber fifty feet high. The slope glistened with the crusty white crystals of gypsum that had given the Great White Way its name. In the far corner of the room the ceiling was pierced by a hole fifteen feet in diameter. This was the bypass route and there was already a rope hanging down the pit, the coiled end lying on the floor.

Thirty feet to the right of the bypass pit, at the base of the regular route, Jim grabbed the handline and climbed up the slope. He clambered over several large rocks and wriggled through the constriction that prevented Emily from taking the same route. Ahead he could see the lights of a dozen rescuers working on the haul system for lifting the litter vertically up the bypass pit.

"How are you guys doing?" he asked.

"We're almost ready."

The maze of ropes, pulleys, and safety cams was completely different from anything Jim had seen before. "Who set up this rig?" he asked.

"The guys who rigged it left last night; they're on the surface. We're not sure how it's supposed to work."

"Where's the belay line for the litter attendant?"

"There isn't one – we ran out of rope. Unfortunately, we don't have all the equipment we need."

"OK," Jim said. "We have a 250-foot rope with us. I'll send someone up with it and you set up a belay for the litter attendant."

Jim climbed back down the slope of the Great White Way to the team below. They put Emily back in the litter and described to her what was ahead. Don Coons put on his vertical gear and prepared for the job of litter attendant. He would ride beside Emily and guide the litter up the pit. There was also the matter of acting as a human shield if any rocks fell down the pit.

"Rope!" A soft whirring sound was followed by a thwack as the end of the belay line hit the wall of the pit. Jim looked up and saw that the rope did not reach the floor. He sent Dave up to ask for more rope, while they hooked Emily and Don into the hauling system. When Emily was ready, Jim climbed back up the trail to the top of the pit to supervise.

A second team was rigging the route between the top of the bypass pit and the top of the Great White Way. When they finished, they came down to the pit to help with the initial haul. The small ledge overlooking the pit was now crowded with people. The clamor made it difficult to think and almost impossible to communicate with the team at the bottom. The haul system had been reconfigured, but Jim thought it looked only slightly better than before.

"Should I tell the people below to come up and help?" Mark said.

"No," Jim said, "tell them there isn't enough room here. They should either wait at the bottom or go to the very top of the Great White Way."

"Jim, they're ready," Bob said.

"Go ahead then."

The haul team started pulling on the rope. The cams bit into the rope and the pulleys multiplied their strength by three, but the rope still moved slowly. Three commands were called out repeatedly.

"Haul!" The team slowly walked backward, pulling on the rope.

"Set!" The team released six inches of rope, permitting the first cam to catch.

"Slack!" The haul team relaxed the rope as another caver slid the second cam back down the main line, taking up the slack. Each set of movements brought the litter three feet closer to the top of the pit; three feet closer to the surface.

"Haul . . . set . . . slack."

"Haul . . . set . . . slack."

"Haul . . . stop!"

One of the cams had jammed into the pulley above it. A six-foot loop of loose rope dangled from the system. If the haul team stumbled now, Emily, Don, and the litter would drop at least six feet, and the shock might sever the main line, throwing all the weight on the emergency belay rope.

Jim was worried. The pulley was jammed, the ropes were tangled, and everything was off-center. No matter what they did, the rope would not budge. Minutes passed as they worked frantically to free the system.

Don shouted from below wanting to know what was causing the delay. Emily stood in the litter, suspended vertically over the cave floor below. She said she was fine, but Don could tell she was in pain from the stress on her splinted leg.

"What's the problem?" Don shouted again, but no one answered.

Forty-five minutes passed with three dozen people working at counter purposes. Too much time. Jim stepped back and shouted.

"Okay everybody, I need quiet. Quiet! Let me think."

Jim sat down to sort out the problem.

Dave Shurtz appeared, panting from his quick jaunt up the slope. "How can I help?" Dave was both a paramedic and an expert at technical ropework. Jim pointed at the jammed system and explained the problems.

"You know," Dave said, "we were working on something like this just last week." He took a spare pulley and a length of webbing from his pack and walked over to the rope. It took him only a few minutes to connect the new pulley and to redirect the load on to one of the lines. Suddenly, the mass of rope and metal turned into a smoothly operating machine. The cams gripped and the pulleys did not jam. Soon the rhythm of the taskmaster echoed up and down the corridors of the Great White Way again.

"Haul . . . set . . . slack."

"Haul . . . set . . . slack."

PETER & ANN BOSTED
Emily starting up the Great White Way.

"Haul . . . set . . . slack."

By the afternoon of the third day, the rescue operation had grown to epic proportions. There were now more than 140 people working on all phases of the rescue and members of the national news media were arriving in force. Bridges and Kerbo were constantly busy dealing with dozens of details and answering the incessant barrage of questions from the press. Throughout the day, bulletins flashed on CNN, and NBC Nightly News ran lengthy segments on the rescue. People around the country were anxiously following the progress of the injured caver hundreds of feet underground.

To cope with the flow of information, Steve Reames was preparing a large tactical map of the cave showing the route Emily would travel to the surface. Greg debriefed each team that came out of the cave to find out what was happening underground. Steve was surprised to hear that the rescue team was still on the lower half of the Great White Way.

"They must be having problems," he told Greg.

Just then, Rick walked into the room. "Could you guys find out how much food and water is at EF Junction?" he said. "Emily should be there in a couple of hours and I want to make sure there are enough supplies. I'm going out to the cave to talk to the press, but I'll have my radio. You can call me there."

"Keep working on the map," Greg said, "and I'll go through the communication logs and the debriefing forms." No sooner had he spoken than another team arrived ready for debriefing.

Steve was still drawing the tactical map when Greg hurried back into the room.

"Have you seen the debriefing sheet for Donald's team?" Greg asked.

"Sure," Steve said, as he walked over to the debriefing table.

"I need to know how much water his team left at EF Junction," Greg said.

"That's easy," Steve said, "None."

"None!?"

"Right. The water jug they were supposed to use to take water from Little Lake Lechuguilla had a hole in it, so they lost most of the water before they made it to EF Junction. What little made it there was drunk by the rigging teams. It's not a problem, other teams also left water at EF Junction."

"No they didn't," Greg said.

"Nonsense," Steve said. "One of the teams took water into the cave yesterday."

"They drank half of it and left the rest at C-61."

"What about the team that went in this morning?"

"They were reassigned to transport ropes. As far as I can tell," Greg said, looking at his clipboard, "there are five to ten food packs at EF Junction and no water. I'm not even sure that the food hasn't been eaten already."

GREG MILLER

P. J. Pearson (standing) leading a general briefing;
tactical map is visible in upper right part of photo.

Steve looked at his watch. "In less than two hours, twenty to thirty dehydrated rescuers will arrive at EF Junction and they won't have any food or water."

"That's what I've been saying," Greg said.

Brian Borton walked through the doorway. "Brian! Where's Rick?" Steve said.

"He's still out at the cave talking to the press," Brian said.

Steve and Greg told Brian about the water problem. Brian asked the radio operator to call Rick.

"No luck," the operator finally said. "He must be in the canyon between the cave and the parking lot."

They couldn't wait for Rick. Brian went to arrange for use of the helicopter and to get food and water containers. Greg went to look for any available cavers. Steve stayed behind to man the debriefing table in case another team returned from the cave.

Minutes later, Brian and Greg returned, with two cavers who had volunteered to carry in supplies. They started loading packs with as much food as they could carry. It only took a few minutes to discover that there was no way two people could be expected to carry ten gallons of water — eighty pounds — into the cave at a dead run.

"Where's the nearest water?" Greg asked.

"Little Lake Lechuguilla," Brian said, "but it would take hours to ferry the water from down there."

"There's another option," Steve said. "If we give them five gallons of water to carry and those collapsible containers, then they can fill up with ten more gallons at the end of the F-survey."

"No way!" Jim said. "That pool at F-21 is barely big enough to fill a canteen."

"No, not that one," Steve said, picking up pencil and paper. "There's a dead-end passage that branches off of the main travel route at F-21." Steve drew a sketch of the passages. "There are several large pools near the end; since the passage is a dead-end, I don't think anyone has been back since we surveyed it several years ago. Most people don't know those pools are there. You can drop off the five gallons at EF Junction and then go fill another ten gallons at those pools. That way you'll have to carry the ten gallons of water only about eight hundred feet." Jim took the sketch map Steve handed him, and then headed for the helipad.

⚜   ⚜   ⚜

Jim Goodbar relaxed slightly as Emily and Don cleared the top of the Great White Way. The five-hour nightmare of technical ropework was finally over, but this was not a good place to rest. The floor was irregular and sloped toward the precipitous drop only a few feet away. Just one more traverse over a small pit and EF Junction would be only 300 feet away.

Jim moved to Emily's side as the litter was disconnected from the haul system. Although she assured him she was OK, Jim could tell that she was in a lot of pain and needed to get out of the litter soon.

As they rounded the final corner to EF junction, they saw a small first-aid kit wrapped in white plastic lying on top of a rock. The supplies were stacked off to one side. Fifteen gallons of desperately needed water and over forty meal packets were piled in the corridor. The rescue team put Emily down in a large flat area and helped free her from the straps and webbing of the litter. Food and water were handed around. There was more than enough.

Dave Belski connected the phone to the pair of wires running down the passage and was soon talking to someone at the entrance. At the command center, Steve wanted to know if the underground team planned to stay at EF Junction for the night.

Jim considered the obstacles they would meet in the Rift. His team still had a few good hours left in them, but the trip through the Rift would be grueling, with three pits to cross, one short crawlway, a long corridor, another pit, and 300 feet of narrow fissure passage. The first pit had been rigged, but they would need the equipment from the Great White Way to rig the others. The entire route through the Rift was relatively narrow with rocky floors. Once they started, there would be no stopping until Emily was all the way through. It could take as long as six hours, longer if there were problems.

Jim, Don, Steve Mosberg, and Dave Shurtz talked with Emily. Her leg was still throbbing from the strain of the haul up the Great White Way, and she was extremely tired. They decided to camp for the night.

While the leaders planned for the next day, Pat walked over to Emily and sat down next to her. She handed Emily a newspaper that had just been brought down from the surface. Emily was astonished as she read the front page headlines of the El Paso Times: "Injured Woman Stranded In Cave." When she realized that her rescue had become a national media event, she was embarrassed.

"What if I only sprained something?"

Pat laughed. "So what? You can't get out on your own. Nobody cares whether your leg is broken or not. We're all here to help."

Rick Bridges was unhappy when the word came from below. He was hoping that the rescue team would get to C-61 ahead of schedule. "Who told them to stop?" he asked Steve.

"It was Emily's decision," Greg said. "Emily, Dr. Mosberg, Jim, and Dave discussed the options and decided to stay at EF Junction."

Phil Koepp was pleased by the news. So far they had been reacting to events as they occurred. They would hear about a problem and then they would send a team out to fix it. But now with the fresh teams of cavers arriving from all over the Southwest, they could prepare the way ahead of Emily.

Phil looked at the tactical map on the wall of the command post. EF Junction was near the center of the map; Emily was almost halfway to the surface. A blue push-pin showed where the rescue team was spending the night.

"Yes," Phil said. By tomorrow they would be more than halfway out.

❧   ❧   ❧

In the cave, Dan Legnini was sweating heavily, but he was glad to be underground. Shuffling papers on the surface had been driving him crazy. Now he was in the Rift doing something he was truly good at: technical ropework.

It was his job to have the entire Rift rigged before morning, when Emily would start moving again. Three pits, spaced only fifty feet apart, lay before him. Dan looked down the first. Smooth, featureless walls dropped into the lower Rift, a hundred feet below. His headlamp was not strong enough to illuminate the bottom.

Dan's teams had carried in as much rope as possible, but it was clear that it was not enough. They would have to disassemble the haul systems at the Great White Way and move the rope and equipment into the Rift. After sending a team to begin the de-rigging process, Dan turned his attention to the pits. Tyrolean traverses would be the name of the game here. First they would rig a single rope across the pit, then hang two pulleys from the rope. The litter would be attached to the pulleys and secured with a belay line. Then a haul-line would be attached to the litter. Emily and her attendant would be pulled across the pit by a team on the far side.

Each traverse would take several hours to set up. Dan appointed Steve Attaway and Steve Sontag to head the teams working on the first two pits, while he focused on the third. As members of the de-rigging team came back with ropes, pulleys, and carabiners, Dan directed them to the team that most needed the supplies. The corridor was noisy now with a dozen rescuers placing anchors and stringing ropes.

At last they were almost ready. There were only five of them left standing now. The others had long since run out of steam and turned in for some sleep. The ropes were secured and the anchors were checked. By all appearances the rigging was complete. But Dan was not done until each tyrolean was tested.

"A volunteer?" Dan asked.

John stepped forward.

"Mark, run the belay," Dan said. "Bob, take the haul line."

John clipped his seat harness onto the pulleys of the tyrolean.

"Ready."

The main line drooped under the load. The pulleys creaked forward, taking John out over the pit, his feet dangling in space.

"Haul slow," Dan said.

The haul team pulled in the rope a few inches at a time, moving their live cargo across the void below. The anchors shifted in place slightly, adjusting to the tension in the rope. Now they were all wide awake despite the late hour. John's feet touched the other side and he scrambled up the rocks to a flat spot away from the edge of the pit.

"Belay off."

Dan stood to one side examining the ropes and webbing.

"We can make it better," he said. "If we move this anchor over just a little, then the haul line won't rub against the wall."

They moved the anchor and repeated the experiment with Dave, the heaviest caver among them. As predicted, the tyrolean worked more smoothly now.

"OK guys, let's test the next one," Dan said.

Dan was determined that when Emily crossed these pits, there would be no malfunctions to slow them down.

⚜   ⚜   ⚜

It was now Wednesday morning. The rescue had been in progress for three days. The command staff gathered in the Fire Station for the first of two daily general briefings.

"Good morning, and welcome to the 0600 hour general briefing for the Davis Mobley incident. My name is P. J.

Pearson. I'm the plans section chief and I'll be conducting this morning's briefing. Does everyone have a copy of the incident action plan for this operational period? OK. Operations?"

Operations Chief Steve Swanke stood and walked to the tactical map in the front of the room.

"Emily is now here at EF Junction," Steve said. "The rescue team is scheduled to start waking up at 0700 hours. Emily has agreed to an in-cave interview with the press via the field phones, and that has been scheduled for 0830.

"Immediately after the interview they'll start down the Rift. The goal for today is Glacier Bay, marked on this map with a brass thumbtack. A line drawing of the cave is included on the last page of the packets you all have. Last night we had teams rig the traverses in the Rift, and the word this morning is that all rigging is in place and has been fully tested. Another team was sent in yesterday afternoon to enlarge the keyhole in the Rift. That task has also been completed.

"Emily is currently scheduled to be out of the cave at approximately noon tomorrow. Please note! If things go well in the Rift today, the rescue team may arrive at Glacier Bay early. If that happens, they may decide to go for the surface tonight. Everyone please let your people know that they may need to extend their shift through the night if this happens. Any questions?"

"Thanks, Steve," P. J. said. "Tim, tell us about logistics."

Tim Stubbs was standing in the back of the room.

"As you can see on the first page of your handout," he said. "I've staffed most of the positions in logistics. Boomer has done an excellent job with his electronics wizardry. Now we have a phone patch at the cave entrance connecting the field phones in the cave to the park radio frequencies. He's also wired another phone patch here at the communications base between the park radio and regular phone lines. The doctor in the cave can now talk directly to any hospital that has a telephone. This system will be used for the press telephone interview with Emily later this morning.

"We now have over five thousand feet of rope in the cave. Another three thousand feet should be arriving by overnight courier sometime this morning. We also have another three hundred carabiners on order; I haven't checked to see exactly when they're arriving, but it should be sometime today. If there's anything else you guys need just let us know and we'll get it for you."

P. J. took the floor again, this time to report on the Plans Section. He described the status of food and water caches in the cave, personnel, and plans for demobilization. Then he turned the floor over to the deputy incident commander.

Dwayne Alire rose from his chair and addressed the group. "Yesterday it was suggested to me by Erin, our public information officer, that the press would like a live interview with Emily. Boomer managed to make this possible with his electronics expertise. Last night we sent Emily a list of questions that the press came up with, and she agreed to the interview this morning provided nothing is asked that was not on the list. The interview should last about five minutes.

"Immediately afterwards we'll have a press briefing here inside the maintenance yard, just outside this door. Please remember who these guys are. Watch what you say. We would like to see that the press receives complete and accurate information from us rather than overheard tidbits taken out of context. If a member of the press approaches you, you can talk about what you're doing and how you're involved with the rescue, but please don't speculate about how Emily is doing, when she will be out, etc."

Finally the floor was turned over to the Incident Commander, Phil Koepp.

"I'd just like everyone to remind their teams to keep safety in mind. As Emily gets close to the entrance there'll

PETER AND ANN BOSTED
Using a tyrolean traverse to move Emily over a pit in the Rift.

be a lot of excitement. I'd just encourage all of you to keep safety a high priority. We don't want to mar our excellent record with any accidents. We already had one minor incident with an out-of-control rappel. That caver received some rope burns on his hands. So please be safety conscious.

"I would also like to thank you and all of your people for an incredible effort. Everything is going well. Remember we have a lot of hard-working cavers underground. Let's do our best to support their efforts."

In the cave, the rescue team was ready to start moving Emily again. Don Coons assembled the crew and outlined the plans for the morning. "Any questions?" he said as he finished.

The room was silent. They all knew their jobs and were ready to get started, even though the fatigue of the last two days was starting to show.

"OK, let's go!" Don said.

They picked up their gear and took their places around Emily, who was already strapped into the litter. Lifting her once again, they continued the slow process of passing the litter down the passage. The Rift was only a few hundred feet ahead of them and it was one of the biggest challenges they would have to overcome. Crossing the first three pits would be only the beginning.

It took thirty minutes to reach the top of Captain Hook's Ladder. They began by connecting Emily to the two pulleys that rode along the first tyrolean traverse line. Three more ropes – a belay line, a haul line, and a brake line – were connected to the litter. The well-rehearsed team took only minutes to prepare for the traverse. Soon, Emily and Don were being towed across the chasm. As they reached the other side, they were pulled up and onto a large flat rock. The traverse itself had taken only ten minutes.

The rescuers were on a roll now. Leaving the litter in place, they transferred the control lines and pulleys to the next traverse rope. The next two pits, Freakout and the adjacent, unnamed one, had been rigged as one long 200-foot Tyrolean. Again the haulers and belayers took their positions and again Emily and Don were drawn over the pit. The ropes stretched and creaked as Emily, litter, and Don reached the halfway point. The team on the far side continued their repetitious refrain of "Haul . . . set . . . slack." Emily soon reached the far side of the third pit and was lifted to the safety of the cavern floor.

Jim Goodbar looked at his watch. He was surprised to find that it had taken only three hours to cross three of the most treacherous obstacles in the entire rescue operation. The rigging elves of the previous night had provided rope systems that worked without a hitch.

The thrill of success surged through the rescue team. They sped Emily several hundred feet down the corridor, pausing only after reaching the DC-10 crawlway. The elves

Emily being carried through the gypsum blocks of Glacier Bay.

had been here too; they had removed the loose rocks on the floor of the belly crawl, to make it possible for the cavers to kneel upright in the smooth-walled tube. A turn to the right, a turn to the left, and Emily was through. The team moved rapidly down the passage; cavers at the end of the procession struggled to keep up.

The rescue crew finally slowed as they approached the last 300 feet of the Rift. The spacious corridor ended abruptly and funneled into an eighteen-inch-wide fissure.

Don had already thought out this part. He ordered everyone into the fissure. They lay on their backs, touching head
to toe, forming a human chain through the narrowest part
of the crevice. The litter was passed over them from hand
to hand until it reached the final tight spot.

But the keyhole was gone. It had been enlarged during the night so the litter containing Emily passed through
without a pause. As they turned the corner, survey station
C-61 – the end of the Rift – came into view. So did several
ten-gallon water bottles and dozens of food packs stacked
on the floor.

Emily's caravan paused only briefly at C-61. The
freshest cavers took over the task of moving the litter while
the others stayed for a short lunch break. The corridors
were now spacious and the passages comfortably large all
along the route to Glacier Bay. When the team reached the
large, flat floor of Glacier Bay, Don ordered them to stop.
They had reached their destination for the day.

⚜   ⚜   ⚜

On the surface, Steve Reames moved the blue pin on
the tactical map to Glacier Bay, right next to the brass
thumbtack that marked the day's destination. With a red
felt pen, he wrote 4:15 p.m. next to the blue pin. They had
reached their goal in only seven hours rather than the
expected ten.

"Are they going to continue?" Greg asked.

"We don't know yet. They're still trying to decide,"
Steve said. "My guess is that they'll spend the night in
Glacier Bay."

"I'm not so sure," Greg said. "They must be feeling
an incredible amount of entrance fever. If I was them, I'd
keep working through the night just to get it over with."

"That's true," Steve said. "If the cave is breathing
in, they should be able to smell the fresh air from the base
of Boulder Falls. But they must be exhausted after three
days underground."

"Entrance fever does strange things to people."

There was the sound of excitement inside the communications room. Bridges, Swanke, and Koepp came out with smiles on their faces.

"They're going to go for it," Rick said. "Emily is coming out tonight."

There was now just one major obstacle left. Although they had already carried Emily through 6,000 feet of rugged cave passage, the 150-foot ascent up Boulder Falls would be the most difficult challenge yet. Don and Emily were particularly apprehensive about being hauled up the vertical shaft. They had spent more than an hour stuck in the Great White Way after the haul system jammed. But the Great White Way was a friendly place compared to Boulder Falls. It was not as steep and it had several ledges to work from if a problem occurred. If the haul system malfunctioned in Boulder Falls, they would be hanging free in the middle of the huge pit.

The cavers set the litter down at the foot of the steep debris slope leading up to Boulder Falls. The passage was crowded with even more cavers sent in from the surface to help with the final haul.

"What's the plan?" Don said to Mark Minton who was working on the rigging.

"The pit was rigged two days ago, so we've had plenty of time to test everything. We're all ready. The plan is to haul Emily up the debris slope and then up the vertical part of Boulder Falls in one long pull."

Don surveyed the situation. "Considering that we will be hanging free for 150 feet, I think we need three ropes," he said. "One for the litter, one to belay Emily, and one to belay me."

Mark climbed back up the slope and returned a few minutes later with three ropes in hand. He connected one to the litter. Don and Emily tied into the other two. Mark and Don then carefully checked all the ropes, straps, and connections.

"OK, we're ready," Mark shouted up the debris slope. The message was radioed to the top of Boulder Falls by walkie-talkie.

The haul team at the top of Boulder Falls began pulling. The ropes tightened and the litter lurched slowly up the steep debris slope with Don walking along to stand guard over Emily. The ropes could easily dislodge a rock from the top of Boulder Falls and Emily was in an extremely vulnerable position on her back in the litter.

When the litter reached the top of the debris slope, it was hoisted until it stood upright. Then Don and Emily were slowly lifted off the floor. Don hung next to the litter, his feet pushing against the wall to keep the litter from banging into the rocks at the base of the pit. Soon Don and Emily cleared the wall and were dangling free in the immense shaft. As the litter was pulled higher, Emily looked down at the sea of anxious faces and realized that she was leaving part of her team behind.

"Thanks everyone." she shouted down. "I love you all." The rescuers burst into a round of applause and cheers.

The ascent was slow and tedious. Each pull of the rope took them six feet higher. When they reached the top thirty minutes later, a new team of fresh litter-bearers took over the job of carrying Emily. The old team had spent four days learning the delicate task of maneuvering the litter through the passages. Emily had grown accustomed to the pattern and rhythm of their movements. The new team and the awkward movements of the litter made Emily nervous, but they were now only a short distance from the entrance.

⚜   ⚜   ⚜

Four hours later, the wind whistled past Emily as she was slowly inched up through the culvert. She could smell the sweet scents of the desert as she passed the iron gate marking the inner entrance to Lechuguilla. Behind her, cavers began flowing out of the culvert like genies from a bottle.

PETER AND ANN BOSTED
Emily being passed through the Rift.

They handed Emily up the short climb just beyond the entrance gate. She came out of the tunnel and stared up the entrance pit into a canopy of stars. From the base of the pit, she could feel the chill of the night air. The warm glow of moonlight silhouetted the familiar oak trees that stood guard around the edge of the pit.

The cavers wasted no time connecting Emily to the final haul system. Don clipped his harness to the large steel carabiner on his belay line and shouted to the surface, "Up slow."

At the top of the pit, the haulmaster called out his now-familiar tune: "Haul . . . set . . . slack." The ropes tightened and the litter was lifted slowly from the soft dirt floor of the entrance chamber. Suddenly, as if the sun itself had been turned on, the surface and everyone on it was bathed with intense halogen light. The TV crews had arrived. This was the moment that television viewers across the country had been waiting four days to see.

The base of the entrance pit was full of cavers now; every face looking up as Don and Emily ascended slowly toward the end of their journey.

"Haul . . . set . . . slack."

"Haul . . . set . . . slack."

"Haul . . . stop! I've got it!"

The metal frame of the litter reached the top of the pit. Emily was pulled up and away as the haulmaster released the attached ropes.

"Belay off."

Jim attached his ascenders to the static rope hanging down one wall of the pit. With a final surge of energy he climbed to the surface, disconnected his harness, and went over to where Emily was sitting up in the litter. She was smiling.

The radio operator keyed the transmitter and sent a simple message: "She's out."

A voice crackled from the receiver. "Good job."

A fresh team took Emily the remaining mile to the waiting ambulance. Several of the cavers who had just

Emily waves goodbye as she is raised up Boulder Falls.

come out of the cave walked along with Emily and her new litter-bearers.

Jim Goodbar and Don Coons stood and waved as Emily and her entourage moved briskly down the hillside.

"We did it!" Jim shouted as he gave Don a hug.

Don lifted the smaller Jim from his feet and spun him wildly about. They stumbled and fell, laughing.

At the hospital, they found that Emily's leg was indeed broken. She had surgery the next day. She hobbled about on crutches for a while, but was soon back caving, as enthusiastic as ever.

⇒ 18 ⇐

THE END OF AN ERA

Pat Kambesis sat on the stone steps of the cabin door watching the sun set over the stark desert hills to the west. She had just finished a long trip into the Western Borehole and was enjoying a relaxing evening lounging around the cabins. Her thoughts were interrupted by a familiar voice.

"Hey Pat, would you meet me in my office?" She turned and saw Ron Kerbo standing in the cabin door.

Kerbo and Pat were old friends and it was not uncommon for Ron to invite her to his office to chat about caves and expeditions. But this time there was something formal in the tone of his voice.

As Pat trudged up the stone path to the cave specialist's office, she had an uneasy feeling in the pit of her stomach. She had a good idea what the meeting was about. During the first year of exploration, LCP had faithfully delivered copies of the survey notes to the park after every expedition. But for more than a year no survey notes had been delivered. As she opened the door to his office she braced herself for the inevitable questions.

"Have a seat." Kerbo cleared some papers from his desk.

"I wanted to talk to you about the survey notes," he continued. "You know that we still haven't gotten copies of any of the survey notes from the last five expeditions."

"Yes, I know," Pat said. "I've talked to the board about it and they have some concerns about the security of the data. They're afraid that with the Freedom Of Information Act . . ."

Kerbo interrupted her. "Look, you guys signed a Memorandum of Understanding and it says that you will turn over all the notes from your expeditions. The park needs the all data you collect to properly manage Lechuguilla."

Pat knew that LCP was obligated to turn over the survey data from expeditions, but she was in a tough position. She knew that the members of the board felt that they had already delivered enough information and they had no intention of turning the notes over to the park.

"I don't want to pressure you, but this is an important issue to us. If LCP has concerns about security, then we'd be glad to talk about them, but first we need to get copies of the survey notes."

"I'll talk to the board and explain the park's position. I'm sure they'll understand."

The survey notes were not the only problem facing the project. Some of the rank and file members of LCP were beginning to complain again about the way the project was being run. The individual cavers who did all the exploration and surveying were gradually feeling more and more alienated. To begin with, Rick had decided to move the project headquarters to his house in Carlsbad. This meant that if you wanted something as simple as a computer printout or to look through the survey notes, you had to drive fifty miles round trip into town.

At the same time, Rick was beginning to focus his energy on other projects. Because of the success of LCP, he was getting lots of attention from the media. He had been on a PBS television special, he was invited on a U.S. caving delegation to Russia, and he went to Alaska on an expedition to find the deepest caves in the United States. LCP was so successful that he was even trying to expand the project to include other National Park caves around the country. All these distractions gave Rick little time to deal with the day-to-day details of LCP. Even something as important as negotiating a Memorandum of Understanding with the park was delegated to other board members.

Pat was one of the few people on the board who paid attention to the problems of the expedition cavers. As a result, it was no surprise that people came to her with their concerns. As the complaints grew to a crescendo, Pat finally decided she had to bring them to the attention of the rest of the board.

People often underestimated Pat. She was small, almost petite, with dark hair, a soft, round face, and child-like features. Her physical size was perfect for caving and she could squeeze down the tightest passages with ease. Many a macho male caver was left eating her dust as she scurried away down a tight, seemingly impenetrable crawlway. Most of all, Pat was fun to cave with. She had a mischievous giggle and she always knew how to enjoy herself.

What most people could not see was that underneath was a smart and serious caver. Her political skills were formidable and she could see through complicated issues that confounded most people. She had a habit of asking just the right "innocent" question that cut to the heart of an issue.

Pat was not looking forward to the next LCP board meeting. Board Meetings were always long, drawn-out affairs that started early in the morning and dragged on late into the night. With the park demanding the survey notes, and the complaints from the cavers, it was certain to be a very contentious meeting.

Over time, the LCP board members had gradually scattered across the country. John Patterson was still in

Denver, but Rick had moved to Carlsbad to be close to the caves, and Pat was now living in Atlanta. In 1989, four new members were added to the board to give the project better regional representation and to bring in people with special skills. Buddy Lane, an old friend of Rick's from Tennessee, was added to give eastern representation. Miles Hecker, a teacher from Wyoming, was chosen to represent the Rocky Mountain states, and Garry Petrie, who was now living in Oregon, was added for his computer skills. Finally, Kiym Cunningham, a geologist from Denver, was recruited to oversee scientific projects.

Carlsbad, New Mexico, is a small oasis in the middle of the dusty desert landscape. The Pecos River provides just enough water to green up a few lawns and fill a few swimming pools. But surrounded by desert, Carlsbad still has a dry and desolate feel. Rick now lived in a small house on the south side of town.

LCP board meetings were usually scheduled during expeditions because most of the directors were already caving in the park. Rick's house was the logical place for the meetings. It was close to the park and yet isolated from the hustle and bustle of the cabins. Most importantly, the survey notes, the computer, and all the corporate documents were at hand.

At nine in the morning on August 7, 1990, cavers began to arrive at Rick's house in Carlsbad. Early arrivals found seats around the living room, while a few stragglers stood in the doorways, holding cups of steaming coffee, trying to revive themselves after many days underground. Rick called the meeting to order and began with a series of minor issues.

During a pause in the business, Pat raised her hand.

"Rick, I've got several topics that need to be addressed."

Rick looked at her coldly. "Okay, go ahead."

"I've been hearing lots of complaints from people on the expeditions. I think we need to talk about them."

"What kind of complaints?" Buddy asked.

"Well, first of all, everyone is upset that the computer and survey notes are no longer kept in the cabins."

"Yes." Garry said.

Miles was nodding in agreement.

"And," Pat continued, "they want more of a say in how the expeditions are run."

"If everyone is so dissatisfied with LCP, how come I don't hear any complaints?" Rick said. "Who are these people?"

Pat was on the spot. She did not want to reveal the names of the people who had told her their concerns in confidence.

"It's probably just the usual clowns and misfits," Rick continued. "What have they got to complain about anyway? They have the privilege of getting to explore the most spectacular caving discovery of the century. If they don't like the way the project is being run, they shouldn't participate. We have plenty of other people who would gladly take their place."

There were a few more comments, but the board members were unwilling to challenge Rick's opinion, and Pat could see that it was pointless to argue. "Well," she said, "if we aren't going to resolve that issue, maybe we should move on to the next topic."

She paused until she had the attention of the rest of the board members. "On the last expedition, Ron Kerbo called me into his office. He was very upset that we haven't given him copies of the latest survey notes."

Rick stood up and looked around the room. "We've talked about this before. There's nothing that requires us to give them the survey notes."

"I thought we signed a Memorandum of Understanding with the park that says we do," Pat replied.

"That isn't what the MOU says," Rick countered.

"Well, let's look at it and see what it says." Pat shuffled through the stack of papers in her lap and began to read:

Copies of all maps, reports, and publications, and other supporting documentation produced or obtained by the project as
a result of its research and/or interpretive activities and expeditions under this agreement, which copies will be provided
free of charge to the United States.

"See, it doesn't say anything about the survey notes,"
Rick said triumphantly.

"What do you think the phrase 'supporting documentation' means?" Pat said, rolling her eyes in disbelief.
"Don't you think survey notes are supporting documentation?"

"You guys negotiated that MOU without my approval, I
didn't even get to read it before it was signed so I don't consider it valid. Anyway, I know something about contracts,
and this memorandum is too vague to stand up in court,"
Rick insisted.

Pat looked around the room. Everyone was nodding
in agreement.

Garry Petrie stood up. "I think it would be dangerous
to give the data to the park. All government agencies are
under the Freedom of Information Act. That means that
anyone could go to the park and get copies. Besides, we've
already given them line plots and maps of the cave. Why do
they need the survey data?"

Rick looked more confident now. "The survey notes
are the corporate property of the Lechuguilla Cave Project.
We did all the work to gather them and we own the copyright." Rick paused to make sure everyone was with him.

"The park service doesn't appreciate how much
money it costs to run this project. We have to buy ropes,
survey gear, and computer equipment. If we turn the notes
over to the park service, they could sell or even give away
our data and then we'd lose a potential source of income."

Pat made one last try. "If we don't give them the
notes, they could cancel our MOU and we'd lose access to
the cave."

Rick smiled. "Pat's just being naive. They'd never
cancel our MOU. Look, we gave them fifty miles of cave on

a platter. We made them famous. They won't kill the goose that laid the golden egg. Besides, with all the pressure from the Carlsbad business community to commercialize the cave, they wouldn't dare risk a confrontation with us."

Pat felt frustrated as Rick went on to other topics. She knew that the park was not going to let the issue drop; the survey notes were just too important to their management plans.

The survey notes had gradually become very important to everyone involved with Lechuguilla. They were important to the explorers because they showed where all the unchecked leads were and they were often the key to making the next big discovery. They were important to the project because of their money-making potential. The survey notes could be used to make maps of the cave, and maps could be sold to park visitors and cavers around the country. Also, every magazine and newspaper that published an article on Lechuguilla needed a map to show the size and shape of the cave. The project could charge a hefty fee for that privilege. Finally, the notes were essential to the park service. They showed where the cave went, whether it was heading outside the park, and where other entrances might be. All this was crucial information for managing and protecting the cave.

Pat was the head cartographer for the Lechuguilla Cave Project and this put her square in the middle of the controversy. Her job was to make maps from the survey notes. With over fifty miles of cave passage, there were thousands of pages of survey measurements and sketches. All these mud-stained packets of paper had to be organized, pieced together, and re-drawn into finished maps. It was a big job, so Pat had a team of a dozen cartographers working with her. To make things easier, they had divided the cave into rectangular sections called quads. Each quad was assigned to a different person. As head cartographer, Pat had all the original survey notes at her house in Atlanta. After each expedition, she would organize all the new notes, make copies, and send them out to the people working on the quad maps.

In the months following the board meeting, tension in the project over the survey notes began to rise. One evening, Pat was sitting at home in Atlanta when the phone rang. It was Garry.

"I thought you ought to know what's been happening on the board."

"What do you mean?"

"Rick's been calling each board member and trying to convince them that you can't be trusted."

"What's he been saying?"

"He's upset that you've been talking to the park. He claims that you've been going behind our backs."

"Ron and I are old friends and I talk to him all the time. Besides, the park is very upset that we won't turn over the notes."

"Rick has convinced the rest of the board that you're a threat to the project. He's got some idea that you're going to turn over the notes to the park. He's even been saying that you're going to make maps of Lechuguilla and sell them."

"What's he going to do?"

"He's out to get you. He's trying to convince everyone that you shouldn't be on the board. Be careful, Pat."

Within a week Pat received another phone call. This time it was Anne Strait, Rick's girlfriend.

"Rick wants you to bring all the original survey notes to the park on the next expedition."

"Why?"

"Some of the copies we have are unreadable, and Rick wants to make new copies."

"I need all those notes to work on the quad maps. Why don't you tell me which copies are unreadable, and I'll make you new ones?"

"No, Rick wants you to bring all the notes. We just need them for a few days to make copies. You'll get them back at the end of the expedition."

Pat suspected that Rick had another reason for requesting all the original data. She also suspected that once she took the notes to the expedition, she would never see them again. As a hedge, she quietly made a complete copy of all the notes. Sure enough, at the next expedition, Rick convinced the board that the survey notes should be kept at his house in Carlsbad.

In 1991, the political landscape at Carlsbad Caverns National Park began to change. In January, Ron Kerbo was promoted to regional cave specialist. The project's refusal to turn over the survey notes had left a bitter taste in Ron's mouth, and he took that bitter taste with him to his new home at the regional office in Santa Fe. In spite of his growing disillusionment with the project, the loss of Ron Kerbo as cave specialist at the park was a major blow to LCP. Even though he was a park service employee, Ron was a caver at heart and he understood and tolerated the eccentricities of LCP. His replacements were not so tolerant and understanding.

Soon after Ron's departure, David Ek was named as his temporary replacement. He immediately called Rick into his office and demanded that the project hand over copies of the notes. Rick complained that photocopying hundreds of pages of survey notes would be too expensive. When Ek offered to pay for the photocopying, Rick demanded that everything be put in writing. All the pieces were in place for a major confrontation between the park service and LCP. The next board meeting was shaping up to be a pivotal event. It was scheduled to take place in Denver in May, 1991.

The weather was cool and rainy when Pat arrived in Denver. Larry Fish, an old friend, picked her up at the airport and together they drove across town, splashing down streets still slushy from the last big snow storm. Larry was a programmer in his early forties and they had become good friends when Pat lived in Denver. Even after she moved to Atlanta, they often chatted on the phone about caving adventures, gossip, and the inevitable politics that surrounded the sport.

"Hey, isn't that Bill's house?" Pat said as she pointed at a red brick house on the corner. "Let's stop and visit."

They quickly turned down a side street and skidded to a halt. The house was on a busy one-way street and they turned to watch the traffic whizzing by as they walked up the steps and rang the door bell. The thick wooden door opened suddenly and a smiling face appeared behind the screen.

"Pat! Great to see you! Come on in."

Bill Yett escorted them down a dark hallway to the kitchen.

"I knew you'd be in town for the board meeting and I was hoping you'd stop by," he said as he motioned toward the kitchen door. "We have lots of things to talk about."

Pat Jablonsky was sitting at the kitchen table sipping coffee.

"Hey Pat, look who's here. It's Pat," Bill said chuckling to himself. For some reason, Colorado had a surplus of cavers named Pat. It was an endless source of amusement and confusion for everyone. Pat Jablonsky looked up from the table and smiled.

Bill Yett and Pat Jablonsky's house was a favorite hangout for cavers in Denver. They always had a pot of chili cooking on the stove, and cavers stayed into the late night hours to talk of new discoveries and cave politics.

"So you're here for the board meeting," Bill said.

"Yeah, fun way to spend a weekend," Pat joked.

"I hear Rick and the rest of the board are already in town having dinner."

"They're all probably bad-mouthing me right now."

"Actually, I've heard something else through the grapevine," Bill said. "A friend of mine overheard some of the board members talking. They're planning to vote you off the project at this meeting."

The realization that Rick was actually plotting to remove her from the board hit Pat hard. She did not sleep well that night. The next morning was cool and rainy, and the dark skies added to her somber mood. John Patterson picked her up early and they headed for the meeting. It was scheduled to take place at the Federal Center, a U.S. Government installation across town. Kiym Cunningham worked as a geologist there and had reserved a room for the meeting.

As they drove up to the gate, a military policeman stepped out of the guard house and motioned for them to stop. He walked slowly around the car, peering into each window, scanning the interior. As he reached the driver's side, John rolled down the car window.

The M. P. stared intently at John. "What is your business here?" he said.

"We're going to a meeting in building forty-seven," John replied.

"Could I see some identification please."

He took their drivers licenses and disappeared back into the guard house. A minute later he returned with two visitor's badges.

"You must wear these at all times," he said as he motioned them through the gate. The Gulf War was winding to a close, and the government was still concerned about terrorist attacks. All federal installations were under very tight security. The security check only added to Pat's sense of foreboding.

The meeting was held in a large conference room. Kiym unlocked the door and the board members filed inside and took seats around a big square table. Rick stood up and called the meeting to order. They began to work their way through a long list of mundane items. Eventually, they came to the first hot topic: the survey notes. Despite increasing pressure from the park, the project still had not turned over the notes. The board members began rehashing the same old issues: "Will our copyright be protected?" "Will the park sell our data to magazines?" "Is the MOU valid?"

This time Rick had a new argument. He stood up and faced the group. "Look, you guys," he said, "even if we do turn over the notes, we should use them as a bargaining chip. You know I wanted to get volunteer status for LCP when we negotiated the MOU. Since you guys blew the negotiations and left it out, this is a great opportunity to get volunteer status. Otherwise, we'll have to wait five years until the MOU expires.

"What do you mean 'volunteer status'?" Pat said.

"It's a special designation that the superintendent can grant to any group doing work in the park. It's an honor, and it also gives everyone Workman's Compensation. That way if any of us are injured while working in the cave, the government will pay for medical expenses and lost wages. It would also mean the park would have to pay for ropes and equipment."

Rick's new argument impressed the board members. They decided to continue withholding the data while pressing their demands. Rick volunteered to talk to the park superintendent and explain their position.

Now came the item of business that Pat was dreading. Rick stood up again. "It's time to re-elect officers."

The room was suddenly quiet. Pat braced herself for the attack she sensed was coming. Her attention was focused on Rick. She was expecting him to begin reciting a long list of her transgressions against LCP, but Rick would not look at her. Instead, he was staring intently at the group. His eyes shifted from person to person as he tried catch someone's attention. Pat looked around the room. The other board members were fidgeting nervously in their seats, staring at the floor or the table, avoiding Rick's gaze.

A few moments passed in total silence, then Pat felt a wave of relief sweep over her. It was obvious that whatever conspiracy Rick had cooked up was not working. The other board members just would not go along with a plan to expel her from the project. In a few minutes all the board members were unanimously re-elected to another term in office.

The park service responded quickly to the board's decision to press for volunteer status while still withholding the notes. In June, the park hired Dale Pate as the permanent replacement for Ron Kerbo. Dale was a longtime Texas caver. He had spent many years exploring caves in Mexico. Working in these large Mexican cave systems requires a high degree of coordination and teamwork. He expected trust and cooperation from cavers and he did not like LCP's confrontational attitude. In addition, Ron Kerbo had warned Dale about the problems with the project. Dale was not sympathetic to the demands of LCP.

Soon after he was hired, Dale began to increase the pressure on the project. He and the park superintendent, Wallace Elms, composed another letter requesting the survey notes. They rejected the project's arguments by saying:

> As managers of the 76 known caves located within the boundaries of Carlsbad Caverns National Park, computerizing the survey and inventory data for these caves is a high priority. Having this, and other such information about the caves that we manage, is the primary reason we issue caving permits to caves which are not open to recreational caving.

The strains within the project continued to grow over the summer. With the pressure from the park, Rick became even more protective of the survey notes. There were so many complaints that when the August expedition rolled around, Garry Petrie decide to bring his own copy of the notes. He left them in the hut so that everyone could use them, but they mysteriously disappeared from the cabin and were never seen again. Now, except for Pat's secret copies, Rick had the only set of notes for Lechuguilla Cave.

In the middle of all the turmoil, Pat got another invitation to meet with park management. She was in the park for an expedition when Dale Pate dropped by the cabins.

"Hey Pat, Wally would like to meet with you while you're here."

"Wally who?" she thought. Suddenly she realized who Dale was talking about. "You mean Wallace Elms, the park superintendent?"

"Yes," Dale replied.

Pat knew the meeting would be important, so she invited Pat Seiser, Don Coons, and Carol Vesely along for moral support. They would also make good witnesses in case Rick once again accused her of undermining the project.

A few days later, Pat and her friends walked into the administration building of Carlsbad Caverns National Park. The secretary escorted them into a large conference room. The room was a distinct contrast to the dusty, converted offices of the cave specialist. It was beautifully decorated in a Southwestern motif with large white-washed walls set off by thick wooden beams. Maps of the park and the caves were neatly arranged on the walls. At one end of the room was a large group of windows with a scenic view overlooking the main entrance to Carlsbad Cavern.

A few minutes later, the superintendent walked in. He was wearing his park service uniform, and he greeted them formally by shaking hands with each one of them. He motioned for them to find seats around the large conference table in the center of the room.

Pat was expecting a serious, possibly contentious conversation, but Elms was friendly, almost apologetic as he began.

"Pat, before I say anything else, I just want to make sure that the cavers don't get the wrong impression. We really appreciate the work that the project has done for us. You guys have done a great job and we really want to continue working with you. But you have to understand, we've got to have those notes. There's just got to be some way we can get the information we need, and still have a good relationship."

"I've tried to tell the board how important this information is to you, but they don't seem to understand," Pat said.

"I'm very surprised that the board doesn't understand my position," Elms said. "This park belongs to the

people of the United States. I'm the manager of this park
and it's my job to protect the caves and land for the people.
We're stewards of this land."

"I know," Pat said. "A lot of people in the project are
frustrated with the board's position."

"You mean the cavers don't support the board? I
thought the board was supposed to represent the people
working in the project."

"Most of the cavers I know think LCP should be
cooperating with the park and should turn over the notes,"
Pat said. Don and Carol nodded in agreement.

"Look, if we're forced to take drastic measures we'll
do it. Please don't make us do that. Please tell everybody
we appreciate what they're doing. But, if we have to get
ugly about it, we will."

Elms politely escorted them to the door and again
shook hands with everyone. The meeting was a real eye-
opener for Don and Carol.

"I hadn't realized how serious this is. They're going
to close the cave if the project doesn't turn over the notes,"
Carol said.

"Yeah, I know!" Pat said. "I've been trying to convince the board that we're in real trouble, but they just
keep blowing me off."

"We've got to do something or all our hard work is
going to go down the drain," Pat Seiser said.

As summer changed to fall, the situation deteriorated
rapidly. The project continued to press its position that the
MOU was vague, that LCP had to have volunteer status,
and the copyrights had to be honored. The park adamantly
refused to negotiate until the data was turned over. In
October, the park took the drastic step of closing the cave:

> . . . until the park receives the required survey data and
> notes, August expedition report, and assurances of continued
> compliance with the terms of the agreement, all surveying
> and exploration trips into Lechuguilla Cave are suspended
> . . . . We are hopeful that these matters will be resolved quickly
> and that operations under our existing Memorandum of

Understanding can be continued. However, we caution that if
they are not resolved within a reasonable length of time, we
will issue a 90-day notice to terminate the agreement.

The park's letter sent shock waves through the Lechuguilla Cave Project and once again Pat's phone began
ringing.

"Hi Pat, this is Kiym. Did you see the letter from the
park?"

"Yeah, I saw it. What do you think about it?"

"We're gonna hang tough on this."

"What do you mean 'hang tough'?"

"We have to stand firm on this. We've got to maintain
a united front. If we let them intimidate us, if we back
down, we're not going to get what we deserve. We're gonna
call their bluff because they wouldn't dare terminate the
MOU."

"Are you kidding?" Pat said. "We can't treat the park
service this way. We need to have a telephone board meeting as soon as possible."

"We don't need a board meeting," Kiym said.

"Yeah, we do! Because we're about to lose it all. Don't
you understand? They're going to terminate the MOU and
we're going to lose everything."

Over the next few days, Pat called each of the board
members and pressed her case for an emergency meeting.
A few days later, they set up a conference call to discuss the
park's letter.

When the discussion started, most of the board members felt that the park was trying to take advantage of
them. Rick summed it up by saying: "The park is trying to
screw us and we've got to take a stand."

Pat knew she had one argument that might work.
"Look, you guys," she began. "No matter what you think
about the National Park Service, you've got to consider the
rest of the people in the project."

"What do you mean?" Buddy said.

"Everyone in the project is pissed at us because we've
cut off their access to the cave. I've talked to these people

and they don't support what we're doing. We don't have their support because we got them kicked out of the cave."

"Well, that was never our intent," Buddy said.

"Maybe Pat's right," Miles said.

"Yeah, this standoff is damaging the project," Garry said.

The arguments went back and forth for a long time, and in the end, Pat prevailed. When they finally called for a vote, Pat, Miles, Buddy, and Garry voted to give the data to the park. Kiym and John abstained, and Rick voted against the idea.

The next day, Pat called the park to let them know the data was coming. Soon afterward, Pat's phone was ringing again. This time it was Garry.

"Rick's at it again. He wants you off the board," Garry said.

"What's the problem this time?" Pat said in disbelief.

"He's upset that you called the park to tell them the data is coming. He says that John Patterson is the secretary and it's John's job to inform the park."

"I have friends in the park," Pat said. "I always talk to the park and I didn't know it was a big secret. Why does he care who tells the park? The important thing is that they're going to get the data."

She paused to think for a moment. "Well I'm tired of this. I'm going to save them the trouble. I'm going to resign."

The next day, on November 15, 1991, Pat Kambesis resigned from the Board of Directors of the Lechuguilla Cave Project. Three weeks later, the survey data was finally delivered to the park. Each page of the notes was rubber-stamped with an LCP copyright notice. In addition, there was a letter demanding certain conditions before the park could accept the data. The conditions included granting volunteer status, supplying ropes for the project, and honoring LCP's copyright. The letter concluded by saying:

> If these points are not agreeable to you, please return all of
> the accompanying data as soon as possible. In such an

eventuality, the LCP is still willing to continue working with the NPS to amicably resolve our mutual problems.

A few days later, Pat called Larry Fish. "Hey Larry, I need to talk to you. I think I might have done something dumb."

"What did you do?" Larry asked.

"I just resigned from LCP."

Larry laughed. "It's about time!"

She filled him in on all the events of the past year.

"What's going to happen now?" Larry asked.

"Well, I don't know," Pat said. "The park is very worried that the cavers are going to react badly to the closing of the cave. They're afraid that after all the work the cavers have done, closing the cave will make them feel unappreciated."

"Everyone I've talked to supports the park and thinks that the LCP board is acting crazy," Larry said.

"Yeah, every day since I resigned, my phone has been ringing off the hook. Everyone I talk to is very upset with the board."

Larry thought for a moment. "You know, the park really needs to know how the cavers feel about this. What if we put together a petition saying that we support the park service? I know a bunch of people would sign it."

Pat quickly agreed, and over the next few weeks they contacted Lechuguilla cavers in Denver, Atlanta, and elsewhere around the country. The key parts of the petition they circulated said:

> We are among those who have mapped sixty miles in Lechuguilla Cave. This letter is an expression of our disappointment with the leadership of the Lechuguilla Cave Project, Inc. It also voices our concern with the state of the relationship between LCPI and Carlsbad Caverns National Park. Because we have no representation on the Board of LCPI, and since the project leadership is not accountable to, and communicative with us, we feel it is time that we speak out on behalf of ourselves.
>
> The fact that we have no voice in the running of the project has always been a sore point among LCP cavers. But we

trusted the intentions and integrity of the Board and believed that they would always strive to do the right thing for the cave, the park, and with respect to us. The Board's actions toward the park during the last few months has badly shaken our confidence in the project. We are dismayed because whether we like it or not, LCPI represents us to the park service and other governmental agencies, to the general public, and to non-LCP cavers. Because of these problems, we urge you to re-evaluate the Memorandum of Understanding with LCPI and suggest that you consider other exploration/survey alternatives.

A few weeks later Pat was again on the phone with Larry.

"I wanted to call you and give you an update on the petition."

"Yes, I was wondering how it's going."

"We've already got more than a hundred signatures."

"That's great."

"Yeah, and I have some other interesting news to tell you," Pat said. "First of all, Miles and Garry have both resigned."

"Wow! That means that three out of seven directors have resigned."

"I also talked to the park. They've spent the last few weeks sorting through all the survey data that LCP gave them. Guess what? The data from the July, 1991, expedition is missing."

Larry laughed. "So they're still holding out data. Boy, that's really dumb."

"There's more. The park is hinting that they have reached the end of their rope with LCP and they're actually going to cancel the MOU."

There was a long pause in the conversation as the impact of canceling the MOU hit home.

Larry finally broke the silence. "What is the park going to do after that?"

"I don't know, but Dale says the park is never going to work with another organization that isn't democratically run."

"What would happen if we put together a new organization and this time did it right?" Larry said.

"Great idea!" Pat said. "You know, it's funny; this cave has had a history of power struggles and political battles. We need to make sure that doesn't happen again."

"You're right. What should we do?"

"Well," Pat said, "for one thing, it should be democratic right from the very beginning."

"Yeah, and there needs to be some kind of regional representation so everyone has a voice in the way the project is being run."

"And a system of checks and balances so no one can subvert the organization."

"How should we start?" Larry asked.

"We've already got more than a hundred people who have signed the petition. They could form the backbone of the organization."

Over the next month, there was a flurry of intense activity among the cavers. They continued to gather more signatures and more support. In just a few short weeks, 120 people had signed the petition. They represented the core of the most active cavers who had worked in the cave. In early March, 1992, the petition was delivered to the park service. At the same time, the cavers formed a committee to create a new organization. Through phone calls, letters, and conversations with cavers around the country, they began hammering out a new constitution. They chose the name Lechuguilla Exploration and Research Network, or LEARN for short. Everyone liked the word "Network." It conveyed the sense of cooperation and democracy that they wanted to instill in the project.

On April 29, 1992, the event everyone was expecting occurred. After several more attempts to get the survey notes for the July expedition, the park mailed the following letter:

Dear Mr. Bridges:

This is to inform you and the other directors that the National Park Service has decided to terminate the

Memorandum of Understanding (MOU) between the NPS and Lechuguilla Cave Project Inc.

The following are some of the factors that influenced our decision. Among these were:

• Lack of timely response to our repeated verbal requests for survey notes and digital survey data which began over a year ago and written requests which began some 10 months ago.

• Resignation of three of the seven members of the LCP's board of directors.

• Lack of a clear indication that the LCPI leadership intends to fully cooperate with the park and other cooperators in all aspects of the management of Lechuguilla Cave and other park caves.

We will be evaluating several alternatives for future exploration and surveying. These will either be directly under NPS supervision with expeditions scaled down in size and scope, or under some other arrangement.

> Sincerely,
> Wallis B. Elms
> Superintendent

Over the spring and summer, the LEARN Organizing Committee worked furiously. They wrote a constitution that was quickly ratified by the 120 signers of the petition. They also started a newsletter and elected regional representatives from all over the United States. Finally, Pat Seiser was selected by the representatives to chair the new organization.

By August, 1992, all the pieces were in place and LEARN submitted a proposal to begin surveying and exploring in Lechuguilla Cave. It was good timing because an oil company was making plans to drill a well just a mile north of the cave. The park service was anxious to push exploration northward to see if the well could endanger any undiscovered passages.

One evening in the late fall, Larry's phone rang. He picked it up and heard Pat's voice at the other end.

"Congratulations!" she said.

"What happened?"

"We did it!"

"We did what?" Larry said. Pat was chuckling as she tantalized him with the big secret.

"I just got a letter from the park and we've been given a permit for four expeditions in 1993."

"Wow!" Larry said.

⇛ 19 ⇚

Bibliography

History

Davis, Donald. "Comments on Lechuguilla Cave, New Mexico." *Rocky Mountain Caving*. Vol. 3, No. 4. Autumn, 1989, p. 17: Report on early history of the cave, including some early Colorado cavers' visits to the cave.

Frank, Edward Forest. "Cave History." *NSS News*. Vol. 46, No. 10. October 1988. National Speleological Society, pp. 378-379: Summary of pre-caver history of the cave, including guano mining claims.

Rhinehart, Rick. "The Underground Hurricane: Digging in Lechuguilla Cave." *Rocky Mountain Caving*. Vol. 3, No. 3. Summer 1986, pp. 38-39: Brief account of the historic CRF digs and the first three digs run by Dave Allured and John Patterson.

The Digs and Breakthrough

Allured. Dave. "Lechuguilla Cave Dig Planned." *Rocky Mountain Caving*. Vol. 2, No. 4. Autumn 1985, p. 3: Announcement for November, 1985, digging trip.

Allured, Dave. "Lechuguilla Cave: A Summary Status Report." *Rocky Mountain Caving*. Vol. 3, No. 4. Autumn, 1989, p. 17 : Report on the May, 1986 breakthrough trip.

Exploration

Allison. Stan. "Breakthrough in the F Survey of Lechuguilla." *Rocky Mountain Caving*. Vol. 5, No. 1. Winter, 1988, pp. 16-17:

360

Personal account of January, 1988, discovery of Lebarge Borehole, Tinsel Town, Land of Awes, Darktown, and the Prickly Ice Cube Room in the Southwest.

Anonymous. "Trip Reports: Lechuguilla Cave." *Southwestern Cavers*. September-October, 1986, pp. 78-79: November 28-30, 1985, digging trip.

Anonymous. "Expedition: August 21-29, 1993." *The Network News*. Vol. 3, No. 1, January 27, 1994. Lechuguilla Exploration and Research Network. pp. 6-8: August, 1993 LEARN expedition, including the Outback and Lake of the White Roses in the Far East, the Jackpot Room, Chandelier Graveyard, and Leaning Tower areas in the West, mop-up in the North Rift, Giant Chiclets Room in the Near East, and survey in the main Rift and Bleeding Hearts area near S&M Crawl.

Belski, Andy. "The Sanitation Expedition: July-August, 1994." *The Network News*. Vol. 3, No. 3, 1994, p. 8. Lechuguilla Exploration and Research Network : July/August, 1994, LEARN expedition, including the North Rift, the Chandelier Graveyard, South Winds, and Chocolate Factory in the West, LaMorada and the Outback in the Far East, and Giant Chicklets, the Orange Bowl, and Tag Hall in the Near East.

Belski, Dave. "Trip Reports: Lechuguilla Cave." *Southwestern Cavers*. January-February, 1988, pp. 11: Jan. 9-10, 1998, trip to the end of the Western Borehole, but no descriptions of survey or designations.

Bridges, Rick. "The Breakthrough in Lechuguilla Cave." *Rocky Mountain Caving*. Vol. 3, No. 3, Summer 1986, pp. 39-45: Personal account of the Memorial Day, 1986 breakthrough and the discovery of the passage all the way to Boulder Falls.

Bridges, Rick and Glaser, Roy. "Push at Lechuguilla or the Lech-A-Gorilla Pushes Back." *Rocky Mountain Caving*. Vol. 3, No. 4, Autumn, 1989, pp. 18-26: September, 1986, trip, including the Land Down Under and the first major push of the Rift.

Bridges, Rick. "The Exploration of Lechuguilla Cave." *NSS News*. Vol. 46, No. 10. October 1988. National Speleological Society, pp. 372-376: Summary of digging trips and exploration up to the discovery of the Overpass in August, 1987.

Bridges, Rick. "The Legend Lives." *Southwestern Cavers*. January-February, 1988, pp. 6-8: January, 1988, expedition including Western Borehole to Huapache and Oasis, Lake of the Blue Giants and Stud Lake in the Mega Maze, and the Lebarge Borehole breakthrough to Chandelier Ballroom and Prickly Ice Cube Room.

Bridges, Rick. "Lechuguilla Cave Expedition." *Southwestern Cavers*. January-February, 1989, pp. 5-7: January, 1989, expedition including High Hopes in the Southwest, the 1988 and 1989 rooms in the West, the Apricot Dome/ Ghost Town areas in the East including the discovery of the S&M Crawl.

Brown, Randy and Davis, Donald. "Current Explorations in Lechuguilla Cave." *Rocky Mountain Caving*. Vol. 10, No. 3, Summer, 1993, pp. 13-14: June, 1993, expedition, including the MA-survey area, Topless Dome, and the Ruby Chamber in the East and the Neverland climb and the area between Keel Haul and Hard Daze Night Hall in the West.

Bunnell, Dave. "Discovery of the Lakes in Eastern Nirvana." *NSS News*. October 1988. National Speleological Society, pp. 385-386: Accounts of the discovery of Stud Lake, Lake of the Blue Giants, and the Moby Dick Room in the Near East. Additional accounts by Rick Bridges of the discovery of the Lebarge Borehole and Tinsel Town.

Burger, Paul. "And the Monster Roared." *Rocky Mountain Caving*. Vol. 6, No. 1, Winter, 1989, p. 17: November, 1988, final ascent of High Hopes and the discovery of Shangri-La.

Burger, Paul. "The Empire Bites Back: The December LEARN Expedition." *Rocky Mountain Caving*. Vol. 11, No. 1, Winter, 1994, pp. 10-11: December, 1993, LEARN expedition, including the Fawn Hall area in the North Rift, Needle Park, Blanca Navidad, and the Fortress of Chaos in the West, and breakdown passage near the Ruby Chamber, Happy Hunting Grounds, and the Lost Pecos River in the East.

Cahill, Tim. "Charting the Splendors of Lechuguilla Cave." *National Geographic*. Vol. 179, No. 3, March, 1991. pp. 34-59: Mostly personal account of a couple of trips into the cave and summaries of some of the latest discoveries.

Coney, Bob and Kathy Minter, John Stembel. "Underground Atlanta: Buffoons in Paradise." *Georgia Underground*, pp. 18-19: Discovery of Underground Atlanta.

Davis, Donald "The Grand Cavern of the Guadalupes: Lechuguilla's Mileage Surpasses Carlsbad Cavern." *Rocky Mountain Caving*. Vol. 5, No. 3, Summer, 1988, pp. 30-31: August, 1988, LCP expedition, including climbing in the Rainbow Room, the discovery of the Mirage Room, and exploration in boneyard near the ABCs Room and Manifest Destiny in the West, some pushing in the North Rift, and exploration in the Chandelier Maze and Voids areas in the Southwest.

Davis, Donald. "Revelations in Lechuguilla Cave." *Rocky Mountain Caving*. Vol. 4, No. 4, Autumn 1987. pp, 19-23: October, 1987, expedition, including discovery of the Emperor's Throne Room and Nirvana in the Near East, and the Western Borehole to Hard Daze Night Hall.

Davis, Donald. "Echoes from Lechuguilla Cave." *Rocky Mountain Caving*. Vol. 5, No. 1, Winter, 1988, pp. 14-15: January, 1988, expedition, including Huapache Highway, Oasis Pool, Long Haul and Keel Haul in the Western Borehole, Lake of the Blue Giants, and Stud Lake in the Near East, and the discovery of the Lebarge Borehole, the Tinsel Town Maze, Land of Awes, the Chandelier Ballroom, Hoodoo Hall, and the Prickly Ice Cube Room in the Southwest.

Davis, Donald. "To Depths Profound." *Rocky Mountain Caving*. Vol. 5, No. 2. Spring 1988, pp. 24-26: March/April, 1988, expedition including Fawn Hall in the North Rift, Manifest Destiny and the Chandelier Graveyard in the West, the Mouse's Delight and Land of Awes sections of the Chandelier Maze, and the discovery of the Voids in the Southwest.

Davis, Donald. "The Inner Realm Expands." *Rocky Mountain Caving*. Vol. 5, No. 4, Autumn, 1988, pp. 21-22: October, 1988, LCP expedition, including the discovery of Seesaw Canyon and the Chicken Little Room in the Southwest, and the Chocolate Factory, the Jackpot Room, and the Mirage Room in the West.

Davis, Donald. "More Treasure Revealed." *Rocky Mountain Caving*. Vol. 6, No. 1, Winter, 1989, pp. 17-19: January, 1989, LCP expedition, including Lechy's Lair and the High Hopes discoveries of Ultra Primo, Blue Velvet Lake, Atlantis, and Vesuvius in the Southwest. The article also documents the discovery of Ghost Town from TAG Hall in the Near East.

Davis, Donald. "Lechuguilla: The Ongoing Saga." *Rocky Mountain Caving*. Vol. 6, No. 2, Spring, 1989, pp. 29-32: March, 1989, expedition including pushing in Ghost Town, continued climbing of the Aragonitemare, and more discoveries in High Hopes, This expedition includes the discovery of Big Sky Country, Pearlsian Gulf, and YO Acres off the Chandelier Maze, Underground Atlanta, and Tower Place above the Chicken Little Room, and the Deliverance Passage, all in the Southwest.

Davis, Donald. "The Eastern Wall Falls." *Rocky Mountain Caving*. Vol. 6, No. 3, Summer, 1989, pp. 22-24: May/June, 1989 expedition including the completion of the Aragonitemare climb and the discovery of the Land of Enchantment, the China Shop, the Land of Fire and Ice, Glacier Way, Grand Guadalupe Junction, and the Lost Pecos River in the Far East.

Davis, Donald. "Pushing the Outback." *Rocky Mountain Caving*. Vol. 6, No. 4, Autumn, 1989, pp. 22-24. 30-31: September, 1989, expedition, including the discovery of Boundary Waters, Gorilla Pit, the Ruby Chamber, and the Wild Black Yonder portion of the Outback section in the Far East as well as some smaller discoveries near Prickly Ice Cube Room in the Southwest and near Hard Daze Night Hall in the West.

Davis, Donald. "Lechuguilla: A Review of the Eighties." *Rocky Mountain Caving*. Vol. 7, No. 1, Winter, 1990, pp. 12-25: Decade-end review of Lechuguillan discoveries, both explorational and scientific and a commentary on the cave's impact on caving.

Davis, Donald. "By Deepest Lechuguilla's Waters." *Rocky Mountain Caving*. Vol. 7, No. 1, Winter, 1990, pp. 26-27. 33: December/January, 1989, LCPI expedition including the connection between Ghost Town and the Aragonitemare, the discovery of Lake of the White Roses as well as some general pushing in the Outback and Bryce Canyon areas in the Far East, and some minor pushing in the Chandelier Maze and High Hopes.

Davis, Donald. "The Nation's Deepest: Lechuguilla of the Guadalupes." *Rocky Mountain Caving*. Vol. 7, No. 2, Spring, 1990, pp. 14-15: March/April, 1990, LCPI expedition, including dives of Stud Lake and Lake of the Blue Giants in the Near East, Pleasure Palace, Firefall Hall, LaMorada, and the Outback in the Far East, Keel Haul and boneyard in the Chandelier Graveyard and FUBAR in the west, and the Chandelier Maze, Shangri-La, and the Deliverance Passage in the Southwest.

Davis, Donald. "To the Deepest Ends: Lechuguilla Passes another Milestone." *Rocky Mountain Caving*. Vol. 7, No. 3, Summer, 1990, pp. 24-25, 30: August, 1990, LCPI expedition, including Piled Higher and Deeper and the Chandelier Graveyard in the West, the Tinsel Town Maze and High Hopes in the Southwest, and survey in Ghost Town. In the Far East, the Outback, TNT Pit, and some pushing in La Morada.

Davis, Donald. "Autumn Wanderings in Lechuguilla Cave." *Rocky Mountain Caving*. Vol. 7, No. 4, Autumn, 1990, pp. 21-22, 30: October, 1990, Doucette expedition, including climbing near Underground Atlanta in the Southwest, and La Morada and the Pleasure Dome in the Far East.

Davis, Donald. "Lechuguilla Addendum." *Rocky Mountain Caving*. Vol. 8, No. 1, Winter, 1991, p. 18: Some corrections and additions to the October, 1990, Doucette climbing trip as well as some scientific observations.

Davis, Donald. "Lechuguilla Marches On." *Rocky Mountain Caving*. Vol. 8, No. 1, Winter, 1991, pp. 18-19: December/January, 1990, LCPI expedition, including mop-up in most of the major maze areas and the discovery of Ghostbusters Hall in the Ghost Town area.

Davis, Donald. "The Push Northwest." *Rocky Mountain Caving*. Vol. 8, No. 2, Spring, 1991, pp. 14-17: March/April, 1991, expedition, including Hudson Bay, Spar City, and the Red Sea/Dead Sea complex in the West, the Chandelier Maze in the Southwest, and Nirvana in the Near East. Brief description of the Emily Davis Mobley rescue.

Davis, Donald. "The Heliocentric Expedition." *Rocky Mountain Caving*. Vol. 8, No. 3, Summer, 1991, pp. 23-24: August, 1991, LCPI [Lechuguilla Cave Project, Inc.] expedition, including Ghostriders Hall area in Ghostown, Northwest Passage in the West, and Big Sky Country in the Southwest. Most of this expedition was involved with the helium tracer study.

Davis, Donald and Garry Petrie. "Chipping Away at the Barrier." *Rocky Mountain Caving*. Vol. 11, No. 2, Spring, 1994, pp. 8-11: March, 1994, Hecker expedition including Blanca Navidad, Needle Park Maze, and Western Borehole near the Chocolate Factory and Hard Daze Night. Garry documents the Far East, including a breakdown maze area near the Ruby Chamber, and surveys near Grand Guadalupe Junction and in the La Morada Maze.

Davis, Donald. "The South Winds of Lechuguilla." *Rocky Mountain Caving*. Vol. 11, No. 2, Spring, 1994, p. 12: April, 1994, LEARN [Lechuguilla Exploration and Research Network] expedition documenting the history and discovery of the South Winds section of the Western branch.

Doucette, Don. "High Climbing Down Deep in Lechuguilla Cave." *Rocky Mountain Caving*. Vol. 6, No. 1, Winter, 1989, p. 16: Documents the first climbing of the Aragonitemare.

DuChene, Harvey R.. "The February Lechuguilla Video Expedition." *Rocky Mountain Caving*. Vol. 5, No. 2, Spring, 1988, pp. 28-29: February, 1988, expedition to video portions of the cave for a Denver Museum of Natural History video production.

Glaser, Roy. "Ecstasy in the Guads." *Rocky Mountain Caving*. Vol. 3, No. 3, Summer, 1986, pp. 45-49: Personal account of the Memorial Day, 1986 trip following the breakthrough from Boulder Falls to the Rift.

Glaser, Roy. "Too Much Cave?" *Rocky Mountain Caving*. Vol. 4, No. 4, Autumn, 1987, p. 24: Mostly a commentary on pushing in Lechuguilla and talk about breakthrough into ABCs Room.

Hose, Louise. "To Lechuguillan Depths." *Rocky Mountain Caving*. Vol. 9, No. 2. Spring, 1992, pp. 15-18: Mostly logistical account of May, 1992, dive trip of Peter Bolt into Lake of the White Roses.

Jones, Peter, "Broken Leg Saga." *Network News*. Vol. 2, No. 2, 1993, pp. 7-9. Lechuguilla Exploration and Research Network : Account of Peter's May, 1993, broken leg and self-rescue from the Western Borehole.

Jones, Peter, "Crawling out of Lechuguilla." *Southwestern Cavers*. May-June, 1993, pp. 42-44: Documents Peter Jones' accident of May 15, 1993, in the Western Borehole near the Leaning Tower of Lechuguilla.

Jones, Peter, "The Lechuguillan Self-Rescue." *Rocky Mountain Caving.* Vol. 10, No. 1, Winter, 1993, pp. 12-14: Documents Peter Jones' accident of May 15, 1993, in the Western Borehole near the Leaning Tower of Lechuguilla.

Kambesis, Pat. "The August Lechuguilla Cave Expedition." *Rocky Mountain Caving.* Vol. 4, No. 4, Autumn, 1987, pp. 17-18: August, 1987, expedition, Captain Hooks Ladder to Deep Secrets.

Kambesis, Pat. "Discovery of the Chandelier Ballroom and the Prickly Ice Cube Room." *NSS News.* October, 1988. National Speleological Society, pp. 386-388: Personal account of these Southwest discoveries in January, 1988.

Kambesis, Pat. "Lechuguilla Cave Update." *Southwestern Cavers.* September-October, 1987, pp. 84-86: August, 1987, expedition, Captain Hooks Ladder to Deep Secrets.

Kambesis, Pat. "October, 1987, Lechuguilla Expedition." *Southwestern Cavers.* November-December, 1987, pp. 102-104: October, 1987, expedition including the first real Apricot Pit push, Barsoom, Christmas Tree Room, ABCs and the start of the Western Borehole.

Kambesis, Pat. "More on the January, 1988 Lechuguilla Expedition." *Southwestern Cavers.* January-February, 1988, pp. 8-9: January, 1988 expedition including Western Borehole to Huapache and Oasis, Lake of the Blue Giants and Stud Lake in the Mega Maze, and the Lebarge Borehole breakthrough to Chandelier Ballroom and Prickly Ice Cube Room.

Kambesis, Pat. "The Chandelier Graveyard Discovery." *NSS News.* Vol. 46, No. 10. October 1988. National Speleological Society, pp. 393: March, 1988, discovery of this section of the Western branch.

Kambesis, Pat. "Lechuguilla Cave Update." *Southwestern Cavers.* July-August, 1988, pp. 48-49: March, 1988 expedition including Chandelier Graveyard in the West, Land of the Lost in the Southwest and lead to the deep point, May, 1988, trip to Sulfur Shores.

Kambesis, Pat. "Pushing the Depths of the Guads." *NSS News.* Vol. 46, No. 10. October 1988. National Speleological Society, pp. 394-399: May, 1988, discovery of Sulfur Shores and the new deep point in the Southwest. In addition, Rick Bridges discusses the impact of the cave on that year's NSS Convention, the push to make Lechuguilla a cave wilderness, and documents the visits of several groups from the popular press into the cave.

Kambesis, Pat. "New Discoveries in the L Cave." *Georgia Underground*, pp. 10-16: Video expedition/High Hopes discovery.

Kambesis, Pat. "Sweet Dreams Beyond the Aragonitemare." *Rocky Mountain Caving*. Vol. 6, No. 3, Summer, 1989, pp. 25-26, 28: Personal account of May/June, 1989, discoveries of passages beyond the Silver Bullet Passage, including Glacier Way, Grand Guadalupe Junction, and the Lost Pecos River in the Far East.

Kambesis, Pat. "Expedition: July 3-10, 1993." *The Network News*. Vol. 3, No. 1, January 27, 1994. Lechuguilla Exploration and Research Network. pp. 5-6: July, 1993, LEARN expedition, including re-survey and mop-up near Hard Daze Night Hall and other passages along the Western Borehole, mop-up from the Colorado Room down through the Overpass, mop-up in the North Rift, the Giant Chicklets Room, and the Outback in the Far East.

Kreager, Ken. "Late News from Lechuguilla." *Rocky Mountain Caving*. Vol. 5, No. 2, Spring, 1988, p. 29: May, 1988, trips into the cave including the discovery of Sulfur Shores in the Southwest.

Lane, Buddy. "Apricot Pit Revisited." *NSS News*. Vol. 46, No. 10. October 1988. National Speleological Society, pp. 380-381: Accounts the discovery of the Mega Maze area, including the Emperor's Throne Room and Nirvana in the Near East.

Lane, Buddy. "Vertical Adventures in Lechuguilla Cave." *NSS News*. Vol. 46, No. 10. October 1988. National Speleological Society, pp. 377-378: Account of first attempts to bottom Apricot Pit and dropping of other pits in the Overpass in August, 1987.

Lappin, Ted. "Finding the Gulf of California." *NSS News*. October 1988. National Speleological Society, pp. 383-385: Personal account of the discovery of the Gulf of California down to the Shoestring Traverse. Additional accounts by Rick Bridges of the exploration of the Western Borehole out to the Leaning Tower of Lechuguilla.

LaRock, Ed and Rich Sloan. "Oy! The Joy of Discovery in Lechuguilla." *Rocky Mountain Caving*. Vol. 6, No. 2, Spring, 1989, pp. 34-35: January, 1989, discovery of the Deliverance Passage near Hoodoo Hall in the Southwest.

Moss, Lyle. "The Adventure Continues." *Rocky Mountain Caving*. Vol. 6, No. 3, Summer, 1989, pp. 24. 27: Personal account of final series of climbs to top the Aragonitemare and the exploration of the passages beyond to the Silver Bullet Passage in the Far East in May/June, 1989.

Parent, Laurence. "Explorers Pit Themselves Against Cavernous Lechuguilla." *New Mexico Magazine*. June 1988, pp. 42-47: Article about the opening of the cave, some of the discoveries, and some on the wilderness designation.

Parent, Laurence. "Mystery of the Breathing Cavern." *National Parks*. July/August 1988, pp. 20-23: Article about the opening of the cave, some of the discoveries, and some on the wilderness designation.

Park Service News Release. "Major New Discoveries Made in Undeveloped Backcountry Cave at Carlsbad Caverns National Park." *Southwestern Cavers*. November-December, 1987, pp. 104-105: October, 1987, finds.

Park Service News Release. "January 25, 1991." *Southwestern Cavers*. January-February, 1991, p. 3: Summary of past three expeditions netting three miles of new cave and stating that Lechuguilla is the deepest cave in the US.

Park Service News Release. "Lechuguilla Cave now Deepest in US." *Southwestern Cavers*. May-June, 1992, p. 30: Documents the dive of Lake of the White Roses and summarizes the discoveries and the new depth figure.

Park Service News Release. "Lechuguilla Cave's Mapped Length Tops 60 Miles." *Southwestern Cavers*. January-February, 1993, p. 5: Hecker-January, 1993, expedition including brief mention of mapping in the Far East and the Northwest Passage in the West.

Petrie, Garry. "Who Discovered Hoodoo Hall?" *Rocky Mountain Caving*. Vol. 5, No. 1, Winter, 1988, p. 17: Personal account of January, 1988, discovery of Hoodoo Hall in the Southwest.

Petrie, Garry. "An Oasis Down Under." *Rocky Mountain Caving*. Vol. 5, No. 2, Spring, 1988, p. 27: March, 1988, discovery of the lakes of Castrovalva.

Petrie, Garry. "Lechuguilla Cave: March, 1989 Expedition." *Southwestern Cavers*. May-June, 1989, pp. 50-51: March, 1989, expedition including discovery of Tower Place and Underground Atlanta, the Deliverance Passage, and YO Acres in the Southwest, and the Chocolate Factory in the West. Only brief mention is made of pushes in the East including Ghost Town and 100 more feet in the Aragonitemare.

Petrie, Garry. "Never Say Never." *Rocky Mountain Caving*. Vol. 6, No. 2, Spring, 1989, p. 32: January/March, 1989, discovery and pushing of S&M Crawl/Ghostown bypass to Apricot Pit.

Reames, Steve. "Expedition: December 27, 1993-January 2, 1994." *The Network News*. Vol. 3, No. 1, January 27, 1994. Lechuguilla Exploration and Research Network. pp. 9-10: LEARN expedition, including pushing in the Chandelier Graveyard, the main Western Borehole, and Blanca Navidad in the West, the Outback in the Far East, and Kryptonite and Fawn Hall in the North Rift.

Rhinehart, Rick. "New Wonders in the Depths of Lechuguilla Cave." *Rocky Mountain Caving*. Vol. 4, No. 3, Summer, 1987, pp. 25-26: August, 1987, expedition, including the discovery of Wooden Lettuce, the Overpass, and the Great White Way.

Roberts, David. "Caving Comes into its Golden Age: A New Mexico Marvel." *Smithsonian Magazine*. November, 1988, pp. 52-65: Primarily an account of author's March, 1988, trip into the cave, but recounts the digging open of the cave as well as some of the other discoveries in the cave.

Seiser, Pat. "3/27/93-4/4/93 Expedition." *The Network News*. Vol. 2, No. 2, 1993, pp. 5-6. Lechuguilla Exploration and Research Network : March/April, 1993, LEARN expedition, including the Northwest Passage and Manifest Destiny in the West, the North Rift, and Nirvana and the Great Beyond in the Near East.

Seiser, Pat. "5/15/93-5/23/93 Expedition." *The Network News*. Vol. 2, No. 2, 1993, pp. 6-7. Lechuguilla Exploration and Research Network : May, 1993, LEARN expedition, including Left Hand Corridor, the North Rift, Mirage Room and Keel Hall in the West, and Pigs in Space in the Near East near the Rustcicles.

Seiser, Pat. "April 2-10, 1994 Expedition." *The Network News*. Vol. 3, No. 2, 1994, pp. 9-10. Lechuguilla Exploration and Research Network : April, 1994, LEARN expedition, including Sugarlands and Glacier Bay in the Upper Cave, the North Rift, Hoodoo Hall and the Chandelier Maze in the Southwest, Pigs in Space in the Near East, and South Winds and the Wild West in the Western branch.

Sims, Steve. "Above and Beyond – Mouses Delight Area." *NSS News*. Vol. 46, No. 10. October 1988. National Speleological Society, pp. 388-392: January, 1988, discovery of this part of the Chandelier Maze in the Southwest and of the Prickly Ice Cube Room.

Sims, Steve. "Lechuguilla: Opening Up Again?." *Rocky Mountain Caving*. Vol. 5, No. 3, Summer, 1988, p. 32: Account of August, 1988, trip, including surveying near Sulfur Shores, Castrovalva, Mouse's Delight, and the second ascent of Seesaw Canyon in the Southwest.

Sims, Steve. "Lechuguilla Opens Up" *Rocky Mountain Caving*. Vol. 5, No. 4, Autumn, 1988, pp. 22-23: October, 1988, discovery of Seesaw Canyon and the Chicken Little Room.

Sims, Steve. "Pellucidar – The Enchanted Room." *NSS News*. Vol. 46, No. 10. October, 1988, National Speleological Society, pp. 379-380: Account of discovery of Pellucidar in the Western branch.

Smith, Gary. "A LEARN Novice's First Expedition." *The Network News*. Vol. 3, No. 1, January 27, 1994. Lechuguilla Exploration and Research Network. pp. 14-15: Personal account of October, 1993, LEARN expedition into the West and North Rift.

Smith, Gary. "Expedition: October 9-16, 1993." *The Network News*. Vol. 3, No. 1, January 27, 1994. Lechuguilla Exploration and Research Network. p. 8-9: October, 1993, LEARN expedition, including Three O'clock Staircase and Jackpot areas in the west, some survey near S&M Crawl, and pushing near Fawn Hall in the North Rift.

Taylor, Michael Ray (ed.). *Lechuguilla: Jewel of the Underground*. Speleo Projects. Caving Publications International: Basel, Switzerland, 1991: Photographic coffee table book with extensive photographs of the major areas of the cave and some exploration history and geology.

Thompson, Norman. "From the Depths of Lechuguilla: A Typical Trip Log." *Rocky Mountain Caving*. Vol. 4, No. 4, Autumn, 1987, p. 24: Personal trip log of a photo trip to Emperor's Throne Room.

Vesely, Carol. "Discovery of the Western Borehole." *NSS News*. Vol. 46, No. 10. October 1988. National Speleological Society, p. 381-383: Accounts the discovery of the ABCs Room and the beginning of the Western Borehole.

Vesely, Carol. "December Discoveries in Lechuguilla Cave." *California Caver*, Vol. 42, No. 3, p. 60-61: December, 1993, expedition including pushing in the North Rift, the Outback in the Far East, a short climb in the Near East, and the discovery of Blanca Navidad in the West.

Vesely, Carol. "Discoveries in Lechuguilla Cave." *California Caver*. Issue No. 200. Fall, 1994, p. 7-8: July, 1994, expedition including pushing in the South Winds in the West, the Deep Voids in the Southwest, near Stud Lake in the Near East, and the Outback in the Far West (including Guano Assumption Pit).

Emily Davis Mobley's Rescue

Bosted, Ann. "A Short Log of the Rescue of Emily Davis Mobley: March 31 to April 4, 1991." *Rocky Mountain Caving*. Vol. 8, No. 2, Spring, 1991, pp. 20-21, 25: In-cave log of the rescue efforts to get Emily Davis Mobley from FUBAR out of the cave.

Bosted, Ann. "Log of the Rescue of Emily Davis Mobley: March 31 to April 4, 1991." *California Caver*. Vol. 41, No. 1, pp. 6-15: In-cave log of the rescue efforts to get Emily Davis Mobley from FUBAR out of the cave.

Bosted, Ann. "The Lechuguilla Rescue: Other Notes." *California Caver*. Vol. 41, No. 1, p. 16: Additional personal reflections on Emily, the rescuers, and the rescue.

Bosted, Ann. "The Lechuguilla Rescue: Suggestions for Improvements compiled during the rescue of Emily Davis Mobley." *California Caver*. Vol. 41, No. 1, pp. 17-18: Contains a list of suggestions for other rescues, including additional gear suggestions.

Legnini, Dan. "Some Statistics." *California Caver*. Vol. 41, No. 1, p. 18: Listing and summary of the gear used in the Emily Davis Mobley rescue.

Petrie, Garry. "The Rescue of Emily Davis Mobley." *Rocky Mountain Caving*. Vol. 8, No. 2, Spring, 1991, pp. 15, 22: Personal account of rescue.

Seiser, Pat. "Moon Over Lechuguilla." *Rocky Mountain Caving*. Vol. 8, No. 2, Spring, 1991, pp. 18-22: Personal account of Emily Davis Mobley Rescue.

Taylor, Michael Ray. "Daring and Danger in a World of Delicate Beauty." *Audubon*. September-October 1991, pp. 74-85: Lengthy article with numerous sidebars that deals primarily with Taylor's trip into the cave and the rescue of Emily Davis Mobley.

Science

Ananiev, Eugeni. "O, Lechuguilla." *Rocky Mountain Caving*. Vol. 10, No. 1, Winter, 1993, pp. 14, 17-18: Personal account of November, 1992, inventory trip to the Far East.

Cunningham, K. I.. "Mammal Skeleton Discovered in Lechuguilla." *Rocky Mountain Caving*. Vol. 7, No. 2, Spring, 1990, p. 16: Documents the discovery of a ringtail cat skeleton in the Land of Awes in the Southwest branch.

Davis, Donald. "'Stalactoids' on Pool Linings in Lechuguilla Cave: More Bizarre Subaqueous Speleothems?." *Rocky Mountain Caving*. Vol. 5, No. 1, Winter, 1988, pp. 15-16: Discussion on possible subaqueous formations along the edges of pools and their localities within the cave.

Davis, Donald. "A Lechuguillan Mystery." *Rocky Mountain Caving*. Vol. 5, No. 1, Winter, 1988, p. 20: Description and possible explanation of a strange. musical moaning near the Liberty Bell.

Davis, Donald. "Some Scientific Notes." *Rocky Mountain Caving*. Vol. 6, No. 1, Winter, 1989, p. 19: Observations on recent finding regarding the elemental sulfur and corrosion residue in the cave.

Davis, Donald. "The February Lechuguilla Scientific Expedition." *Rocky Mountain Caving*. Vol. 7, No. 1, Winter, 1990, p. 28: February, 1990, scientific expedition including some scientific observations in the Far East.

Davis, Donald. "Regarding Würms and Rotated Gypsum Planes in Lechuguilla." *Rocky Mountain Caving*. Vol. 10, No. 3, Summer,

1993, pp. 13, 19: Description of würm variation on subaqueous helictites found in Neverland including possible genesis.

DuChene, Harvey. "Science in Lechuguilla Cave." *The Network News.* Vol. 3, No. 1, January 27, 1994. Lechuguilla Exploration and Research Network. p. 20: Update on current science projects, including microclimate study, studies of the sulfur in the cave, and the proposed oil and gas drilling just outside the park.

Jablonski, Pat. "Extinct Sloth Recovered from Lechuguilla Cave." *The Network News.* Vol. 3, No. 3, 1994, p. 16. Lechuguilla Exploration and Research Network : Report of the recovery of a Pleistocene Shasta ground sloth near the Liberty Bell.

LaRock, Ed and K. I. Cunningham. "The October, 1989, Lechuguilla Microclimate Study Field Trip." *Rocky Mountain Caving.* Vol. 7, No. 1, Winter, 1990, pp. 27, 33: Synopsis of study that included radon, barometric pressure, air velocity and direction, relative humidity, and evaporation rates throughout the cave.

Taylor, Mark. "Climbing Down into the Deepest Cave in the State." *New Mexico Monthly.* March, 1988, pp. 8-10: Trip report on December, 1987, paleontological trip as far as Glacier Bay.

Techniques and Equipment

Kambesis, Pat and Rick Bridges. "Survey Methods and Standards used by the Lechuguilla Cave Project." *NSS News.* October 1988. Vol. 46, No. 10. National Speleological Society, pp. 400-401: Describes what techniques are used and what data are collected by the project.

Kambesis, Pat. "Dry Food." *The Network News.* Vol. 3, No. 1, January 27, 1994. Lechuguilla Exploration and Research Network. p. 20: Tips on keeping food dry in a cave.

Seiser, Pat. "In Case of Accident." *The Network News.* Vol. 3, No. 1, January 27, 1994. Lechuguilla Exploration and Research Network. p. 18: Tips on what to do in case of an accident in Lechuguilla.

Shipp, Melanie. "Lechuguilla Equipment Report." *The Network News.* Vol. 3, No. 1, January 27, 1994. Lechuguilla Exploration and Research Network. pp. 17-18: Tips on equipment for both long and short-term stays in Lechuguilla.

Strait, Doug. "Incandescent Electric Headlight Systems for Long Duration Expeditionary Caving." *The Network News.* Vol. 3, No. 1, January 27, 1994. Lechuguilla Exploration and Research Network. p. 23-34: Description of efficient incandescent light system and a comparison with other lighting systems commonly used in the cave.

Vesely, Carol. "Surveying Efficiently". *The Network News.* Vol. 3, No. 1, January 27, 1994. Lechuguilla Exploration and Research

Network. p. 16-17: Tips on making a survey crew work more efficiently.

Politics

Anonymous. "Final Report: Carlsbad Lechuguilla Task Force." *Rocky Mountain Caving*. Vol. 6, No. 4, Autumn, 1989, pp. 7-8: Reprint of the final report of the Carlsbad Task Force to determine how to best utilize the discovery of Lechuguilla for the benefit of the city of Carlsbad.

Anonymous. "Lechuguilla Study Act of 1989." *Rocky Mountain Caving*. Vol. 6, No. 4, Autumn, 1989, pp. 8, 19: Reprint of two acts to protect and recommend a plan to manage Lechuguilla and to possibly establish a cave research institute in the city of Carlsbad.

Davis, Donald. "Lechuguilla Cave Development Condemned." *Rocky Mountain Caving*. Vol. 6, No. 3, Summer, 1989, p. 9: Response and commentary on Rick Rhinehart's "Paper Dragon" article.

Donahue, Bill. "In Beauty it is Finished: Of Man and Caves and the Lure of Lechuguilla." *Buzzworm*. March/April, 1990, pp. 34-39: Discusses the environmental aspects of Lechuguilla Cave. Most of the article is based on discussions with Dave Jagnow and the 1989 helium experiment.

Kambesis, Pat. "Committees of the Lechuguilla Cave Project." *Rocky Mountain Caving*. Vol. 6, No. 3, Summer, 1989, pp. 11, 14: Outlining the duties of the committee chairs and the responsibilities of each committee in the incorporated Lechuguilla Cave Project.

Kambesis, Pat. "The Collapse of the Lechuguilla Cave Project." *Rocky Mountain Caving*. Vol. 9, No. 2, Spring, 1992, pp. 12-15: Summary of the problems that caused LCPI to be restricted from Lechuguilla.

Kolstad, Rob. "LEARN Documents." *The Network News*. Vol. 1, No. 1, July, 1992. Lechuguilla Exploration and Research Network. pp. 6-9: LEARN constitution and bylaws.

Petrie, Garry. "Understanding Lechuguilla Cave Project, Inc." *Rocky Mountain Caving*. Vol. 6, No. 3, Summer, 1989, pp. 11, 14: Description of the incorporated Lechuguilla Cave Project, the memorandum of understanding with the park service, and the operating procedures for the project.

Rhinehart, Rick. "Kerbo to Head Lechuguilla Cave Project." *Rocky Mountain Caving*. Vol. 4, No. 3, Summer, 1987, pp. 23-25: Documents the new management plan for Lechuguilla, including comments on the plan from Roy Glaser, Rick Bridges, and John Patterson.

Rhinehart, Rick. "Publicity Continues to Promote Lechuguilla Wilderness Concept." *Rocky Mountain Caving.* Vol. 5, No. 3, Summer, 1988, pp. 21-22: About the proposed wilderness designation for Lechuguilla.

Rhinehart, Rick. "Lechuguilla Cave Project to Sign New memorandum of Understanding." *Rocky Mountain Caving.* Vol. 6, No. 1, Winter, 1989, p. 10: Documents the signing of the MOU with the National Park Service as well as the incorporation of the Lechuguilla Cave Project. The article also includes mention of some of the recent internal political woes of the project.

Rhinehart, Rick. "The Paper Dragon: Commercialization and Lechuguilla Cave." *Rocky Mountain Caving.* Vol. 6, No. 2, Spring, 1989, pp. 11-13: Speculative article and comments on the possibility of commercializing Lechuguilla.

Rhinehart, Rick. "Wilderness Lost: The Rush for the Commercialization of Lechuguilla Cave." *Rocky Mountain Caving.* Vol. 6, No. 2, Spring, 1989, pp. 8-9: Summary of proposal by Carlsbad city residents to commercialize Lechuguilla and stop proposed wilderness designation.

Rhinehart, Rick. "Lechuguilla Cave Project Yields to Park Service Pressure." *Rocky Mountain Caving.* Vol. 8, No. 4, Autumn, 1994, p. 6: Report of the contested Lechuguilla survey notes being handed over to the National Park Service.

Rhinehart, Rick. "LEARN Offers Representation for Former Lechuguilla Cave Project Members." *Rocky Mountain Caving.* Vol. 9, No. 1, Winter, 1992, p. 8: Documents formation of LEARN and the projects philosophy and goals.

Rhinehart, Rick. "NPS Assumes Management of Lechuguilla Exploration." *Rocky Mountain Caving.* Vol. 9, No. 1, Winter, 1992, p. 8: Documents problems between the NPS and LCPI, and the restriction of the latter from further exploration in the cave.

Rhinehart, Rick. "Surveying Continues Within Lechuguilla Cave." *Rocky Mountain Caving.* Vol. 10, No. 4, Autumn, 1993, p. 8: General summary of exploration taking place during 1993.

Taylor, Mark. "The Secret Cave." *Outside.* April, 1988, pp. 17-18: Mostly describes the beauty of Lechuguilla with some comments on the proposed wilderness designation.

Yett, Bill. "Some Thoughts on Carlsbad Politics and Lechuguilla Cave." *Rocky Mountain Caving.* Vol. 6, No. 2, Spring, 1989, pp. 9-10: Comments on the proposed commercialization of Lechuguilla.

20

INDEX

◇ C ◇

◇ D ◇